PSU Chemtrek

Small-Scale Experiments for General Chemistry

2013–2014

Written by Stephen Thompson
Edited for Penn State by Joseph T. Keiser

Hayden-McNeil Sustainability

Hayden-McNeil's standard paper stock uses a minimum of 30% post-consumer waste. We offer higher % options by request, including a 100% recycled stock. Additionally, Hayden-McNeil Custom Digital provides authors with the opportunity to convert print products to a digital format. Hayden-McNeil is part of a larger sustainability initiative through Macmillan Higher Ed. Visit http://sustainability.macmillan.com to learn more.

Hayden-McNeil Publishing
14903 Pilot Drive
Plymouth, MI 48170
www.hmpublishing.com

Keiser 6095-8 F13

History

A Brief History of *PSU Chemtrek*
By J. T. Keiser

This project started in 1991. That year I was hired by Penn State University as their Director of General Chemistry Laboratories and given the job of running and improving their introductory lab courses. I could see what some of the problems were—the labs were too cookbook, students spent too much time setting up experiments and too little time actually doing experiments, students did not think very deeply about the experiments they did, reports typically were not started until nearly a week after the experiments were completed, and in the best cases the feedback (grades) came two weeks after an experiment was completed. But, it was hard to imagine how to improve things. The Penn State lab is large (216 students at one time), and the frontline teachers are typically first-year graduate students. How could I make the experiments more open-ended and not end up with bedlam? I struggled to find a solution, and then a friend gave me a copy of *Chemtrek*.

In *Chemtrek* I found solutions to most of the problems. Small-scale made it possible to do more open-ended experiments safely, within our time constraints, and within our budget. Students could "tinker"—attack a problem from several different directions, analyze results during the lab period, and then gather more data if necessary. The waste problem was dealt with at its root—the experiments generate very little waste. I loved the idea of having students make their own instruments, and how this reveals the relationship between form and function. In short, I wanted to bring *Chemtrek* to Penn State. Well, not exactly. I wanted to adapt *Chemtrek* for use at Penn State.

The plan was to build on the *Chemtrek* foundation. In 1992 I visited Stephen Thompson at Colorado State University, and began working towards this goal. In the fall of 1992, a small honors lab class (Chem 14H) was taught using some of the *Chemtrek* experiments. In the '93/'94 academic year we began using *Chemtrek* in our mainstream lab courses (Chem 14 and 15). In the fall of 1994, the first edition of a customized version of *Chemtrek*, called the "Penn State Version of *Chemtrek*," was produced. This involved an agreement between Prentice-Hall and Penn State in which Penn State licensed the right to use fifteen of the original *Chemtrek* experiments, edit them, and blend them with local material. This first "Penn State Version of *Chemtrek*" was followed by nine more between 1995 and 2003. In total, ten editions were produced and printed at Penn State.

In 2004, a new approach was taken, one in which Hayden-McNeil assumed responsibility for printing the lab manual under a licensing agreement between Prentice-Hall, Penn State, and Hayden McNeil. The title of the 11th edition was shortened to "*PSU Chemtrek*." Subsequent editions have also used this title.

Along the way, I have tried to fairly reward the contributors and keep the price of the manual down. The original author, Stephen Thompson, and Prentice-Hall have received royalties from all of the Penn State editions. Once Penn State had contributed a significant amount of work to the project, then a portion of the royalties went to Penn State. These are kept in a special account that is used for projects that will improve the running of the labs—i.e., Penn State's royalties are reinvested into Chem 111 and 113. The price of the manual has hardly changed in 10 years. Ultimately, the students have benefited from this arrangement. They have received an excellent, up-to-date lab manual at a fair price.

Contents

Preface

Chemtrek is a laboratory text designed for use by students in a two-semester general chemistry laboratory program for science majors at the college or university level. The chapter topics have been selected to complement areas of chemistry normally presented in an introductory science major's lecture course. The material in the text has been used in the instructional laboratories of a major university over a period of ten years and has thus been thoroughly class-tested and revised numerous times.

There are probably dozens of laboratory manuals in print that fit the above description—so why consider another one? The answer is that *Chemtrek* presents an entirely new, innovative, small-scale, inexpensive, safe, efficient, and extremely effective way to get students involved in the excitement and promise of experimental chemistry.

Chemtrek is the outcome of nearly two decades of research and development in the use of small-scale methods, equipment, and techniques in instructional contexts. The small-scale approach is based on the use of nontraditional, plastic equipment that was originally developed for use in the fields of clinical chemistry, microbiology, and recombinant DNA research. All of the equipment is inexpensive and readily available (worldwide) at chemical supply houses. *Chemtrek* is extremely easy to implement and requires minimal conversion costs. An instructor's technical manual is available and provides necessary information for ordering supplies, preparing solutions and other laboratory necessities as well as for organizing the logistics for any number of students in the laboratory course.

The small-scale *Chemtrek* approach provides solutions to most of the multitude of difficult problems associated with teaching the undergraduate chemistry laboratory. *Chemtrek* is inexpensive to implement because only small quantities of chemicals are required. The small amounts and low cost for chemicals have many synergistic effects in other areas of instruction. Solution preparation time and costs are significantly reduced and inventories can be cut to a bare minimum. Faculty and students need not feel inhibited about exploring interesting additional experiments that always seem to surface naturally during laboratory investigations. "Small" means that you can even consider exotic or expensive materials that would be unthinkable in a traditional lab program.

Small-scale experimental methods have proven to be much safer for the student, the instructor, and the institution. The disposal of wastes is cut to an absolute minimum in the *Chemtrek* program. In fact, an attempt has been made to build in environmental safety and awareness in the design stage rather than to try to control things at the execution stage. It is perhaps crucial to point out that the experiments in *Chemtrek* are not just scaled-down or miniaturized versions of the mundane, traditional "cookbook" approach to experiments. By the way, I have strongly resisted attempts to label the *Chemtrek* approach as microscale or microchemistry. It is not. However, it certainly is on a smaller scale than classical macroscopic experimentation.

Long experience in developing instructional laboratories has made me painfully aware of the enormous problems inherent in the use of scientific instrumentation in an instructional context. Most modern instruments are expensive to buy, difficult to maintain, and are regarded by most learners as problematical "black boxes." My approach in *Chemtrek* is to ask students to build their own instruments wherever possible. This approach is based on the use of an inexpensive multimeter as the basic measuring device—and the only black box allowed! The meter can be connected to various, inexpensive sensors to produce simple but effective devices that can be student-built, are user-friendly, and that reveal the relationship between form and function. Only in this type of context can students begin to gain insight into the hows and whys of instrumental design.

I wrote *Chemtrek* for students. Students actually work from, with, and through laboratory texts. Each chapter represents a particular area of chemistry and is divided into three parts: Introduction, Background Chemistry, and Laboratory Experiments. The Introduction situates the chemistry within a life or application context and tells students why they are being asked to do the experiments. The Background Chemistry section provides more specific details about various chemical aspects of the experiments, without answering the major questions in advance. Students are encouraged to read the Introduction and Background Chemistry before coming to lab. A Pre-Laboratory Quiz is provided so that students can test themselves on the reading material.

Different types of information have been integrated within the Laboratory Experiments sections. Students are encouraged to record real-time observations, answer questions, get involved in peer discussions, design experiments, and interact with their instructor. Every chapter contains qualitative and quantitative aspects of both theory and experiment, and each ends with an application, an unknown sample for identification and analysis, or a research project.

In teaching chemistry laboratory with *Chemtrek*, we have already seen some serendipitous advantages to small-scale methods. Small-scale focuses the students' attention on having insights, on realizing concepts, on understanding intelligible processes, and on the value of constantly questioning textual and instructional authority! Small-scale provides a new way to teach creative problem solving, the processes of invention and discovery, analytical thinking, effective writing, and the elements of descriptive chemistry.

"Great problems are solved by being broken down into little problems. The strokes of genius are but the outcome of a continuous habit of inquiry that grasps clearly and distinctly all that is involved in the simple things that anyone can understand."

—Bernard J.F. Lonergan,
Insight, A Study of Human Understanding

Acknowledgments

It has taken a long time to write this book. It would have never happened at all if it were not for the encouragement of my undergraduate and graduate students at Colorado State University. We academics must always remember that the students are the reason for the university!

I would like to express my appreciation to the U.S. Department of Education Fund for the Improvement of Post-Secondary Education and the Carnegie Corporation for a Mina Shaughnessy Scholar Award that allowed me two summers of time to write and reflect. I have been enriched by the Woodrow Wilson and the Camille and Henry Dreyfus Foundations for giving me the opportunity to meet people with extraordinary energy, enthusiasm, and dedication to teaching. I would also like to thank the faculty and cadets of the Chemistry Department of the United States Air Force Academy for a most delightful and productive year as a visiting professor.

I would like to thank Randy Matsushima, John Schmidt, Bob Breuer, John Murray, Marilyn Bain Ackerman, K. Vasudevan, Louise Saddoris, Pete Markow, Steve Sadlowski, Alan Kopelove, Ed Brehm, Shawn Fujita, Sri Bringi, Carl Schanbacher, John Stringer, John Haase, Rene Elles, and Don Dick for their insights, suggestions, hard work and faith.

I can never repay the debt of friendship to Rob Cohen, Bill Cook, Ted Kuwana, Thad Mauney, Ed Waterman, and Mike Braydich. These friends never failed to shine light during my own dark struggle with the flight from understanding.

Without doubt, no project like this could ever be successful without the total commitment from dedicated technical staff. Mrs. Jackie Resseguie was there at the beginning, providing continuous encouragement throughout the project, and solved all of the enormous logistical problems in the actual implementation of *Chemtrek*. Thanks also go to all her staff, particularly Lynne Judish, who helped enormously in the development work. I would also like to thank the staff at Technical Texts for their patience and help in creating the final product.

Finally, my heartfelt thanks go to my wife Marsha Schlepp Thompson, who produced this camera-ready text and chemical structures (on a MacPlus) from my handwritten draft and endless revisions. She coordinated the whole project with equanimity, good humor, grace and love!

Stephen Thompson

Acknowledgments

Introduction

Small Is Beautiful

A Discussion with the
Student about the
Advantages of Using
Small-Scale Equipment
and Techniques in the
Study of Science

The Need for a New Approach in the Laboratory

I recognize that most of you are thinking seriously about a career in science and that only a few of you wish to be chemists. However, I would like to try to explain why the chemistry laboratory is one place where you can actually do science and start becoming a scientist. The laboratory, unlike the lecture room, is one place where you can and should question and test all those accepted facts about how nature works. Doing science, rather than listening to someone else talk about it, always generates new perspectives and new ways of synthesizing knowledge. Professors and textbooks (including this one) should only serve as a guide. I have every confidence that you can make original observations, design new types of experiments, and seek out new knowledge—even though you may only be a freshman!

I am sure that you are asking the question, "Why should I have to take a *Chemistry* laboratory, of all things?" One answer is that a knowledge of chemistry and of the experimental methods by which chemical information is obtained has proved to be useful in almost all areas of science and technology. Chemistry is the study of matter and its transformations. Chemists have invented and refined a unique and powerful ideography (pictorial way of representing matters) that can be used to rationalize and explain the results of over two centuries of experimentation with matter. Matter is described by three-dimensional structures consisting of atoms held together by a variety of electronic forces. These structural representations have proven to be crucial concepts in fields as diverse as designing new plastics and genetic engineering. Transformations of matter are pictured in the form of dynamic chemical reactions in which old bonds are broken and new arrangements produced. What is truly remarkable about this view on matter is that it was constructed out of the information from chemical experiments carried out on real gases, liquids, and solids—long before anyone had actually "seen" a molecule. What is perhaps even more astonishing is that the molecular images produced by the scanning tunneling microscope, a new microscope capable of resolving individual atomic dimensions, appear to confirm and support the chemical ideography. The congruence of scientific imagination and technological image clearly demonstrates that chemistry is an information science of great beauty, utility, and predictive power.

The development of the creative scientific approach to solving problems has come at a time when the scale of human interference in natural processes has reached dangerous levels. Life in the global village is becoming increasingly complex and subject to technological disintegration. We are faced simultaneously with devastating population increases, severe soil erosion, environmental degradation, and potentially disastrous global climate changes. Energy production from fossil fuels becomes increasingly costly, both in terms of the waste of nonrenewable resources and in the aquatic and atmospheric degradation caused by combustion products. The technological backlash is inevitable and will occur worldwide. The disasters at Minamata (Japan), Three Mile Island (United States), Bhopal (India), Chernobyl (Soviet Union), and Valdez in Prince William Sound (United States) attest to the destructive potential. The headlines become more strident everyday: "Can dry armpits cause a world crisis?," "Is the 1988 drought a result of the greenhouse effect?," "There is a hole in the ozone layer again!," and "Exxon-Valdez—America' Chernobyl."

It is now more important than ever to remain skeptical about the claims made about new "breakthrough" technologies, especially those in the areas of energy production, biotechnology, and agriculture. The thoughtful application of human scientific wisdom and an ongoing commitment to conservation are the keys to solving these very complex problems.

Small—And the Best of All Worlds!

The chemistry laboratory is a good place in which to begin to understand the scientific principles inherent in some of these complex issues. One of the strengths of the scientific approach to problem solving is the experimental testing of concepts. The concepts derive from human imagination and are found to be true or false by the test of their behavior. The constant tension and interplay between insight, imagination, thought, and experimentation constitute the foundation of all methods, including science.

I am sure that most of you have not had the opportunity (or the inclination or the time, for that matter) to compare various texts for the chemistry laboratory. I have, and I would like to explain how this book is different and why I believe that the difference is important. Earlier in this introduction, I pointed out that chemistry is the study of matter and its transformations. It would seem practical and sensible to study small amounts of matter wherever possible. After all, unless you want large amounts for some reason, 10 milligrams of matter is as representative of matter as, say, 100 grams. The reason is obvious. Molecules are so small—10^{20} molecules ($\sim$ 10 mg) is as good as 10^{24} molecules ($\sim$ 100 g)! All the chemical investigations included in this text have been designed to require only small amounts of matter, usually in the tens of milligrams and less than one milliliter range. There are some tremendous advantages to working with small amounts of matter:

- Small-scale experiments are *much safer* for you.

- The use of small amounts of chemicals means that there is *less waste* to dispose of.

- The use of small amounts naturally leads to *conservation* of valuable resources.

- Small-scale systems tend to be *user-friendly* and facilitate scientific comparisons, even in complex environments.

- Small scale means *less expensive*, for you, the student, and for the institution.

Experimental chemistry carried out on a small scale requires apparatus and instruments that are different from the traditional, large-scale glass and metal ware that most of us usually associate with chemistry laboratories (beakers, test tubes, ring stands, Bunsen burners, etc.). Fortunately, there have recently been tremendous advances in the development of sophisticated small-scale equipment for use in the fields of genetic engineering, clinical chemistry, and recombinant DNA. Much of the nontraditional small-scale equipment is made out of plastic, and most of it was originally designed to be disposable. We are going to reuse it and recycle it wherever possible. The plastics are polystyrene (e.g., microreaction trays), polyethylene (e.g., pipets and microburets), and polypropylene (e.g., straws—yes, the very kind you use to drink your sodas). All three plastics have chemical properties that can be exploited in the innovative design and use of tools for science. All have surfaces that are nonwetted by aqueous solutions. Nonwetted surfaces make the storage, transfer, and delivery of aqueous solutions much easier than, say, glass surfaces. The high surface tension of water means that in the presence

of a plastic, a drop can be its own container and a reproducible volume increment at the same time. The ease of production of small drops from plastic tubes leads naturally to digital methods in volumetric work. Counting drops can circumvent the problems inherent in the analog methods of meniscus reading. The low softening and melting point of these materials, together with the ease with which they can be stuck, bent, cut, and otherwise mutilated naturally leads to innovative construction. Of course, in an experimental science such as chemistry, there is occasionally a need for glass or metal materials. When this need arises, we will not hesitate to use small quantities and small tools.

The modern scientific research laboratory also contains many types of sophisticated and expensive instrumentation—such as gas chromatographs, nuclear magnetic resonance spectrometers, pH meters, and electronic balances. These instruments are often interfaced with dedicated microcomputers and are therefore referred to as "smart" instruments. Unfortunately, these "smart" instruments are "black boxes" that may be operated by anyone who knows which button to push, hence the cliché, "smart instruments, dumb students." In this laboratory course you will have the opportunity to build many of the instruments needed for quantitative chemical studies. The instrument design has deliberately been kept as simple as possible to enable you to focus on the fundamental operational principles. When you build your own scientific instrument,

- *You* know how it works.

- *You* can fix it when it breaks.

- *You* can play with it whenever you wish to.

- *You* begin to understand the connection between form and function.

- *You* begin to understand the real nature of experimental error and approximation.

- *You* can usually take on the more sophisticated versions with confidence.

How to Use this Book

Each chapter of *Chemtrek* contains three major divisions: Introduction, Background Chemistry, and Laboratory Experiments. The Introduction gives you an overview of a particular area of chemistry and tells you why you are being asked to carry out the laboratory experiments. The Background Chemistry contains more information about the chemical principles that are important in the laboratory experiments. You should read the Introduction and Background Chemistry sections before you go to the laboratory. Find out for yourself whether you have grasped the main ideas by taking the Pre-Laboratory Quiz. Go back to the Introduction and Background Chemistry, and I am sure that you will be able to find the answers fairly easily.

Each section of the Laboratory Experiments will usually include questions and requests to do calculations. These will typically be in one of two formats: "bullet (•)" questions, and "Q" questions. Bullet (•) questions are generally hints. They do not need to be answered, although it may be helpful to do so. "Q" questions, however, should always be answered in your notebook whenever they arise. They are designed to tie together the theory associated with the preceding experiments. The bulk of your report grade will be based on your answers to these questions. Your instructor will give you additional information as to how you will be expected to write your laboratory reports. One of the most important skills a scientist must acquire is the ability to write as thoughts occur and as experiments evolve. Learning to write as you work in the laboratory is not easy. However, you will find the more you write, the better you will become. If you keep an ongoing scientific diary, you will be amazed at how your communication skills will develop and mature. The actual format of your laboratory report that is required by your instructor will be given to you during the first laboratory session.

The Relationship Between Laboratory and Lecture

It is virtually impossible for the laboratory course to be completely coordinated with the lecture course—they represent two entirely different methods of learning. However, your instructor has planned the sequence of laboratory work very carefully so that you will not be confronted with major new concepts until you have encountered them in lecture. Occasionally, you may find that you have not had much time to assimilate lecture concepts before you start using them in laboratory. Don't panic. Read the Introduction and Background Chemistry and don't hesitate to ask your instructors (in both laboratory and lecture) for help. This is an educational institution, and we are here to help you!

Laboratory Safety

Experimentation in a chemistry laboratory always has an element of danger and risk associated with it. This is particularly true if the surroundings, tools, and techniques are new and unfamiliar. In the process of writing this text, I have performed all the experimental procedures dozens of times (some of them hundreds of times). I did this in order to critically assess the risk factors inherent in each step. It is obviously impossible, in any situation, to be sure that there is zero risk. However, the risk can be kept to an absolute minimum by using a small-scale approach (as in this text) and by adhering to the following precepts:

• Recognize in advance, before you come to laboratory, which operations are likely to involve more risk than usual. Your instructor will give you information about these operations at least one week ahead of the laboratory.

• Try to be safety conscious when you work in the laboratory. Be aware not only of your personal safety, but also of your peer group safety.

• Recognize that even a safe task could possibly be dangerous if not carried out according to instructions.

- Be aware of the general safety features appropriate to the room, laboratory, and building that you are working in. Again, your instructor will familiarize you with the location of fire extinguishers, safety showers, and the steps to take if the fire alarm goes off.

- Wear your eye protection.

- Only work in the laboratory when an instructor is present. Experience is invaluable in unusual or unforeseen situations.

- Report any accident, *however slight*, to your instructor. Don't wait; report it immediately.

- Don't eat or smoke in the chemistry laboratory.

I have found from experience that the majority of accidents in undergraduate laboratories are caused by:

- The insertion of glass tubing through cork or rubber stoppers.

- Cuts caused by broken or chipped glassware.

- Burns from touching hot metal or other heated objects.

The use of small-scale plastic equipment has been found to eliminate many of these problems. However, it is important to recognize that numerous chemicals and solutions that you will be using are corrosive and can cause burns. Your instructor will provide you with the appropriate cautions and inform you of the steps to take if you do spill chemicals. Most of the chemicals and materials needed for the laboratory experiments will be placed either at a location near your workspace, called an "arms reach station," or at a convenient central location in the room called "reagent central."

1

Experiment 1

Calorimetry

Adapted by Caitlin Conn and Patrick Crooks from *The Chemurgy of Peanuts* by Genevieve Miller.

Introduction

NOTE: If you are allergic to peanuts, please inform your instructor or TA immediately so that you can be assigned a different experiment.

Energy is crucial to the survival of every living thing. As humans, our bodies need to remain within a relatively narrow temperature range. We "burn food" (internally) to stay warm. We also burn food to provide energy to do work. All bodily functions require energy—walking, talking, exercising, even studying and sleeping.

The burning of our food to produce energy can be viewed in a general sense as a type of combustion reaction. A combustion reaction is defined in *Chemistry: The Central Science* as "[a] chemical reaction that proceeds with evolution of heat and usually also a flame." This textbook goes on to say that most combustion reactions involve oxygen (1). The reactions in our bodies don't produce flames, but they do involve oxygen, and they do produce energy that is often released as heat.

You may have heard of "burning calories" in reference to exercise. Please note that calories are not substances that are burned—i.e., "burning calories" is an inaccurate way of speaking. A calorie is simply a unit that is a measure of energy. During exercise, the body burns food to release energy (or a part of our bodies, such as fat), and that energy can be measured in different units, such as calories.

In this experiment you will examine the calorie content of a common food item, peanuts—i.e., you will measure how many calories of heat are released when peanuts are burned. You will also be burning paraffin. Paraffin is the material that candles are made of. When you burn a candle, paraffin is combusted, and energy is produced in the form of light and heat. You will be determining the heat released by the combustion of paraffin as part of this lab.

In order to determine the heat produced from the burning of peanuts and paraffin, you will build your own calorimeter out of household items. A calorimeter is defined as "an apparatus that measures the evolution of heat" (1).

Lastly, you will do some theoretical calculations to help you understand the relationship between calories and work.

Background Chemistry

Overview

The metabolic reactions that take place inside our body are vital to our existence. One of the most fundamental examples of metabolism is digestion. The process of digestion is most certainly a chemical one—it is an example of a combustion reaction: food reacts with oxygen to generate energy.

Foods produce the same amount of energy whether they undergo combustion under metabolic conditions or they are burned outside the body. We can, then, calculate the energy value of food by burning it and measuring the amount of heat that is released from the reaction. To ensure accuracy, chemists use calorimeters, devices that measure temperature changes from chemical reactions, to determine the energy produced by a reaction.

Food energy is measured in Food Calories (indicated with a capital "C", sometimes abbreviated as "Cal"). One "Food Calorie" is 1000 times bigger than a "scientific calorie"—that is, 1 Cal = 1000 cal = 1 kcal. One scientific calorie is the energy required to raise the temperature of 1 g of water by 1 °C from a standard temperature at 1 atmosphere pressure. For clarity, throughout this lab we will use the symbol "FC" to indicate Food Calories, and "cal" to indicate scientific calories.

In this experiment, you will measure the amount of energy released by the combustion of several different substances. The energy released during combustion will raise the temperature of a measured volume of water in a simple calorimeter. We can determine the exact amount of energy released because we know the specific heat of water. The specific heat of water is 1.0 cal per g per °C, or 1 FC per kg per °C. By measuring the temperature change in a known mass of water, you can determine the amount of energy that the water has absorbed.

Energy released = (mass of H_2O heated) × (temperature increase) × (specific heat of H_2O)
(Eqn. 1) (2)

Paraffin Calorimetry

Paraffin can be burned to release energy. The energy content of paraffin, the type of paraffin typically found in candles, is 10.0 kcal/g (3). Another word for paraffin is "alkane," which is a particular type of organic molecule. Just as there are many alkanes, there are many different kinds of paraffins. Most paraffins are not very reactive at room temperature and one atmosphere pressure, but they can be burned by increasing temperature and/or pressure. Paraffin combustion produces water and carbon dioxide and releases energy (4).

Besides being used in candles, paraffin was being considered as a potential rocket fuel as of 2003. NASA noted the increased safety and decreased pollution that would result from using paraffin as an energy source (5). Paraffin is also used as a cosmetic and is frequently applied to the skin to soften it.

Peanut Calorimetry

Peanuts are known for their high energy value. On average, a peanut contains 6 Food Calories per gram of energy. In fact, one pound of peanut butter contains the same energy found in 32 eggs or 2.5 pounds of steak. It is this high energy value and the low cost of peanuts that led George Washington Carver to encourage the consumption of nuts during the Depression.

Peanut oil can be represented by the molecule in Figure 1.1 with the formula $C_{57}H_{104}O_6$. Please note that at each vertex, a carbon atom is present. In addition, hydrogen atoms (not shown) are present at each vertex, as many as necessary to provide four bonds to each carbon.

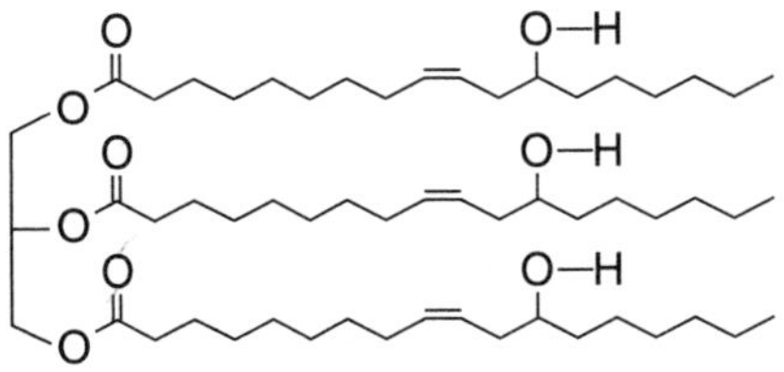

Figure 1.1 The molecular structure of peanut oil. (2)

The combustion reaction for the peanut oil shown in Figure 1.1 is given in Equation 2.

$$C_{57}H_{104}O_6(l) + 80\ O_2(g) \rightarrow 57\ CO_2(g) + 52\ H_2O(l) + \text{heat}$$
(Eqn. 2) (2)

Energy Conversion

Energy can be measured in many different units. You may need to refer to the textbooks available to you in the lab to complete some of the questions in this experiment. You will also need to use two other energy units: "foot-pound" and "Joules." A foot-pound is the energy required to lift one pound one foot high. A table of useful conversion factors is provided below. You will use this information to relate energy and work. Be sure to properly cite any additional sources that you find in your lab and use to complete the questions.

Table 1. Useful Conversion Factors[6]

1 Cal = 1000 cal = 1 kcal
1 cal = 3.08 foot-pounds
1 J = 0.738 foot-pounds
1 cal = 4.18 J

References

1. Brown, Theodore L., H. Eugene LeMay, Jr., and Bruce E. Bursten. *Chemistry: The Central Science.* 10th Edition. Page G3. Pearson Education, Inc.: Upper Saddle River, NJ, 2006.

2. Miller, Genevieve. *The Chemurgy of Peanuts.* Chemistry 111 Make-up Lab. Spring 2008.

3. "The Energy Content of Fuels: A Physical Science Activity." *University of Virginia Physics Department.* October 25, 2008. <http://galileo.phys.virginia.edu/outreach/8thGradeSOL/FuelEnergy.htm>.

4. McMurry, John. *Organic Chemistry.* 7th Edition. Page 91. Thomson Learning, Inc.: Belmont, CA, 2008.

5. "Candle Stick Rocketship." *NASA.* January 9, 2003. October 25, 2008. <http://science.nasa.gov/headlines/y2003/28jan_envirorocket.htm>.

6. Walker, Jearl. *Fundamentals of Physics Part 3.* John Wiley and Sons, Inc.: Hoboken, NJ, 2008.

7. Markow, Peter G., *Estimating the Calorie Content of Nuts,* Chemical Education Resources, Inc., Pennsylvania, 1993. (Many of the experiments in Genevieve Miller's make-up lab, Reference 2, are based on this publication.)

Quiz Outline

Typically there is no quiz on this lab. A post-lab quiz on Experiment 3 (Small-Scale Techniques) is generally given on the day of this experiment. Check with your TA to be sure.

NOTE: Please bring an empty soda can (or two!) to lab for this experiment.

Laboratory Experiments

Flowchart of the Experiments

Section A.	Construction of a Calorimeter

Section B.	Combustion of a Candle

Section C.	Combustion of a Peanut

Section D.	Energy and Work

Section A.   Construction of a Calorimeter

Goal: To build a functional small-scale calorimeter that is capable of determining the amount of heat released in a chemical reaction.

Before You Begin: You are about to build a device similar to the one in the diagram shown below. As you work through this section, refer to the diagram to facilitate the construction of your calorimeter. You may work in pairs for this experiment.

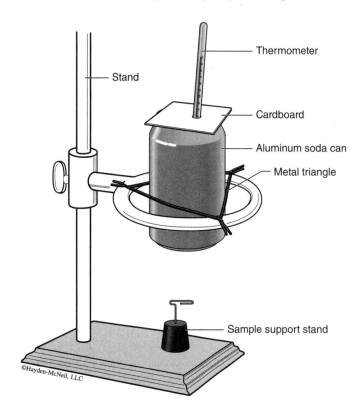

Figure 1.2 Small-scale calorimeter.

Experimental Steps:

1.   Obtain 1 empty aluminum soda can, 1 metal triangle, a square piece of cardboard about 15 cm × 15 cm, a ring stand (this consists of a stand, a ring, and a clamp), and a thermometer. These materials will be used to construct your calorimeter.

2.   Suspend your can in the middle of the ring using the provided materials. Experiment with different setups if necessary. You may not need to use all the provided materials. Check with a TA to make sure your setup is sufficient.

3.   Place the cardboard square on top of the can, and put a mark on the place directly above the hole in the top of the soda can. Punch a hole in the cardboard square at the spot you marked, and insert the thermometer in this hole. The hole should be small enough to hold the thermometer in place. Place the cardboard square on top of the soda can and adjust the position of the thermometer until the bulb extends into the can about 5 cm from the bottom.

| **Section B.** | **Combustion of a Candle** |

Goal: To measure the heat released by a burning candle using a homemade calorimeter.

Experimental Steps:

1. Carefully measure 200.0 mL of distilled water by filling your 100 mL volumetric flask twice. Remove the thermometer assembly from the soda can and pour the water into the can.

2. Reposition the thermometer assembly and measure the initial water temperature. Record this temperature in your lab notebook.

3. Obtain a candle and the bottom part of a Petri dish (the smaller part). Stand the candle up in the Petri dish.

4. Determine the mass of the combined candle and Petri dish. Record your value.

5. Transfer the candle and dish to the ring stand, directly underneath the calorimeter. Adjust the can clamp so that the bottom of the can rests 1–2 cm above the top of the candle.

6. Light the candle and let it burn. When the temperature of the water has risen by approximately 10 degrees, gently blow out the candle and record the final temperature of the water. Stir the water before taking a reading.

7. Find the new mass of the candle and Petri dish system and record the value.

Questions:

Q1. Find the energy released per gram of paraffin. Put your answer in terms of Food Calories/g.

Q2. The accepted energy content value for paraffin is 10,000 cal/g. Convert this value to Food Calories per gram.

Q3. How does the value you found compare with the accepted value of the energy content of paraffin? Calculate your percent error.

Q4. (a) What are some possible sources of error in this experiment?

(b) What is the largest source of error?

(c) What can be altered in the experiment to improve the accuracy of the calorimeter?

8. Make any change to your calorimeter that you think will improve its accuracy and repeat steps 1–7.

Q5. (a) What change did you make to your calorimeter?

(b) Did you get a more accurate result for the energy capacity of paraffin?

Q6. Create a table that organizes all of your data from both trials.

Q7. Patrick thinks that burning the candle until the temperature has risen only 5 degrees will yield more accurate results, but Caitlin thinks that it won't make a difference. Who is right, and why?

Section C.	**Combustion of a Peanut**

Goal: To measure the heat released from burning a peanut using a homemade calorimeter.

Experimental Steps:

1. First obtain a paper clip and a cork, which will be used to construct a peanut support stand.

2. Straighten one end of the paper clip. Insert the end of the paper clip into the center of the end of the cork which has the smaller diameter. You will place the peanut support stand on the base of the ring stand used in the calorimeter assembly. (See figure in Section A.)

3. Carefully measure 200.0 mL of room temperature water. Remove the thermometer assembly from the soda can and pour the water into the can. Record the amount of water used.

4. Reposition the thermometer assembly.

5. Select half of one peanut for your study. (Two peanuts come in a typical shell. You should be using half of a single peanut.)

6. Determine the mass of the peanut half. Record this value.

7. Transfer the peanut half to the support stand by inserting the free end of the paper clip into the peanut half. Position the peanut support stand underneath the can so that the peanut is 1–2 cm below the bottom of the can.

8. Measure the initial water temperature. Record this temperature.

9. Ignite the peanut. (This may take several attempts. Be careful not to burn yourself. Using tweezers to hold the match may help.) Extinguish the match by putting it into some water.

10. Immediately after the peanut stops burning, determine the final temperature of the water. Record this temperature.

11. What remains of the peanut is called the "peanut residue." Allow the peanut residue to cool to room temperature. Determine the mass of the peanut residue.

12. Record the mass of the peanut burned by subtracting the mass of the peanut residue from the initial mass of the peanut.

Q8. Calculate the amount of energy released per gram of peanut burned in units of Food Calories/g.

Q9. Find the accepted value for the energy content of a peanut in Food Calories/g by reading the nutrition information on the peanut bag. Calculate the percent error of your value compared to the accepted value.

13. Repeat steps 5–12, this time using a *whole* peanut.

Q10.   Calculate the amount of energy released per gram of peanut burned. How does this value compare to that of the first trial using the peanut half? Should these values be different? Why or why not?

Q11.   Create a table that organizes all of your data from both trials.

Q12.   The peanut residue is similar to charcoal, a compound of pure carbon. Consider the combustion reaction of charcoal and use this information to calculate a theoretical energy yield for the peanut residue. (Use data from either trial.)

$$C(s) + O_2(g) \rightarrow CO_2(g)$$
ΔH_f of Carbon Dioxide $= -393.5$ kJ/mole

Q13.   Add the heat released by the burning peanut to the theoretical value for the heat of combustion of the peanut residue to get the total theoretical heat of combustion of the peanut. Divide this by the original mass of the peanut to get a theoretical heat of combustion for a completely burned peanut in Food Calories/g. How does this value compare to your previous calculated values? How does it compare to the accepted value?

Section D.   Energy and Work

Goal: *To connect the concepts of energy and work.*

Experimental Steps: 1.   One foot-pound is the amount of energy expended when a force of one pound acts through a distance of one foot along the direction of the force. Have one lab member perform an action of work and convert the amount of work done into foot-pounds. For example: step up 0.5 foot on a stool rung or lift a 1-pound book three feet.

Q14.   Convert the amount of work you just did into Food Calories.

Q15.   (a) Make an educated guess of how many grams of peanuts you would have to eat to do the amount of work you did in question 1. (Assume that all the potential energy in the peanut is completely combusted in the body and turned into usable energy.)

(b) Now calculate how many *grams* of peanuts are required using the nutritional information from the peanut label.

(c) How many *peanuts* would this be, assuming they all have the same mass as the peanut you weighed in Section C?

Q16.   Was your guess higher or lower than your calculated value?

Q17.   When running, an average person burns 0.653 Food Calories/mile-pound. How many Food Calories does a 150-pound person burn when running a mile?

Q18.   Theoretically, how many *grams* of peanuts would you have to eat to run a mile? (Assume, again, that all the potential energy in the peanut is completely combusted in the body and turned into usable energy.) How many *peanuts* would this be? Does this answer surprise you?

Experiment 2

Spectroscopy

The Interaction of Light and Matter

"We all *know* what light is; but it is not easy to *tell* what it is."

— Samuel Johnson

Introduction

In certain parts of South America there exists a most beautiful and remarkable species called the railroad worm (*Phrixothrix*). Yellowish-green luminous spots are arranged in eleven pairs on the worm's abdominal segments, and on its head there are two additional red luminous spots. When the worm is disturbed all the spots give off light, and as it undulates through the night, it looks like a miniature railroad train. Of course, this biological midnight express emits an amazingly small amount of energy in the form of visible radiation (light) compared to the many other natural and manmade sources. Our world is literally inundated with all kinds of radiation, much of it coming from our own sun. Daylight that comes from the sun is a very small part of the spectrum of electromagnetic radiation. From cosmic rays to radiowaves, the total electromagnetic spectrum includes all the known types of radiation (see Table 2.1).

Radiation may be described in one of two ways: either as a stream of energy pulses (photons) or as energy waves sent out from a source (worms, suns, etc.) at the speed of light. Scientists dodge the bullet by using whichever interpretation works best to explain an experiment involving radiation. The photon and wave theories are linked by Planck's Law:

$$E = h\nu$$

where E is the photon energy in joules (J), ν is the frequency of the radiation (Hz or s^{-1}), and h is Planck's constant (6.63×10^{-34} Js). Wavelength and frequency are related by

$$c = \lambda\nu$$

where c is the speed of light (3×10^8 ms^{-1}), λ is the wavelength of the radiation (often reported in nm), and ν the frequency. It is useful to note that energy and frequency are directly proportional to each other, whereas energy is inversely proportional to wavelength.

Sources of radiation are extraordinarily diverse, ranging from complex nuclear fusion reactions in supernovae to burning zirconium foil in photographic flash cubes. In spite of this diversity, the amount and type of emitted radiation are intimately related to the chemistry of the processes that produce the radiation. It is this link that forms the basis for the science of spectroscopy. *Spectroscopy* is the study of the interaction of electromagnetic radiation with matter. When matter is energized (excited) by the application of thermal, electrical, nuclear, or radiant energy, electromagnetic radiation is often emitted as the matter relaxes back to its original (ground) state. The spectrum of radiation emitted by a substance that has absorbed energy is called an *emission spectrum*, and the science is appropriately called *emission spectroscopy*.

Another approach often used to study the interaction of electromagnetic radiation with matter is one whereby a continuous range of radiation (e.g., white light) is allowed to fall on a substance, and then the frequencies absorbed by the substance are examined. The resulting spectrum from the substance contains the original range of radiation with dark spaces that correspond to the missing, or absorbed, frequencies. This type of spectrum is called an *absorption spectrum*. In spectroscopy the emitted or absorbed radiation is usually analyzed, i.e., separated into the various frequency components, and the intensity is measured by means of an instrument called a *spectrometer*.

The resultant spectrum is mainly a graph of the intensity of emitted or absorbed radiation versus wavelength or frequency. There are in general three types of spectra: continuous, line, and band. The sun and heated solids produce *continuous spectra* in which the emitted radiation contains *all* frequencies within a region of the electromagnetic spectrum. A rainbow and light from a lightbulb are examples of continuous spectra. *Line spectra* (illustrated in Figure 2.l) are produced by excited *atoms* in the gas phase and contain only certain frequencies, all other frequencies being absent. Each chemical element of the periodic chart has a unique and, therefore, characteristic line spectrum. *Band spectra* are produced by excited *molecules* emitting radiation in groups of closely spaced lines that merge to form bands.

These categories of emission and absorption spectra contain tremendous amounts of useful information about the structure and composition of matter. Spectroscopy is a powerful and sensitive form of chemical analysis, as well as a method of probing electronic and nuclear structure and chemical bonding. The key to interpreting this spectral information is the knowledge that certain atomic and molecular processes involve only specific energy ranges. Table 2.1 shows the regions of the electromagnetic spectrum and the associated energy transitions that occur in atomic and molecular processes.

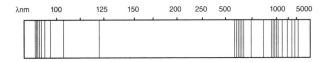

Figure 2.1 Line spectrum of hydrogen.

A simple example of the energy changes involved in particular transitions and the resulting spectrum is the hydrogen emission spectrum. This spectrum is especially interesting for historical, theoretical, and practical reasons. Over a period of 40 years, from 1885 to 1925, all of the lines in the emission spectrum in the ultraviolet, visible, and infrared regions were found experimentally and were identified with various electron transitions. Spectroscopic experiments like the above gave the major experimental evidence for the Bohr theory of the atom and eventually for the modern quantum theory.

Much of the scientific knowledge of the structure of the universe, from stars to atoms, is derived from interpretations of the interaction of radiation with matter. One example of the power of these techniques is the determination of the composition, the velocities, and the evolutionary dynamics of stars. The source of the incredible amount of energy produced by the sun is nuclear fusion reactions going on within the hot interior (temperature 40×10^6 K). Two fusion cycles, the carbon cycle and the proton cycle, convert hydrogen nuclei into helium nuclei via heavier nuclei, such as carbon 12 and nitrogen 14. The enormous radiation of energy from the hot core seethes outwards by convection. This radiation consists of the entire electromagnetic spectrum as a continuous spectrum. Towards the surface of the sun (the photosphere), the temperatures are much lower, and the cooler atoms of different elements all absorb at their characteristic frequencies. The radiation that shoots into space towards the earth is a continuous emission spectrum with about 22,000 dark absorption lines present in it (Fraunhofer lines), of which about 70% have been identified. These absorption lines—i.e., missing frequencies—prove that more than 60 terrestrial elements are certainly present in the sun.

Stellar spectroscopy via satellites has shown unequivocally that all the known elements of the periodic chart are made in complex sequences of fusion reactions in stars. The absorption lines also have different intensities at different temperatures, and the spectra are therefore excellent indicators of the temperature of a given stellar atmosphere. Absorption lines of stellar spectra can also be used to measure star velocities (relative to the earth) by measuring the Doppler effect. When a source sends out light of a specific frequency, the frequency remains the same only if the distance between the source and receiver stays the same. If the source is moving towards the earth, the light will appear to be of a higher frequency—i.e., bluer—than the light of a similar source in the laboratory. Conversely, the light of a receding source appears to be of lower frequency and, thus, redder (see Figure 2.2). The Doppler effect is easily measured by comparing the stellar spectrum with the spectrum of matter made luminous in the laboratory.

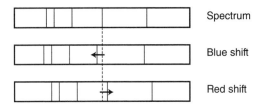

Figure 2.2 Spectral shifts due to the Doppler effect.

The science of spectroscopy can take us into the subatomic world or out into the farthest distance of space. The development of lasers is now causing a revolution in many areas of spectroscopy. These coherent, almost monochromatic, sources can be used to study extraordinarily fast chemical processes, as well as such previously inaccessible processes as flames and combustion. Recent research has shown that all living objects emit low-intensity radiation that may be detected and analyzed with modern photoelectronic techniques.

Table 2.1 Spectral Regions in the Electromagnetic Spectrum

Type of Radiation (i.e., Spectral Region)	Energy Range (E, Joule)	Frequency Range (ν, Hz)	Wavelength Range (λ)	Energy Transition
γ-ray	4.0×10^{-14}	6.0×10^{19}	$<5 \times 10^{-3}$ nm	Nuclear
X-ray	$4.0 \times 10^{-14} - 2.0 \times 10^{-17}$	$6.0 \times 10^{19} - 3.0 \times 10^{16}$	$5 \times 10^{-3} - 10$ nm	Inner-shell electrons
Vacuum UV	$2.0 \times 10^{-17} - 1.1 \times 10^{-18}$	$3.0 \times 10^{16} - 1.7 \times 10^{15}$	$10 - 180$ nm	Middle-shell electrons
Near UV	$1.1 \times 10^{-18} - 5.7 \times 10^{-19}$	$1.7 \times 10^{15} - 8.6 \times 10^{14}$	$180 - 350$ nm	Valence electrons
Visible	$5.7 \times 10^{-19} - 2.6 \times 10^{-19}$	$8.6 \times 10^{14} - 3.9 \times 10^{14}$	$350 - 770$ nm	Valence electrons
Infared	$2.6 \times 10^{-19} - 4.0 \times 10^{-21}$	$3.9 \times 10^{14} - 6.0 \times 10^{12}$	770 nm $- 50$ μm	Molecular vibrations
Far Infrared	$4.0 \times 10^{-21} - 2.0 \times 10^{-22}$	$6.0 \times 10^{12} - 3.0 \times 10^{11}$	$50 - 1000$ μm	Molecular rotations
Microwave	$2.0 \times 10^{-22} - 6.6 \times 10^{-25}$	$3.0 \times 10^{11} - 1.0 \times 10^{9}$	$0.1 - 30$ cm	Molecular rotations
Radiowave	$< 6.6 \times 10^{-25}$	$< 1.0 \times 10^{9}$	> 30 cm	Nuclear and electron spin

Background Chemistry

"The most directly compelling evidence for the quantization of energy comes from the observation of the frequencies of light absorbed and emitted by atoms and molecules."

— *P. W. Atkins*

Atoms, ions, and molecules contain electrons that occupy discrete energy levels. The actual energy of each state (level) is dependent upon several factors: the nuclear charge, the distance of the electron from the nucleus, and the number of electrons between the nucleus and the electron in question. The transition of an electron from one level to another must be accompanied by the emission or absorption of a discrete amount of energy. The magnitude of this energy depends on the energy of each of the levels between which the transition occurs.

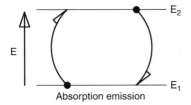

Figure 2.3 Energy Level Transitions

In the instance illustrated above in Figure 2.3, the energy involved in the electron transition (ΔE) will equal the energy difference between E_2 and E_1:

$$\Delta E = E_2 - E_1$$

For *energy emission* to occur, electrons must first be given energy from some external process—e.g., an electrical discharge, a combustion reaction, or a heated wire. They are then said to move from the *ground state* to an *excited state*. The excited electrons then "relax" back to their original levels, and energy is emitted. The number and type of these transitions depend on the particular structure of the energy levels in a given chemical species and on various quantum selection rules. These properties are unique to each individual species and give rise to an emission of energies that characterizes that species. If the value of ΔE lies within the visible region of the total electromagnetic spectrum, then the frequency corresponds to visible light, and the emission can be seen by the eye. From a practical point of view, since

each electron can undergo many transitions and since many species have many electrons, emission spectra usually consist of a very large number of discrete frequencies.

The wave theory of radiation is particularly useful in providing models for interpreting the behavior of light emitted from atoms. Radiation is a form of energy consisting of oscillating electric and magnetic fields that move the direction of propagation at the speed of light. The wave motion, which is illustrated in Figure 2.4, is described in terms of some fundamental properties such as amplitude A, wavelength λ, and frequency ν.

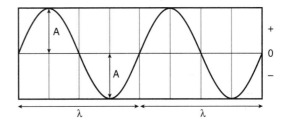

Figure 2.4 A Wave

The frequency is defined as the number of waves (of wavelength λ) passing a point per second. The relationship that links λ and ν is:

$$c = \lambda\nu$$

The human eye is sensitive only to a tiny band of radiation of the total electromagnetic spectrum. This band, called white light, ranges from about 400 nm to about 800 nm in wavelength and is made up of the colors of the rainbow. Table 2.2 shows the wavelength ranges within the spectrum of white light:

Table 2.2 Wavelength Ranges of Colors in White Light

Color	Wavelength (nm)
Violet	400–430
Blue	430–490
Green	490–570
Yellow	570–590
Orange	590–640
Red	640–750

The energy of the various colors of light can be easily calculated using Planck's law,

$$E = h\nu$$

where E is the energy (in Joules), h is Planck's constant (6.63×10^{-34} Js), and ν is the frequency of the radiation.

The separation of light into its spectral components can be done by refraction or diffraction. In this series of experiments, the separation of light into its component colors is accomplished by diffraction in a device called a spectroscope. A spectroscope is simply a box with a slit at one end (to let in light) and a light-separating device at the other end. The separating device you will be using is called a transmission diffraction grating, and it consists of a sheet of transparent plastic that has thousands of tiny grooves ruled on it. The way in which the grating works to separate light into colors is by wave interference. Imagine that light of one color (monochromatic) is shown on the grating in Figure 2.5.

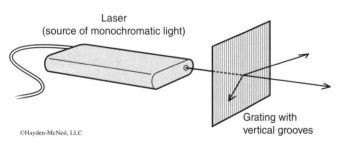

©Hayden-McNeil, LLC

Figure 2.5 Diffraction of laser light.

The grating device in Figure 2.6 illustrates wave interference. Viewed from above, the light waves can be seen as a series of straight lines representing the crests of the waves and the grooves look like tiny openings in the plastic. As these waves hit the grating, ripples of light come from each hole.

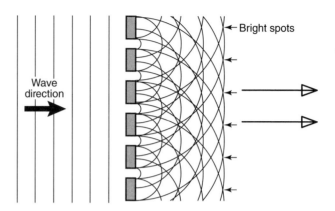

Figure 2.6 Light falling on the grooves of a grating.

The ripples move outward and interfere with each other. Where the crests are in the same place (crest lines cross), the waves will actually add to give a higher wave and a bright spot of light, which is called constructive interference. Destructive interference occurs when crests and valleys meet; the waves will almost cancel each other, resulting in darkness. Figure 2.7 illustrates these differences.

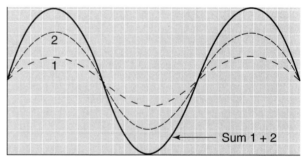

Constructive interference

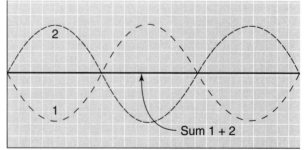

Destructive interference

©Hayden-McNeil, LLC

Figure 2.7 Constructive and destructive interference.

The overall cumulative effect is that the light is bent at an angle to the incident beam. This phenomenon is called *diffraction* and the angle is called the *angle of diffraction* θ. A quantitative relationship can be derived from the geometry as shown in Figure 2.8.

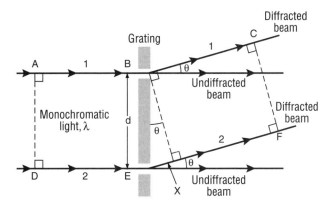

Figure 2.8 Geometry of diffraction.

Where d is the distance between two adjacent grooves, θ is the angle of diffraction and 1 and 2 are two rays of monochromatic light of wavelength λ. Now both rays, 1 and 2, are traveling at the same speed (the speed of light), and after hitting the grating, both are bent at an angle θ. Ray 2, however, has to travel a little bit farther (distance x) than ray 1 in the same amount of time. This path length difference causes a delay in ray 2, and interference can occur. If the path difference is an integral number of wavelengths, then constructive interference will occur. From simple geometry, for constructive interference, x = nλ (where n = 1, 2, 3...) and, since x/d = sin θ, then x = d sin θ, thus

$$n\lambda = d \sin \theta$$

For a given number of grooves per cm and when n = 1 (said to be first order), the angle of diffraction depends on the wavelength of the light. White light, or any other kind of light composed of a combination of colors, will be separated into the individual component colors.

Three common terrestrial sources of visible radiation are the electrical discharges in gases, thermal energy from combustion, and heated metals. A convenient source in the laboratory is the electrical discharge tube—i.e., a glass tube that contains metal electrodes at each end and is filled with a gas, such as hydrogen, helium, or mercury, at a low pressure. A high voltage is placed across the electrodes, and when the current is switched on, a stream of fast-moving electrons shoots through the gas from the cathode to the

anode. Energy is transferred from the electrons to the gas atoms, and the electrons in the gas atoms are excited to higher energy levels. The return of excited electrons to the ground state results in the emission of light, which may be analyzed with a spectroscope. A simple discharge tube is pictured in Figure 2.9.

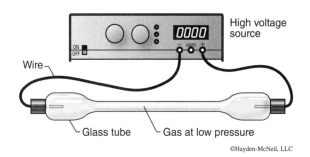

Figure 2.9 A simple discharge tube.

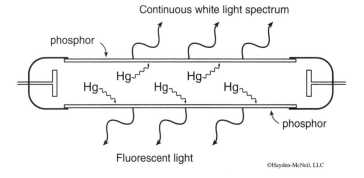

Figure 2.10 A fluorescent lamp.

Some practical devices are the common fluorescent light, neon signs, and street lights. A fluorescent lamp (such as the one pictured in Figure 2.10) is a discharge tube that is filled with a mercury vapor at low pressure. The inside walls of the tube are coated with a phosphor of calcium halophosphate ($Ca_5(PO_4)_3F_{1-x}Cl_x$) doped with Mn^{2+} and Sb^{3+}. Mercury atoms are excited by the process discussed above and emit their characteristic spectrum, which is in both the visible and in the ultraviolet spectrum (mostly UV, at 254 and 185 nm). This UV radiation is absorbed by the Sb^{3+} and passed on to the Mn^{2+}. The Sb^{3+} dopant gives off blue light, and the Mn^{2+} gives off orange light; the combination appears as white light.

Many solid substances—e.g., sodium chloride (NaCl)—may be excited by the thermal energy (heat) of flames. The heat comes from the exothermic combustion reactions occurring in the flame, e.g.,

$$CH_4 + 2O_2 \rightarrow CO_2 + 2H_2O + heat$$

Solid sodium chloride consists of sodium ions (Na^+) bonded to chloride ions (Cl^-). In a Bunsen burner flame, these ions are dissociated, and the separated Na^+ ions combine with free electrons in the flame to form sodium atoms:

$$Na^+ + e^- \rightarrow Na$$

Electrons within the neutral sodium atoms can then be excited to higher energy levels by the heat of the flame:

$$Na + heat \rightarrow Na^* \text{ (an excited Na atom)}$$

The excited atoms then "relax" back to the ground state and emit light:

$$Na^* \rightarrow Na + h\nu \text{ (light)}$$

The emitted light is characteristic of all of the electronic transitions that occur with energy differences corresponding to visible radiation. Analysis of the light by means of a spectroscope gives the atomic emission spectrum of sodium. In this series of experiments, you will be able to measure wavelengths of the emitted light, but not intensity. This is because you will be looking at the spectra by eye. Various types of detectors are available for measuring radiative intensities, and if they were used, a quantitative analysis for the amount of concentration of a chemical element could be accomplished.

Continuous emission spectra contain so many emitted frequencies of radiation that the lines overlap and the light looks like a rainbow. Common terrestrial sources of continuous emission are fluorescent lamps, ordinary incandescent lightbulbs, heated metals in general, and flames containing soot. Notice that all these sources are solids—e.g., the wire filament in a lightbulb and soot particles in a candle flame. The atoms and molecules in heated solids are continuously bumping against each other because they are so close. This dynamic contact results in much of the energy being transferred as kinetic energy which is not quantized. As the temperature of a solid is raised, more and more of the radiation is emitted at shorter wavelengths.

Additional Reading

1. Henderson, S. T., *Daylight and Its Spectrum*, John Wiley and Sons, New York, 1977. Everything you wanted to know about the sun and its emission spectrum.

2. Kippenhahn, R., *100 Billion Suns*, Basic Books, Inc., New York, 1983. A wonderful, readable book about the birth, life, and death of the stars (the nonterrestrial ones!).

3. Herzberg, G., *Atomic Spectra and Atomic Structure*, Prentice-Hall, Inc., New York, 1937. A classic and, in my opinion, still the best book on this subject.

4. Feynman, R. P., *QED: The Strange Theory of Light and Matter*, Princeton University Press, Princeton, N.J., 1985. Feynman's dedication is beautiful—"what one fool can understand, another can." This book should be read by all faculty and students, but particularly faculty!

5. Ingle, J. D., *Spectrochemical Analysis*, Prentice-Hall, Englewood Cliffs, N.J., 1988. A more advanced book, but has all the practical details. Encyclopedic.

Quiz Outline

Your quiz will NOT cover all of the information below, but it will cover some subset of the information given below.

Define spectroscopy.

Be able to determine the equation of a line from two data points.

Explain the difference between a line and continuous spectrum, and give an example of a source of each type.

Be able to explain the difference between an emission spectrum and an absorption spectrum.

Be able to categorize the various types of electromagnetic radiation (the far left hand column of Table 2.1, in the Introduction section of this experiment) and know what kind of energy transition is associated with each type of radiation (i.e., the correlation between the columns at the two extremes of Table 2.1). Also, you should know roughly the correlation between the extreme columns and the RELATIVE energies, frequencies, and wavelengths. (For example, could you tell me if visible radiation is of higher/lower energy/frequency/wavelength than microwave radiation?)

Be able to describe what is meant by the term "white light," and the wavelength range (in nm) that white light covers. Also be able to list the colors of the spectrum from the highest to the lowest frequency.

Be able to describe in a few sentences what a "transmission diffraction grating" is. (A figure might help, but it is not a must.)

Be able to draw the set-up of a discharge tube (Figure 2.9).

Be able to outline in a few sentences how you will calibrate your spectroscope (Section D).

Sample Pre-Laboratory Quiz

1. Define spectroscopy. (2 pts)

2. Explain the difference between an absorption and an emission spectrum. (2 pts)

3. Rank the following types of radiation according to the energy range associated with it.

   (Put 1 next to the highest energy, 2 next to the second highest, etc.) (1 pt)

   Microwave   Visible   Infrared   Ultraviolet (UV)

4. Explain what is meant by "white light." Include the approximate wavelength range associated with "white light." (2 pts)

5. Outline in a few sentences how you will calibrate your spectroscope. (3 pts)

Laboratory Experiments

Flowchart of the Experiments

Section A.	**Characterization of a Transmission Diffraction Grating**

Section B.	**Construction of a Pizza Box Spectroscope$^{©}$**

Section C.	**Exploring Spectroscope Specifications**

Section D.	**Wavelength Calibration of the Spectroscope**

Section E.	**Atomic Line Spectra and Electronic Transitions; Electrical Discharge Tubes**

Section F.	**Flame Emission Spectra**

Requires one four-hour class period to complete.

Section A.   Characterization of a Transmission Diffraction Grating

---

Goals: *(1) To use laser light of wavelength 632.8 nm to determine the number of grooves on a diffraction grating. (2) Calculate the groove distance of a diffraction grating from first-order diffraction data.*

Discussion: You will be using a small piece of plastic diffraction grating to spread visible light into its various colors. This amazing little device has thousands of narrowly spaced lines on it. The exact number can be determined by sending light of a single wavelength through it, and measuring the diffraction angle. Then the diffraction equation for constructive interference (derived in the background section) can be used to calculate d, the groove spacing, and from there it is easy to determine the number of grooves per centimeter.

Experimental Steps: 1.   Somewhere in the room there should be a demonstration setup similar to the one pictured below. This setup involves a helium-neon laser, so named because the laser tube is filled with these gases. It emits mainly red light at 632.8 nanometers (nm). The diffraction grating used is the same type that you will be using in the spectroscope that you will build in Section B.

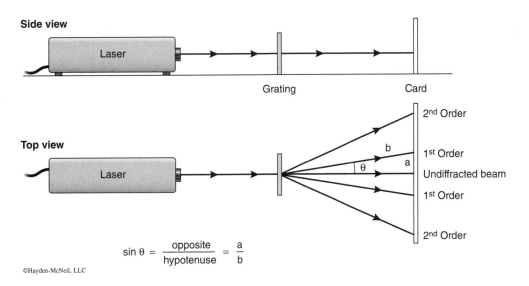

$$\sin \theta = \frac{\text{opposite}}{\text{hypotenuse}} = \frac{a}{b}$$

©Hayden-McNeil, LLC

2.   Measure the values of a and b at the setup in your room. It may also be possible to observe second-order spots.

You will need these values for your homework, so record them below and in your notebook.

a =

b =

Section B.   Construction of a Pizza Box Spectroscope©

Goal: *To construct a simple but rather accurate spectroscope containing a built-in quantitative calibration system.*

Discussion: All of the materials you need for building the spectroscope are located at Reagent Central or at your arm's reach station.

Experimental Steps: A diagram of the completed instrument is shown below. (Your instructor will probably have a sample spectroscope available to show you, too.)

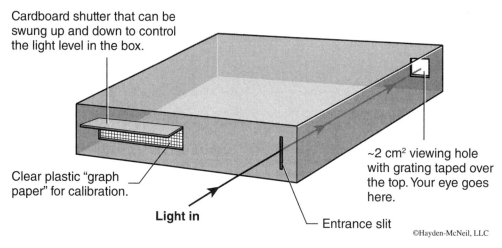

Cardboard shutter that can be swung up and down to control the light level in the box.

Clear plastic "graph paper" for calibration.

Light in

Entrance slit

~2 cm² viewing hole with grating taped over the top. Your eye goes here.

©Hayden-McNeil, LLC

Figure 2.11 Completed Pizza Box Spectroscope©.

1.   Lay your pizza box out flat. Use your razor knife to cut out the shaded portions shown in the diagram on the next page. (Use a piece of corrugated cardboard as a cutting board. The soapstone lab benchtops are actually quite soft.) Also make the U-shaped cut indicated in the diagram. Don't worry too much about the exact dimensions at this point. Almost anything in this experiment can be fixed with black tape!

     CAUTION: Please be careful—these blades are sharp.

2.   Now put the box together tightly using black electrical tape. The only light permitted in should be through the openings that you have cut.

3.   Use a small piece of black tape to temporarily tape the shutter in the "closed" position.

Template for Cutting the Spectroscope Box

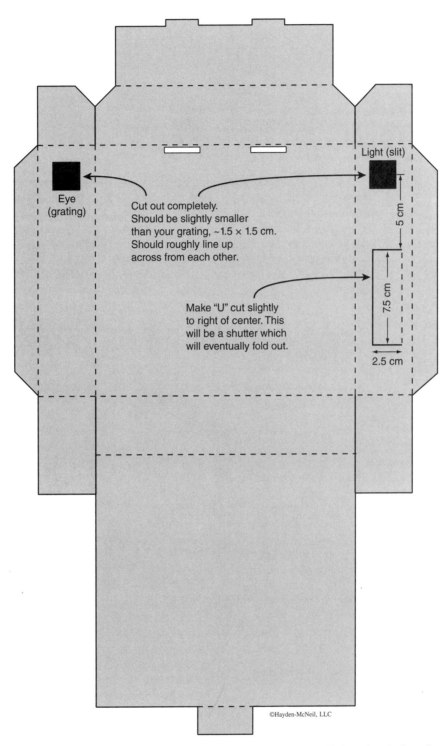

Eye (grating)

Light (slit)

Cut out completely. Should be slightly smaller than your grating, ~1.5 × 1.5 cm. Should roughly line up across from each other.

Make "U" cut slightly to right of center. This will be a shutter which will eventually fold out.

5 cm

7.5 cm

2.5 cm

©Hayden-McNeil, LLC

Cut out completely the 2 shaded regions above. Also, make the one U-shaped cut indicated.

4.   Now use 2 pieces of black electrical tape to define an approximately 1 mm entrance slit.

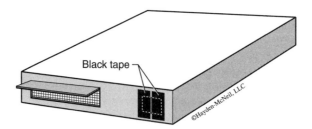

5.   Obtain a piece of plastic diffraction grating and orient it correctly on the box *before* taping it permanently with black tape. To do this, hold the box so that you can look into it through the square hole, and point it vertically so that light from the fluorescent light enters the slit. Hold the grating over the square hole with your index finger while still looking into the box. You should see a visible spectrum (rainbow) to the right of the slit. If a *thin* horizontal rainbow is observed, then rotate the grating 90° (see figure below). Try to handle the grating by the edges as much as possible.

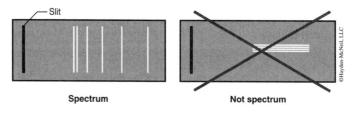

View Inside the Box

Once you are satisfied, carefully tape the grating to the box (tape around the edges).

NOTE: The entire spectrum should fit in the window. If it does not, then the window may need to be enlarged.

6.   Show your completed spectroscope to your TA before moving on.

NOTE: You will need your spectroscope to complete your homework assignment. After that, it is yours to keep!

Section C.   Exploring Spectroscope Specifications

Goal: *To be able to determine the specifications for your spectroscope.*

Discussion: It is always wise to explore the good points and the limitations of any instrument before launching out and spending time and money (tuition!) using it. Obviously, the spectroscope that you have built has many limitations. However, the nice thing about an inexpensive, simple, self-built machine is that you should have no inhibitions about using it, breaking it, changing it, or fixing it. In fact, you have a unique opportunity to write the specifications for your own spectroscopic instrument.

NOTE: If you wear spectacles, you might find it easier to take them off when looking into the spectroscope.

Questions: Q1.   What are the dimensions of your spectroscope? Also include shutter dimensions.

- This may seem like a silly question, but it's not. What is the actual location of the spectrum? Is it really inside the box? See if a neighbor can see the rainbow coming out of the window of your spectroscope when it is pointed at the light. Hint: This is the same grating that was used in Section A with the laser.

This is analogous to looking at a fish in the water. Your mind assumes that light travels in a straight line. So when something bends light, as water does in the illustration below (or a grating, or a mirror), your mind incorrectly thinks that the light is coming from straight ahead. This false image is called a "virtual image," to distinguish it from an image which is a genuine source of light. Thus, the fish below appears to be further away from the person than it actually is.

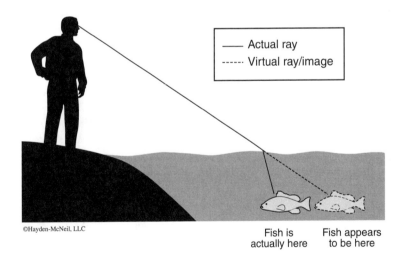

—— Actual ray
------ Virtual ray/image

©Hayden-McNeil, LLC

Fish is   Fish appears
actually here   to be here

Q2.   Now draw a sketch of a top view of your spectroscope. Imagine that your spectroscope is used to view an external source of light that emits only two wavelengths of light—one blue and the other red. Show the paths of the actual rays and the virtual rays in a similar manner to how it is shown in the previous figure.

Q3.   Determine the dimensions of the spectrum observed when you look at a fluorescent light. Briefly explain how you determined it. Now lets change some things. Vary the slit *height* by either covering part of it with an additional piece of black tape, or perhaps with your finger.

Q4.   How does changing the slit height change the fluorescent light spectrum?

        Now vary the slit *width* by unpeeling one of the pieces of electrical tape and repositioning it onto the box. (An alternative way to do this is to use two pieces of tape to fix a *wide* slit. A third piece of tape can then be placed on top of one of the other two to obtain narrower slit widths.)

Q5.   If you make the slit wider or narrower, what happens to the fluorescent light spectrum? Draw a few simple pictures to illustrate what you see.

Q6.   What is the relationship between the distance of the fluorescent light from the spectroscope and the characteristics of the spectrum? Hint: There should be a small battery-operated fluorescent light somewhere in the room which is easier to experiment with than the ceiling fluorescent lights.

Section D.   Wavelength Calibration of the Spectroscope

Goal: *To carry out a calibration of your spectroscope by using known spectral lines in the emission spectrum of a fluorescent light.*

Discussion: All scientific instruments must be calibrated before any quantitative measurements can be made. Commercial instruments are almost always calibrated by the manufacturer before they are actually used in the factory or laboratory. A transparent piece of graph paper is a suitable measurement device, but the only way to calibrate it is to be able to view a visible spectrum that has emission lines of exactly known wavelength. The light emitted from a typical fluorescent light is such a spectrum.

Experimental Steps: 1. At your arm's reach station there should be some precut pieces of transparent graph paper. Take one and use your permanent marker to label some of the lines along the x-axis (e.g., 5, 10, etc.). (This will make it easier to quickly determine the location of a particular line.) Then tape this scale onto the box in the "shuttered" opening of your spectroscope. If you have done it correctly, then when the shutter is partway open you should be able to view the fluorescent light spectrum, and also read your x-axis labels.

                         2. When you have your graph paper positioned properly, then you should mark its exact location in some fashion. That way, if it accidentally gets moved (or, if you want to take it off for any reason), then you can replace it without messing up your calibration.

3. Now narrow the slit to about 0.5 mm and point your spectroscope directly up at the brightest part of a fluorescent light. It helps if you shut one eye!

The spectrum that you can see is actually composed of two types of spectra: a continuous and a line emission spectrum, *superimposed* on each other. This superimposition produces a rainbow with three fairly prominent lines of light in it.

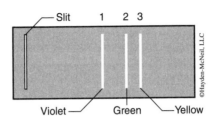

View of Spectrum Inside Box
The 3 prominent lines are superimposed
on a continuous emission spectrum

The three lines 1, 2, and 3, are violet, green, and yellow and are the strong emissions from Hg vapor in the fluorescent tube. These lines have well-known wavelengths and we can use them to calibrate the spectroscope:

Line 1, violet   436 nm   —5   3   17-3   14   >
                                          ─────   ──── = ──── =
Line 2, green   546 nm   —10 17   546-436 =   110   55

Line 3, yellow   580 nm   —   22

4. Take another piece of black tape and place it at the bottom of the slit to adjust the slit length so that the bottom of the emission lines falls exactly on the bottom line of your graph paper.

5. Note the exact location (in terms of the number of lines on your graph) of each of the three emission lines. (Remember, you should always **estimate one decimal place beyond the markings of any instrument.** For example, if an emission line fell in between two graph lines, then it might be listed as 10.5 graph lines. But if it was exactly on one of the lines, then it would be recorded as 10.0 graph lines.) It may help to slowly open and close the shutter (while looking at the light) to get the best reading.

6. Now plot a graph of wavelength of emission lines 1, 2, and 3 versus distance. Use a wavelength axis from 400 nm to 650 nm. Draw the best straight line you can for your three points. Check with your TA before moving on.

This graph is the spectroscope calibration line, which will enable you to find the wavelengths of unknown spectral lines, bands, etc., in any emission or absorption spectrum.

Questions: Q7. What is the optimum shutter setting for viewing only the emission spectrum? What is the optimum shutter setting for reading the graph?

Q8. Determine the equation for the calibration line. (Why not write this on top of your spectroscope for easy reference? Also, adding your name and today's date on top of the box would enable someone else to trace this calibration equation to the raw data which it is based on.) By using this equation, you can easily convert a spectroscopic measurement into wavelength in nm without having to look at your graph.

Q9.   Would this calibration line work for your neighbor's spectroscope?

Q10.   What is the main thing that would need to be changed in the current design to ensure that the calibration line was the same for any spectroscope (with the same size box)?

Q11.   How does the slit width affect the calibration line?

Section E.   Atomic Line Spectra and Electronic Transitions; Electrical Discharge Tubes

Goals: *1.   To obtain the atomic line spectra of light emitted from electrical discharge tubes.*

                  2.   To be able to calculate photon wavelengths, frequencies, and energies from line spectra data.

Experimental Steps: 1.   Electrical discharge tubes containing (a) hydrogen and (b) helium are along one side of the room and are connected to a high-voltage supply. Ask your instructor to switch them on for you.

                  CAUTION: Be careful not to touch the tubes or metal strands or you will get an electrical shock.

                  2.   View both discharge tubes before making any measurements so that you can get a good idea what line spectra look like.

                  NOTE: You might find it advantageous to increase the slit width to about 1 or 2 millimeters.

                  3.   Now view the tube containing hydrogen gas. This is not very bright so you must view it quite closely, perhaps about 10 to 20 cm away.

                  •   Use your spectroscope calibration equation to determine the wavelength of the spectral lines that are prominent.

                  •   Be careful to record the color of the lines (as viewed through the spectroscope), and the overall color of the emitted light (i.e., as viewed by the naked eye).

                  4.   Now use your spectroscope to observe a discharge tube filled with helium gas.

                  •   Note some differences between hydrogen's emission spectrum and helium's.

Questions: Q12.   Why were you encouraged to increase the slit width (above)?

Q13.   For *only the hydrogen discharge* tube, make a chart of the following information:

a.   color of the tube as viewed by eye (i.e., without a spectroscope),

b.   color of a given line (as viewed through the spectroscope),

c.   calculated wavelength,

d.   accepted wavelength (i.e., from some literature reference),

e.   % error.

You will need your data on the hydrogen emission lines for homework. Therefore, *record the data below and in your notebook.*

Line Color	Calculated λ (nm)
Pinkish Red	548.3
violet	436
Blue	545.1
	656 nm

Section F.   Flame Emission Spectra

Goal: *To observe flame emission spectra emitted from chemical species produced in Bunsen burner flames.*

Discussion: Many substances, particularly alkali metal and alkaline earth salts, produce brightly colored flames when they are heated by a Bunsen burner. This is because electrons in the metal atoms are excited to higher energy levels by the heat of the flame. When the electrons fall back to lower energy levels, light is given off. Since the spacings of the electron energy levels are different for different elements, the colors given off vary from element to element. This same process is responsible for the bright colors of fireworks. Flame emission spectroscopy is a powerful method for qualitative and quantitative identification of many elements.

NOTE: Generally this section will be performed by your TA as a demonstration.

Experimental Steps: 1.   Somewhere in the room there should be a station with a rack containing wooden splints that have been soaked in various salt solutions.

2.   Insert one end of a splint containing a particular salt solution into the flame, and observe the predominant color(s).

3.   Use the procedure above to examine *with the naked eye* emission from the available salt solutions. (The use of a spectroscope is difficult, and not that helpful in this section.)

4.   Note the colors associated with the ions examined.

Question: Q14.   Note the colors associated with the ions examined.

Section G.   Homework

Homework: HW1.   In Section A, you measured how far the first-order spots are bent away from the undiffracted beam.

(a) Use the two-dimensional diffraction relationship $n\lambda = d \sin\theta$ to calculate the groove spacing, d. Be careful with units—a good tip is to work in meters.

(b) Calculate the number of grooves per centimeter for your grating. Hint: if the groove spacing was 0.1 ft, then how many grooves would you have per foot?

(c) Suppose you were given the exact same setup described in Section A, except that a different grating with fewer grooves/cm was used. How would you expect this to affect the location of the first-order spot? (Explain how you arrived at your conclusion.)

HW2.   As a homework project, look at and describe the spectral characteristics of four sources of light different from the ones you studied in lab. Some suggestions are white light from a TV screen, street lights (there are many types), neon signs, and the fluorescent lights on the *second* floor of Whitmore.

Draw some pictures to illustrate the differences between the spectra from the various sources.

Make a table which lists: (a) the light source, (b) the color of the source observed visually (i.e., with the naked eye), (c) the color(s) of maximum intensity for each source when viewed through a spectroscope, and (d) the wavelength range for each source.

HW3.   (a) Briefly (100 words or less) explain what Fraunhofer lines are, and why they are significant.

(b) Use your spectroscope to view the reflection of the sunlight from either the sky or clouds using a fairly narrow slit width (approximately 0.5 mm). **Do not look directly at the sun, even through your spectroscope.**

(c) Note the location in graph lines of the three strongest Fraunhofer lines. Determine the three wavelengths, and indicate what elements cause them.

HW4.   The chart on the next page shows the electron energy states of the hydrogen atom. On the right side is given the wavelength of light necessary to ionize an electron from any given point. For example, in order to ionize an electron from its lowest energy state (i.e., to promote an electron from the state n = 1 to n = ∞), a photon with a wavelength of 91 nm is required. Which series of lines (Lyman, Balmer, etc.) did you observe with your spectroscope? How did you figure it out? What final energy level is involved?

HW5.   (a) You have previously determined (Section E) the wavelengths of the hydrogen emission lines. Now determine the frequencies and energies of the light you have observed from the hydrogen discharge tube.

        (b) Determine exactly which electron transition (e.g., 2 → 1) corresponds to each line in the spectrum you observed for hydrogen.

        To do this, you will need to use Bohr's equations regarding the energy differences between the various allowed states for an electron in a hydrogen atom. (These are given in your Chem 110 text, and almost all general chemistry textbooks.) At this point you should know all of the variables except for n_i, the initial state of the electron for each line observed. Hint: For emission of light, ΔE is negative, since the system is losing energy.

HW6.   Wint-O-Green Life Savers spark in your mouth when chewed. Use the hydrogen discharge tube as an analogy to explain what is going on at the atomic level to produce these sparks.

        Note: This question is related to a take-home experiment in your lab kit. You should do this experiment. Instructions are below.

Take Home Experiment #1
Sparking Life Savers—A Demonstration of Triboluminescence

1. Find yourself a room with no windows (a closet or bathroom will do).

2. Take your Wint-O-Green Life Savers and a mirror with you.

3. Wait 5 minutes for your eyes to adjust to the darkness.

4. Pop the candy in your mouth and immediately bite down while keeping your mouth open (avoid salivation of the Life Saver, as this experiment will not work if the candy is moistened).

5. You should be able to view blue sparks of light coming from your mouth!

The Allowed Electron Energy States for the Hydrogen Atom

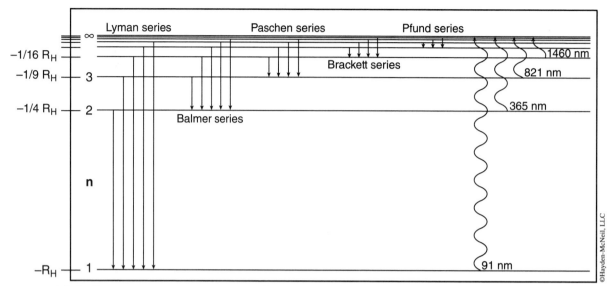

Energy associated with various states of the hydrogen atom in terms of the Rydberg constant (R_H).

Down arrows refer to the transitions of the electron from one allowed energy state to another.

Curvy arrows represent the λ of light necessary to promote an electron from any particular point to $n = \infty$ (i.e., to ionize the atom).

Experiment 3

Small-Scale Techniques and the Absorption of Light

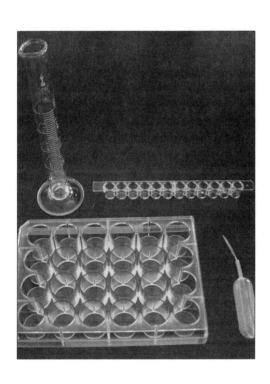

Introduction

Behavioral psychologists tell us that sighted people receive more than 90% of the information about the world through their eyes. The subtleties of line, perspective, shadow, texture, and color form the complex representation of the world we see. These perceptions require three elements: an object, a medium, and an eye–brain system. The medium is light. A source of visible radiation sends out oscillating electromagnetic energy traveling at the speed of light. As the light moves through molecules in the air and impacts on objects, the oscillating energy field interacts with the outer electrons in matter. The light–electron coupling takes less than a picosecond, but in this very short interaction time, a tremendous amount of information is encoded in the light. Eventually, the changed light may pass through the pupil of an eye, travel through the lens and the aqueous humor, and strike the retina. The tiny light detectors, called rods and cones, contain molecular antennas that absorb the light. Rod cells form black and white images in dim light, and cones are responsible for color vision in bright light. The light-absorbing visual pigments consist of a protein, opsin, that is covalently linked to a molecule called 11-cis-retinal. Vision begins when light absorbed by the visual pigments causes the retinal to change its shape, a process called photoisomerization. Shape changes in retinal then trigger a series of changes in the attached protein, which in turn catalyze the conversion of hundreds of secondary messenger molecules into an active state. This conversion is the first step in a cascade of reactions that eventually produces a signal in the brain.

The human eye–brain system is a remarkably flexible and sensitive detector. Recent research in the chemistry of vision has shown that only one photon is required to produce a physiological response in an individual receptor. A person with good color vision can discriminate minute color differences—on the order of wavelength differences of 1 or 2 nm! Of course, there are variations in the response of different humans to light stimuli. About 6% of males are color deficient in some part of the spectrum compared to less than 0.1% for females. However, these variations do not change the fact that the human visual system is very good at deciphering much of the information encoded in light. You have already used your own visual system to investigate the electronic structure of atoms by means of the technique of atomic emission spectroscopy. The encoded information in light emitted from excited atoms is the detailed record of all the electronic energy-level transitions occurring in those atoms. The real key to revealing quantitative information is the use of appropriate standards, calibrations, and comparisons.

Another fundamental way in which valuable information can be obtained from light probes is to measure the *amount* of light energy absorbed or reflected by matter. The amount of light absorbed or reflected depends on the number of interactions that occur between the photons and the absorbing molecules. The absorption is therefore proportional to the amount or concentration of molecules in the chemical system. It is interesting to note that this relationship between the amount of light absorbed and the amount of absorbing species is a general one that holds for all types of radiation. Again, the key to a practical measurement system is the use of appropriate visual comparison standards. Small-scale absorption standards allow the eye–brain system to discern rather small differences in light absorption.

Background Chemistry

Chemistry is the study of matter and its transformations. The experimental practice of chemistry has traditionally relied on the use of large-scale metal or glass apparatus. This equipment is used for carrying out chemical reactions and for the storage, transfer, and quantitative delivery of all forms of chemical substances. Recently, there have been tremendous advances in the development of sophisticated small-scale equipment, much of which is now being used in the clinical, microbiological, and recombinant DNA fields. Your chemistry laboratory course has been designed to utilize some of the outstanding advantages of doing chemistry on a small scale. *Small scale* means that small quantities of chemicals are used. The disposal of small quantities of chemical wastes is relatively simple, inexpensive, and more importantly, much less of a threat to the environment. Doing science on a small scale almost always leads to much greater safety in the laboratory. It is hoped that you will find the equipment user-friendly and efficient and that it will allow you to be far more involved in interesting chemistry than is possible in traditional university laboratories.

Much of the nontraditional small-scale equipment is made out of plastic, and most of it was originally designed to be disposable. We are going to reuse it and recycle it wherever possible. The plastics are mainly polystyrene (e.g., microreaction trays), polyethylene (e.g., pipets and microburets), and polypropylene (e.g., straws). All three plastics have chemical properties that can be exploited in the innovative design and use of tools for science. All have surfaces that are nonwetted by aqueous solutions. Nonwetted surfaces make the storage, transfer, and delivery of aqueous solutions much easier than, say, glass surfaces. The high surface tension of water means that in the presence of a plastic, a drop can be its own container and a reproducible volume increment at the same time. The ease of production of small drops from plastic tubes leads naturally to digital methods in volumetric work. Counting drops can circumvent the problems inherent in the analog methods of meniscus reading. The low softening and melting point of these materials, together with the ease with which they can be stuck, bent, cut, and otherwise mutilated naturally leads to innovative construction. Of course, in an experimental science like chemistry, there is occasionally a need for glass or metal materials. When this need arises, we will not hesitate to use small quantities and small tools.

One of the most innovative applications of small-scale plastic equipment has been in the area of colorimetry and spectrophotometry. As you have already seen in the spectroscopy laboratory, the interaction of light with matter provides scientists with a powerful probe for investigating the structure, function, and dynamics of any chemical system. The analysis of light emitted from excited atoms and molecules is only one example of this general approach.

Another technique that is used extensively in many areas of science is that of light absorption by a chemical system. Consider white light falling on a solution of red food dye. The solution looks red because the complements of red, mainly blues and greens (490–560 nm), have been absorbed by the molecules of red food dye dissolved in the solution. Bluish-green light is absorbed by these molecules because there are electronic energy-level transitions in the molecule that correspond to the photon energy of bluish-green light. In other words, the food dye molecules become excited. The question is, what happens to the extra energy that the molecules have absorbed? Unlike the excited gas–phase atoms in the spectroscopy experiment, the excited food dye molecules do not emit radiation (although other organic molecules under the right conditions will emit light, e.g., fireflies and railroad worms). The extra energy is removed continuously by solvent molecules bumping billions of times per second against the excited food dye molecules. As a result, there is a small but imperceptible increase in the thermal energy of the solvent. The basic reason for this different mode of energy transfer is that all of the molecules in a solution are much closer to each other than they are in the gas phase. Many, many more collisions occur between solution molecules than gas molecules, each collision removing a small amount of energy. Solutions that have colors other than red undergo the same processes. In general, the observed color is the color that is transmitted. The absorbed color is complementary to the observed color. You can predict the absorbed color (approximately) using a color wheel like the one shown on the next page. Try it. What color of light is being absorbed by your blue jeans? (Orange.)

Table 3.1 Absorbed and Observed Colors of Solutions

Wavelength (nm)	Color Absorbed	Color Observed
380–435	Violet	Yellowish-green
435–480	Blue	Yellow
480–490	Greenish-blue	Orange
490–560	Bluish-green	Red
500–560	Green	Purple
560–580	Yellowish-green	Violet
580–595	Yellow	Blue
595–650	Orange	Greenish-blue
650–780	Red	Bluish-green

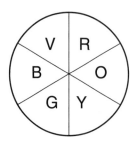

Figure 3.1 A "color wheel", such as the one shown above, gives a rough sense of which colors are complementary.

The color of the light absorbed by a molecule largely depends on the electronic energy levels of the molecule. These levels are determined by the chemical structure of the molecule, i.e., by the number and arrangement of the electrons. Red food dye, for example, has a very different arrangement of electrons than a blue food dye, as shown in their respective structures in Figure 3.1.

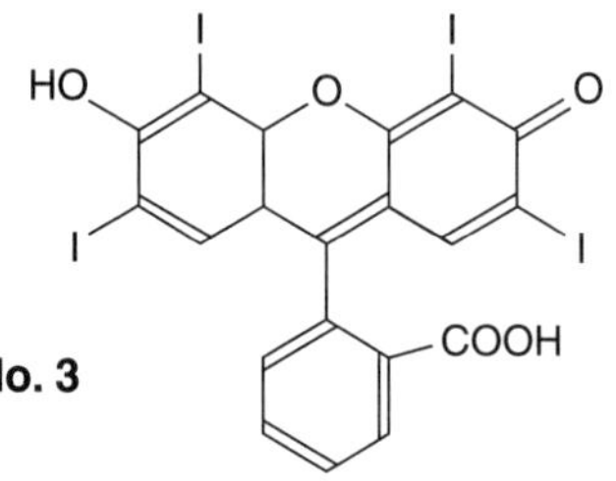

FD and C Red No. 3

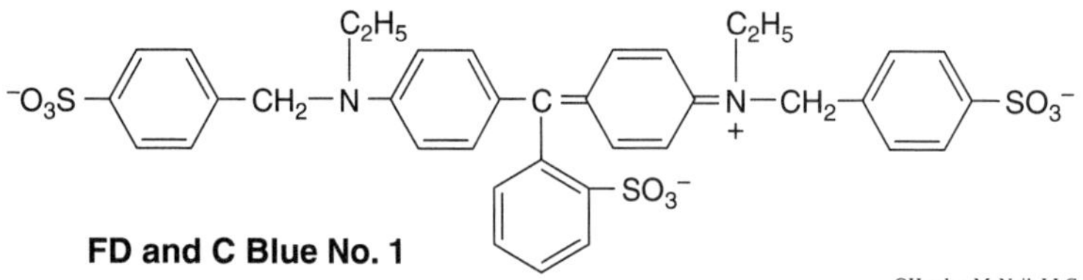

FD and C Blue No. 1

©Hayden-McNeil, LLC

Figure 3.2 The chemical structures of two food dyes.

A careful analysis of the light absorbed and transmitted by a molecule can be used to provide information about the chemical structure. In this series of experiments, however, we will be more concerned with the amount of light absorbed by colored solutions. Light absorption of this type follows a very general law known as Lambert, Bouger, and Beer's law (commonly abbreviated as Beer's law). Beer's law states that if monochromatic radiation is allowed to fall on a solution, then the amount of light absorbed or transmitted is an exponential function of the concentration of the absorbing substance and of the length of the path of light through the sample. Mathematically, the law is expressed as

$$T = 10^{-abc} \text{ or } -\log_{10}T = abc$$

where T is called the transmittance, a is a constant that depends on the substance absorbing the light, b is the path length of light through the sample, and c is the concentration of absorbing substance in the solution. The law is often expressed in linear form as

$$A = abc$$

where A, the absorbance of the solution is defined as

$$A = -\log T$$

One of the earliest and most useful applications of light absorption phenomena was in a technique of chemical analysis called colorimetry. In *colorimetry*, a set of solutions of known concentrations of some light-absorbing substance—e.g., food dye—is placed in a series of containers. An unknown concentration solution is then compared with the calibration set, either by eye or with the aid of a simple instrument. Once a match is obtained, the concentration in the unknown solution can be determined. Modern instrumentation has enabled much greater accuracy and sensitivity to be achieved in light absorption analysis. In instruments called *spectrophotometers*, the amount of light absorbed or transmitted is accurately and quantitatively detected and measured by solid state electronic devices. Sophisticated micro-spectrophotometers are now commercially available in which light absorption of 0.1 mL of solution can be automatically measured with great accuracy.

Quiz Outline

The quiz for this experiment is generally given the week AFTER you complete it. (There is usually a quiz on a different topic the week of Exp. 3. Check your syllabus.)

The Experiment 3 quiz will cover the main points of the entire experiment, including the Introduction and Background Chemistry sections. Also, questions from the articles on small-scale chemistry in your Chem 111 Student Packet may be included.

Notebooks will not be collected this week.

Sample Post-Laboratory Quiz

1. (a) Explain what is meant by "wash, rinse, and fill technique."

   (b) What is the advantage of this approach?

2. A student takes 3 drops of a 0.150 M solution and adds 7 drops of distilled water to it and stirs. What is the concentration of the resulting solution? Show your work if you want full credit.

3. What is meant by the term "standard deviation." What does a "standard deviation" tell you?

4. A given thin-stem pipet is used to deliver ethanol and then water. How do you expect the average drop size to vary in these two cases? Explain your reasoning.

5. In Section G you were asked to design an experiment to determine the ratio of two dyes present in lime Kool-Aid. Briefly describe the experiment you designed.

6. Your course packet contains an article entitled, "Microreactors Eyed for Industrial Use." Cite three significant advantages and one significant disadvantage of these microreactors that are mentioned in this article.

Laboratory Experiments

Flowchart of the Experiments

Section A.	Modifying Thin-Stem Pipets

Section B.	General Pipet Techniques

Section C.	Pipet Calibration for Quantitative Volumetric Work

Section D.	A Comparison of the Accuracy of a Small-Drop Pipet vs. a Standard 25 mL Glass Buret

Section E.	Quantitative Dilution of Solutions

Section F.	Standard Color Solutions and Colorimetry

Section G.	Colorimetric Analysis of a Beverage

Section H.	A Practical Application of Colorimetry

Requires one four-hour class period to complete.

Section A.	**Modifying Thin-Stem Pipets**

Goal:

To learn how to modify thin-stem pipets to make simple, constant drop-volume delivery devices.

Discussion:

Throughout this course you will be using several types of pipets for both qualitative and quantitative delivery of solutions.

Experimental Steps:

Thin-Stem Pipet

The thin-stem pipets (hereafter simply referred to as pipets) can be used directly, without any alterations. However, the long stem length tends to make positioning the tip difficult, so the pipet is used only to carry out qualitative transfer.

Large-Drop Pipet

The large-drop pipet is much more useful than the pipet.

1. Choose one of the pipets from your kit. Cut off the stem at a point about 2 cm from the bulb. This will be referred to as a "large-drop pipet." (Save the stem. You can use it to make a microstirrer.) Note: Make the cut at a right angle.

The large-drop pipet will be used most frequently in this course.

Small-Drop Pipet

You will occasionally need a pipet that delivers much smaller volumes (drops). Your instructor will demonstrate this method before you try.

1. Hold a new pipet firmly between the index finger and the thumb of your dominant hand at a position on the thin stem just beyond the bulb.

2. Hold very firmly so that the bulb is in the palm of your hand.

3. Curl the thin stem between the index finger and second finger of your other hand and grasp tightly. The finger knuckles on both hands should be touching.

4. Pull slowly in opposite directions and the stem will stretch. Keep pulling until the stretched part is more than 4 or 5 cm long.

5. Use sharp scissors to cut off the pulled out part about 1 to 1.5 cm from the original thin stem. Save the cut-off part.

NOTE: Don't be alarmed—only total geniuses and world-class weight lifters can do it the first time around! Try again.

Large-drop pipets deliver approximately 0.03 mL/drop. Small-drop pipets deliver approximately 0.02 mL/drop. More exact calibrations of your particular pipets will be made in Section C.

Section B.   General Pipet Techniques

Goals: *(1) To investigate some of the factors that control drop volume. (2) To learn how to handle large-drop and small-drop pipets for the quantitative delivery of solutions.*

Experimental Steps: 1.   With a hand lens, examine the tips of the pipets you made.

Draw a picture of the end cross sections in your notes.

- Do you notice anything different about the small-drop pipet?

2.   Fill 2 wells of a 24-well tray with green food dye solution.

NOTE: The green dye solution is in a plastic bottle at your arm's reach station. The dye is to enable you to see the solution more easily.

3.   Fill 2 wells of a 24-well tray with distilled water.

NOTE: Before you begin any experiment, you have to assume that the bulb of every pipet is dirty and must be cleaned with distilled water.

4.   Begin by cleaning the small drop pipet. Suck a little distilled water up into the bulb and shake it so that all internal surfaces have been wetted.

5.   Holding the small-drop pipet vertically, expel the distilled water into a waste cup. Press firmly to get those last drops out.

6.   Now suck up a little bit of green food dye, shake to rinse the bulb, and expel into a waste cup.

7.   Squeeze the bulb and suck up some green food dye.

Note how much the bulb fills with one squeeze.

NOTE: This sequence (steps 4–7) is significant. It starts with a *wash* solution (distilled water in this case). Then a *rinse* is accomplished **with the solution you are interested in transferring**. Lastly, the bulb is filled with the solution of interest. We will refer to this as *wash*, *rinse*, and *fill* or, alternatively, "good transfer technique."

This approach is often used to prepare all types of plastic and glass transfer devices. It has the advantage of not requiring a drying step, i.e., in the procedure described above, if the last rinse had been with distilled water, then a drying step would have been necessary to prevent the remaining drops from diluting the green solution. But, since the last rinse was with the green solution, no significant dilution occurs when the pipet is filled.

8.   Now deliver some drops back to the well. With your hand lens, look at the drops as they leave the tip.

- Draw pictures in your notebook to show how they form and fall off the tip.

- What happens if the small-drop pipet is held at different angles?

- Compare the tips of the stretched to the unstretched pipets.

The small-drop pipet tip has an oval, somewhat flattened, shape. This is due to the fact that the pipets are manufactured with a seam.

9.   Practice producing pools of various sizes on your plastic reaction surface (one is in your lab kit) and then suck the pools up completely.

Sometimes small bubbles will be formed in the stem of a pipet and the first drop will not form properly. Simply waste the first drop to the surface or waste cup and then continue and drops will be uniform.

NOTE: For quantitative work it is best to adopt a standard method of making a small-drop pipet and to use a standard delivery technique. These practices are discussed in the next section.

Section C.   Pipet Calibration for Quantitative Volumetric Work

Goals: *(1) To decide on a standard delivery technique for repetitive delivery of drops of solution at uniform volume. (2) To use that technique to calibrate a small-drop pipet.*

Experimental Steps: 1.   Select the small-drop pipet.

2.   Use the good transfer technique (described in the previous section) to fill it with green dye solution.

3.   Tare a weigh boat on one of the balances.

4.   Hold the small-drop pipet *vertically* about 1 cm away from the boat. Deliver one free-falling drop. Record the mass (don't forget your units). You should take a reading as soon as it settles (within 5–10 seconds). Don't wait too long—these balances are sensitive enough to measure the evaporation of water (i.e., the drop is slowly getting smaller). Re-tare the balance. Drop a second drop and record its mass. Repeat this procedure until you have determined the mass of 9 drops.

- Calculate the average drop mass. Assume a density of 1.00 g/mL and calculate the average drop volume.

It would be nice to determine the precision (repeatability) of the drop volume. A professional way to do this would be by calculating a "standard deviation" for the data. A standard deviation tells you that about two-thirds of the data falls between the average ± one standard deviation. (This assumes a "normal" or "bell-shaped" distribution of data, and that the data set is large.)

For example, for the data set 4.0, 5.5, 6.0, 4.5, 4.5, 5.5, the average is 5.0. The standard deviation is around 0.5, since 4 of the 6 data points (two-thirds) fall in the range from 4.5 to 5.5. Therefore, this value could be reported as 5.0 ± 0.5.

- *Estimate* the standard deviation for your data set using the two-thirds rule given above. Show your answer to your TA before moving on.

The standard deviation can be calculated exactly using the following formula:

$$\text{s.d.} = \left[\frac{\sum_i (x_i - \overline{x})^2}{N - 1} \right]^{\frac{1}{2}}$$

where x_i represents an individual data point, x represents the mean or average value, and N stands for the total number of data points.

Applying this equation to the data set given above gives:

$$\text{s.d.} = \left[\frac{(4.0-5.0)^2 + (5.5-5.0)^2 + (6.0-5.0)^2 + (4.5-5.0)^2 + (4.5-5.0)^2 + (5.5-5.0)^2}{6-1} \right]^{\frac{1}{2}}$$

$$\text{s.d} = 0.77$$

It is preferred to round the standard deviation to one significant digit. Therefore, the answer should be reported as 5.0 ± 0.8. The actual standard deviation is a little bit larger than the estimated value in this case. But in both cases, around two-thirds of the data points fall within ± one standard deviation of the average.

- *Calculate* the standard deviation for your data set using the formula given above.

5.   Label your calibrated pipet with (a) the calibration value (average ± one standard deviation), (b) your initials, and (c) the date. This can be done using the "permanent" marker in your kit. You will need to put a piece of clear tape over what you have written since the marks rub off fairly easily.

6.   An alternative (but less accurate) way to calibrate a pipet is to use a container with a known volume. For example, the volume of each well in a 1 x 12 strip is 0.40 mL. If you count the number of drops required to fill one of these wells, then the average drop volume can be determined.

Record the number of drops required to fill one well in a 1 x 12 with the pipet held at (a) a 90° angle, and (b) a 45° angle, and calculate the average drop size in each case.

- How does the angle affect the drop size?

After watching several thousand students do these experiments, I found that pipets are best held in a *vertical delivery position*. Let's use the vertical delivery as *standard delivery technique*. (If you prefer another method, that's OK. Nevertheless, your delivery technique must be consistent!)

7.   The surface tension of the solution being delivered by a pipet also affects the drop volume. A pipet drop calibration for a dilute aqueous solution cannot be used for a solution containing another solvent or a solute that significantly changes the surface tension.

Count the number of drops required to fill a 1×12 well with distilled water. Using the same pipet (rinse and fill), count how many drops are required to fill it with 95% ethanol.

- Does ethanol have a higher or lower surface tension than water?

All of our quantitative transfers in this class involve dilute aqueous (water–based) solutions, so this added complication will not cause us any problems.

Please save your calibrated pipet in your kit. You will need it in a later experiment.

Section D.   A Comparison of the Accuracy of a Small-Drop Pipet vs. a Standard 25 mL Glass Buret

1. Weigh two small cups (a small beaker could alternatively be used). Set up a standard 25 mL glass buret. Fill it with distilled water. (Any type of water would work fine for these volume measurements, but distilled water will help to keep the buret tip clean.) Use the buret to deliver 1 mL as accurately as possible into one of your cups. Reweigh the cup plus water, and calculate the volume delivered.

2. Now use your calibrated small-drop pipet as the delivery device. Repeat the experiment above.

   - Which device more accurately delivered 1 mL?

   - Are you surprised by your results? Explain.

Section E.   Quantitative Dilution of Solutions

Goals: *(1) To be able to use a standardized pipet technique to quantitatively dilute a standard solution. (2) To calculate the concentration of any diluted solution.*

Experimental Steps: 1. Clean a 1×12 well strip. Remove water by slapping the strip onto a paper towel and using a cotton swab.

2. Fill a well of a 24-well tray with standard blue food dye solution.

   Note the *concentration* of the food dye on the label.

3. Use good technique to fill a small-drop pipet with blue food dye solution.

4. Hold the small-drop pipet *vertically* about 0.5 to 1 cm above each well of a 1×12 strip and deliver free drops in the following sequence: 10 drops to the first well, 9 drops to the second well, 8 drops to the third, and so on. Save any unused dye in the 24-well tray.

5. Wash the small-drop pipet and fill it with distilled water.

6. Use standard technique to deliver 0 drops of water to the first well, 1 drop to the second, 2 drops to the third, and so on, until you have added 10 drops of water to the eleventh well.

7. Stir by gently swirling a microstirrer in each well.

Touch the stirrer to a clean paper towel between each well. Be careful not to spill the liquid.

NOTE: The process you have just completed is called a *serial dilution* of the blue food dye.

Now let's calculate the concentration of blue food dye in the solution in each well. The solution in the first well is undiluted and has the concentration stated on the label of the original container. In any sample dilution process, the final concentration of the diluted solution can be calculated from

$$C_i \times V_i = C_f \times V_f$$

where

C_i = initial concentration V_i = initial volume

C_f = final concentration V_f = final volume

If the drops are of the same volume, and if we assume that the volumes are additive, then we can calculate the food dye concentration in the second well by

$$C_i \times 9 \text{ drops} = C_f \times 10 \text{ drops}$$

because 9 drops of dye at C_i were diluted to a total final volume of 10 drops (9 drops dye + 1 drop water). If C_i is known, then C_f can be calculated.

•   Calculate and report the concentration of food dye in each well. Don't forget to report the units.

NOTE: Keep the 1×12 well strip with the solution in it for the next two sections. This strip is called strip 1 to distinguish it from the other strips you will be using later in the laboratory.

Section F.   Standard Color Solutions and Colorimetry

Goal: *To use a color standard system as a calibration in the determination of an unknown concentration solution.*

Experimental Steps: NOTE: The serial dilution of blue food dye solution carried out in the previous section can now be used as a color standard to determine the concentration of unknown solutions of the same type.

1. Obtain a sample of the *unknown* blue food dye solution from your arm's reach station. Use it to fill a well in your 24-well tray.

    •   Make a note of the well number!

2. Clean the small-drop pipet used earlier and use *good transfer technique* to suck up some of the unknown.

3. Put strip 1 on the plastic surface. Clean another 1 × 12 well strip (let's call it strip 2). Use standard technique to deliver 10 drops of the unknown to well 7 of strip 2.

4. Gently pick up strip 1 and strip 2 with the unknown, put one on top of the other, and view at an angle that allows you to look through the *sides* of both strips simultaneously.

5. Slide them relative to each other and compare the "intensity" of blue in the unknown with the color standards.

6. Find a match for the unknown. If the match is in between two wells estimate where in between.

   • Determine the concentration of the unknown food dye solution and report it in your record.

   NOTE: The type of analysis you have just completed is a simple but powerful and widely used method of chemical analysis called colorimetry. Colorimetry is based on the principle that the amount of light absorbed by a sample is proportional to the number of absorbing molecules interposed in the path of the light. In your experiment, the light source is the fluorescent light reflected by a white surface. As the light passes through the solution, red light is absorbed, leaving blue light to enter your eye–brain detection system.

7. Clean both strips.

Section G.   Colorimetric Analysis of a Beverage

Goal:

To design and execute a colorimetric analysis of a beverage.

Experimental Steps:

You are presented with the following problem. Lime Kool-Aid is artificially colored with two FD and C food dyes: a blue and a yellow dye. You are provided with standard solutions of blue and yellow food dyes, and a sample of the powder used to make the drink.

   • Design and execute a colorimetric analysis which will allow you to analyze the soft drink. You may cooperate with others on this part if you would like.

   • A sample Kool-Aid solution can be made by adding 0.1 g of Kool-Aid (kept near the balances) powder to 10 mL of water.

   • Find the ratio of the two dyes present in the beverage.

   • Explain what you did in your notes.

Section H.   A Practical Application of Colorimetry—Chlorine in Water

Goals:

(1) Detect levels of chlorine in drinking water. (2) Remove the chlorine. (3) Understand why chlorine is added to drinking water.

Discussion:

Drinking water is required to be chlorinated, although it cannot exceed 4 ppm due to regulations of the EPA. According to the CDC, there should be at least 0.2 ppm chlorine in drinking water to ensure that any microorganisms have been killed. A chlorine level higher than 2 ppm will leave an unpleasant taste or odor in the drinking water. According to the 2011 Water Quality Report done by the State College Borough Water Authority, the range of detection for chlorine in State College was 0.72–1.39 ppm.

One way to test for chlorine levels in water is through colorimetry. Chlorine reacts with orthotolidine (OTO) to produce a yellow color. The intensity of the yellow color is proportional to the amount of chlorine. By comparison with a set of color standards, the concentration of chlorine in tap water can be determined.

Experimental Steps:

1. Turn your tap water on and let it run for 60 seconds.

2. Clean the left side of the test cell at your Arm's Reach Station thoroughly with distilled water. Fill the cell with tap water.

3. Put 5 drops of OTO into the same cell. Put the top of the cell on and shake.

4. Compare the color and estimate the concentration of chlorine in the unfiltered tap water.

5. Dump out the measured water and clean the cell and top with distilled water.

Discussion:

A Brita filter consists of 2 main components: (a) charcoal for removing organics and chlorine, and (b) an ion exchange resin that has been coated onto small plastic beads. There should be a broken open Brita filter at your Arm's Reach Station. Take a look at it; notice the two types of particles. In Experiment 10 you will learn more about the ion exchange resin. Today we will focus on the charcoal.

Organic compounds and chlorine stick to the surface of carbon. The particular type of carbon in these filters is called "activated charcoal," which refers to the fact that this charcoal is made under conditions that produce many tiny pores in the charcoal and hence a large surface area to react with molecules in water.

Experimental Steps:

6. Pour approximately 300 mL of tap water into a Brita filter. Let the water filter through. (Your TA may have done this already. Check the room's front lab bench.)

7. Pour the filtered tap water from the bottom chamber of the Brita filter into the left side of the test cell.

8. Put 5 drops of OTO into this same cell.

9. Compare the color and estimate the concentration of chlorine in the filtered tap water.

   • How does the filtered tap water compare with the unfiltered tap water? What happened?

The Use and Abuse of Aluminum and Its Compounds

Introduction

What do solid rocket fuel, rubies and sapphires, most RVs, antiperspirants, London buses, fireworks, and 50% of writing paper have in common? All of these products contain aluminum metal or aluminum compounds of various kinds. Aluminum is the most abundant metallic element and the third most abundant element in the earth's crust. The metal itself has not been found in nature because it is very reactive. The major naturally occurring compounds are oxides [e.g., bauxite ($Al_2O_3 \cdot 2H_2O$)] and silicates (e.g., many clays).

The basic process for the manufacture of aluminum metal was invented independently (in 1886) by two 22-year-olds: Charles Hall, a student at Oberlin College, Ohio, and Paul Hèroult, a Frenchman. The modern electrolytic method of production is based on the same process: the reduction of bauxite (dissolved in cryolite) with an electric current. This invention has brought aluminum, in little more than a century, from a chemical curiosity costing over $1,000 per pound to the world's second most commonly used metal. The Hall-Hèroult process consumes almost 5% of the electricity output of the United States!

There is now a wide variety of aluminum alloys used for a multitude of purposes, from thin foils in the food industry, through every engineering industry, to high technological applications in aeronautics, space exploration, and electronics. Unfortunately, metallic aluminum is rather expensive to make, primarily for two reasons. Most of the high-grade bauxite deposits occur outside of the United States, and the Hall-Hèroult process is extremely energy intensive. Changes in the international situation and the depletion of these high-grade deposits are forcing the aluminum industry to use lower grade ores, with correspondingly higher prices (in spite of much research into new methods).

At the same time as these economic pressures are being felt, there is also considerable environmental concern about the broadcast of aluminum beverage cans in the environment. In an ironic twist, the properties of aluminum that are responsible for its widespread use in modern society are also those that are cause for concern in the environment. Aluminum does not corrode in the same way as iron and steel. The aluminum surface reacts rapidly with oxygen in the air to form a tenacious thin film that effectively stops further corrosion. The discarded aluminum can has become almost immortal! It is estimated that the can has an average "lifetime" in the environment of more than 100 years—unless you pick it up and recycle it!

The recycling of solid wastes, particularly metals, is a societal issue of great importance. In our so-called technologically advanced society, we still try to dispose of the ever-increasing mountains of solid waste by the most primitive of methods: burying or burning. Landfill disposal is rapidly becoming expensive, difficult, and dangerous. Urban areas with high population densities are running out of suitable sites for garbage dumps, and old sites are causing severe local and groundwater pollution. Municipal incineration of garbage, which typically includes a mixture of plastics, paper products, metals, garden wastes, etc., is expensive and causes air pollution due to emission of a wide variety of toxic combustion products including NO_xs and SO_xs. Conservation of the valuable resources that are currently being squandered, together with recycling programs to reduce energy and material costs, are the *only* solutions to these solid waste problems.

Interestingly, it is in the area of recycling of metals, in particular aluminum, where the most progress has been made. Recycling of large-scale aluminum structural materials has been going on for a long time, and over the last ten years a number of recycling programs for aluminum cans have proved to be successful. The problem of recycling cans that end up in municipal garbage is still not solved, however. Only in the arena of industrial scrap aluminum, such as construction materials, do we see recycling. The aluminum is usually shredded, melted down, cast, and then made into another aluminum product.

One of the most widely used groups of aluminum compounds is the alums. A true alum is a double salt combination of aluminum sulfate and a group IA or ammonium sulfate, e.g., $KAl(SO_4)_2 \cdot 12H_2O$. The pulp and paper industry alone consumes more than 50% of the one million tons of alum produced annually in the United States. In order to make writing paper, etc., the open spaces in the cellulose fibers must be "filled" with substances that stick strongly to the fibers and stop ink from "bleeding." This is accomplished by adding clay and pine or other rosins (size) to the wet pulp. To fix the rosin strongly to the cellulose fibers, "papermakers" alum is added. The positive aluminum ion "neutralizes" the negative charge on the rosin and allows the rosin to chemically bind to the fibers. The slurry of treated pulp is poured onto screens of a papermaking machine, and the resulting mat is washed, dried, and rolled to produce a smooth sheet of paper like this one.

Unfortunately, this 100-year-old method of sizing paper has been found to have a serious flaw. The aluminum salts present in the paper, together with moisture, produce an acidic reaction that results in a pH of 4.8 or less[1]. The acid catalyzes the breakdown of the cellulose, destroying its strength and suppleness and eventually making the paper very brittle and brown. The extent of the problem is typified by an inventory of the 13.5 million volumes at the Library of Congress. Of these, 3 million are too brittle to handle, and each year about 70,000 more volumes are added to this group. Research has shown that other methods of sizing paper—using calcium carbonate, for example—can produce acid-free paper. The paper industry is moving more and more in this direction, but because of the costs involved, about 50% of paper is still sized with alum in the traditional manner.

Several methods are now being used to save some of the more rare and important books that are disintegrating. Photography can produce excellent master copies, but the cost is high: up to $100 per book. A new large-scale plant that is being built will be able to treat about 9,000 volumes every week. The process involves vacuum-pumping the books until they are dry and then treating them with diethylzinc ($Zn(C_2H_5)_2$) to neutralize acid and react with moisture. The cost per volume is about $3.

Alum compounds are also used extensively as flocculating agents and phosphate-removal agents in water and waste treatment plants. Other uses include soap, greases, fire extinguisher compounds, textiles, drugs, cosmetics, plastics, and pickles (look on your jar!). Aluminum oxides and hydroxides are very commonly manufactured compounds. The oxides are used in ceramics and catalysts, and the pharmaceutical grades of aluminum hydroxide are used in commercial antacid medicines.

---

1. The reaction is given on pg. 7-4.

Background Chemistry

The average American consumes more than 250 cans of carbonated beverages every year. More than 800 billion cans have been manufactured since 1950. With this kind of market, it is obvious that the beverage container industry is extremely competitive, with an increasing demand for a wide variety of packaging materials. The major container materials are refillable and nonrefillable glass bottles, steel cans, aluminum cans, and plastic bottles. Aluminum cans have about a 25% market share for packaged soft drinks and about a 50% share for the packaged beer market.

The modern all-aluminum can is, in a sense, the evolutionary descendant from the all-steel can, which was first test-marketed in 1936 and which became successful in the early 1960s. Much of the success of the aluminum can package is due to the many technical advances that have been made. One of the first major convenience improvements was an aluminum top for the steel can. Although the new top made the cans lighter and easier to open, the consumer still had to use a punch-type opener. In 1962, ALCOA introduced the easy-pen, pull-tab opener for aluminum can ends, which provided for easier gripping and safer openings. The nonremovable opener—such as Reynold's "Stay-on-Tab" and ALCOA's tabless "Easy-pen" end—was developed (1974) as a response to safety and environmental complaints. Other design improvements, which utilized the chemical properties of aluminum, were the drawn-and-ironed two-piece construction and the use of lighter-weight alloys. All these advances have made possible high-speed production (>1000 cans per minute) with maximum use of material (containers weighing less than 26 pounds per thousand).

Many factors play a part in the selection of a particular material for can construction. Manufacturing costs, recyclability, breakage, product purity, and consumer satisfaction are all important. All beverage container materials interact chemically with the solutions contained by them. Steel cans must be electroplated in order to reduce the corrosion that occurs with acidic soft drinks. Chemicals from plastic containers slowly dissolve in the beverage and can cause taste and health problems. Aluminum cans are also susceptible to corrosion by acids and bases and must be coated on the inside walls by a lacquer, resin, or plastic coating. The aluminum alloy (in sheet form) that is used for cans contains about 1 to 2% magnesium, which gives optimum performance at the lowest cost.

Aluminum is a very reactive metal. A clean metal surface reacts instantaneously with dioxygen to produce a thin, transparent, and tough layer of aluminum oxide (Al_2O_3) that protects the metal from further corrosion. This oxide layer is *amphoteric*, which means that it is dissolved by both acids and bases. Bases—e.g., potassium hydroxide (KOH)—dissolve the oxide layer quickly:

$$Al_2O_3(s) + 2KOH + 3H_2O \rightarrow 2KAl(OH)_4$$

The very soluble $KAl(OH)_4$ is thus produced. Once the oxide layer has gone, potassium hydroxide can then directly attack the metal:

$$2Al(s) + 2KOH + 6H_2O \rightarrow 2KAl(OH)_4 + 3H_2(g)$$

where the (s) and (g) mean solid and gas, respectively. The products of this reaction are soluble $KAl(OH)_4$ and dihydrogen gas. It is interesting to note that this is the reason why basic (alkaline) products like detergents, cleaners, and drain openers are never stored in an aluminum container. The aluminum container would slowly disappear!

Once the aluminum has been dissolved and is in solution, a variety of very useful products can be produced by carrying out further chemical reactions. In this experimental series, an alum, potassium aluminum sulfate dodecahydrate, will be synthesized. The addition of sulfuric acid (H_2SO_4) will cause two sequential chemical reactions to occur. Initially, before the addition of all the acid, the $KAl(OH)_4$ is neutralized by the acid to give a thick gelatinous precipitate of aluminum hydroxide, [$Al(OH)_3(s)$]:

$$2KAl(OH)_4 + H_2SO_4 \rightarrow 2Al(OH)_3(s) + K_2SO_4 + 2H_2O$$

As more sulfuric acid is added, the precipitate of aluminum hydroxide dissolves:

$$2Al(OH)_3(s) + 3H_2SO_4 \rightarrow Al_2(SO_4)_3 + 6H_2O$$

Both of these reactions are very *exothermic* (give off heat). The solution now contains dissolved aluminum sulfate [$Al_2(SO_4)_3$], potassium sulfate (K_2SO_4), and a slight excess of sulfuric acid (H_2SO_4). The solution can now be cooled, and potassium aluminum dodecahydrate [$KAl(SO_4)_2 \cdot 12H_2O$] will slowly crystallize out of the solution:

$$Al_2(SO_4)_3 + K_2SO_4 + 24H_2O \rightarrow$$
$$2[KAl(SO_4)_2 \cdot 12H_2O](s)$$

In the experiment, the crystallization process is sped up by providing a small "seed crystal" of alum for the newly forming crystals to grow on. Cooling is needed because alum crystals are soluble in water at room temperature. *Alum* is a generic name for a variety of aluminum compounds that are combinations of aluminum sulfate and a group IA metal sulfate.

The success of a synthesis, like that of alum, is judged by the yield of the compound of interest and by its purity. In the industrial or laboratory manufacture of chemicals, the quality-control evaluation usually involves both a qualitative and a quantitative analysis. *Qualitative analysis* is finding out what elements or substances are present in the sample, and *quantitative analysis* is the determination of how much of each component is in the sample. The synthesis of almost-pharmaceutical grade alum in this laboratory provides you with an opportunity to carry out some simple qualitative analysis tests for the components of potassium aluminum sulfate dodecahydrate.

Additional Reading

1. King, F., *Aluminum and Its Alloys*, John Wiley and Sons, New York, 1987. A good basic source of technical facts and figures. The only place where I could find a reference to the alloy used to make beverage cans!

2. Kaplan, S. (ed.), "100 Year History 1882–1982 and Future Probe," *Beverage World,* New York, 1982. The 100th Anniversary Issue of the trade journal *Beverage World.* A remarkable collection of "inside" information and history on the packaging, marketing, production, distribution, franchising, ingredients, and future of beverages.

3. Abelson, P. H., "Brittle Books and Journals," (editorial), *Science 238, 30* October, 1987. A short and to-the-point editorial.

4. Swanson, J. W., "Internal Sizing of Paper and Paperboard," *TAPPI Monograph Series* No. 33, New York, 1971. Where I found out about sizing—fascinating.

5. "Aluminum" video—an excellent movie showing the process by which bauxite ore is converted to aluminum. Recommended for everyone, but especially for those in the College of Earth and Mineral Sciences. See Dr. Keiser if you would like to sign this out.

Quiz Outline

Be able to answer pre-lab quiz questions similar to those asked in the sample quiz for this experiment.

Also know the following information:

- two reasons why aluminum metal is expensive to produce

- two uses of alum

- the chemical formula for aluminum oxide

- the name of an aluminum compound used in many antacids

- the meaning of "dodecahydrate"

Sample Pre-Laboratory Quiz

1. Explain the difference between the corrosion of iron and the corrosion of aluminum.

2. What is an "alum"?

3. Aluminum metal reacts vigorously with aqueous potassium hydroxide (as you will see today!). Write out a complete and balanced chemical equation for this reaction.

4. The equation for the synthesis of alum is:

$$2Al + 2KOH + 4H_2SO_4 + 22H_2O \rightarrow 2[KAl(SO_4)_2 \cdot 12H_2O] + 3H_2$$

A student started with 0.0602 g of aluminum foil. (a) Assuming that aluminum is the limiting reagent, calculate the expected yield of alum. The student obtained 0.4822 g of alum at the end of the experiment. (b) What was the % yield? Molar Masses: Al = 27.0 g, K = 39.1 g, S = 32.0 g, O = 16.00 g, H = 1.00 g.

5. Assume that one aluminum can is completely reacted with oxygen to produce aluminum oxide, and that this energy can be completely converted to electrical energy. How long could this energy keep a 60 watt lightbulb burning? (Show your work.) Al = 26.98 g/mole, O = 16.00 g/mole, ΔH_f (Al_2O_3) = 1670 kJ/mole, one can = 14 g. 1 watt = 1 J/sec.

Laboratory Experiments

Flowchart of the Experiments

Section A.	Recycling Aluminum: The Synthesis of Alum (Potassium Aluminum Sulfate)

Section B.	Qualitative Analysis of an Alum Sample

Section C.	Melting Point Determination

Section D.	A Practical Use for the Reaction of Aluminum with a Base

Requires one four-hour class period to complete.

CAUTION: Several chemicals used in this experiment are dangerous. Potassium hydroxide, sulfuric acid, and drain cleaner are all corrosive. Eye protection must be worn. If you get any of these chemicals on your hands, etc., wash well with cold water and inform your instructor.

Section A.	**Recycling Aluminum: The Synthesis of Alum (Potassium Aluminum Sulfate)**

Goal: To make an excellent grade of alum (potassium aluminum sulfate, $KAl(SO_4)_2 \cdot 12H_2O$) from scrap aluminum foil.

Discussion: You will find that aluminum metal is quite reactive and can be used as starting material for a wide variety of commercially important chemicals.

Experimental Steps: 1. Cut out a piece of regular aluminum foil (~1" × 2"), and weigh it accurately on an analytical balance. It should weight between 0.06 and 0.1 grams.

2. Cut the foil into very small strips and put all the strips into a small, *clean*, plastic cup.

3. Fill a Styrofoam coffee cup with hot water from the coffee urn in the front of the room to about 2 cm from the brim.

4. Transfer about 3/4 of a pipet of 1.5 M KOH to the aluminum in the small cup. The easiest way to do this is to first transfer 1/2 of a pipet full, followed by 1/4.

5. Float the small cup on top of the hot water in the Styrofoam cup. Swirl to wet the metal strips. Place the entire setup under your hood. The lower vent can be adjusted as necessary.

    • Record what you see.

Question: Q1. Explain your observations above in terms of a chemical reaction.

Experimental Steps: 6. Swirl gently every few minutes until all of the aluminum dissolves. If the solution stops bubbling then you may need to change the hot water (to increase the temperature), or add a *little* more KOH. (Note: If you add too much, it may be difficult to recover your crystals later.)

7. While the dissolution is going on, prepare an apparatus for microfiltration.

    (a) Construct an all-purpose clamp by cutting twice (about 8 cm) down a straw, peeling one half back and cutting it off, as shown on the next page.

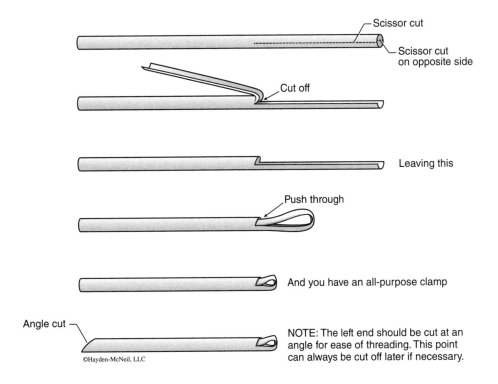

©Hayden-McNeil, LLC

(b)   Now make a stand by punching a hole about 5 cm from one end of another straw. (There should be 1/4" hole punches in the front of the room.) Cut about 8 cm off the other end of the same straw. The 8 cm piece will serve as the filtration column.

(c)   Place the stand in a 96-well plate.

(d)   Push a filter paper circle (already punched out for you) down the filtration column with a slim straw.

(e)   Insert a column cap (red plastic cap) onto the end and gently push the paper circle down against the cap.

The microfiltration apparatus is pictured below:

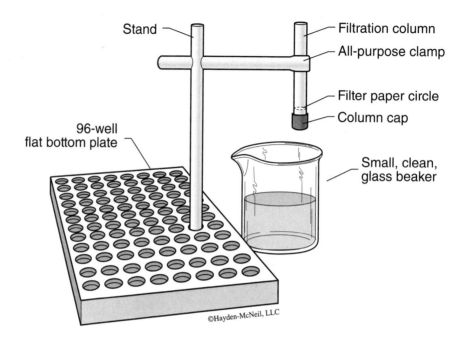

8. The aluminum should have dissolved by now. Suck up all the liquid from the cup with a clean pipet, *but try to avoid the black impurities as much as possible.*

9. Place a small, clean, glass beaker under the filtration column.

10. Transfer the liquid into the filtration column.

11. Allow the solution to filter via gravity until all the liquid has come through.

    Note: This filtration step, and the upcoming ice bath step, may take some time. While these operations are going on, there are a number of things you can (should!) do.

    •   Bring your notebook record up to date.

    •   Read ahead and prepare for the upcoming steps in this section.

    •   Look up alum in the Merck Index. Copy down molar mass, solubility in alcohol, solubility in water, and melting point information.

    NOTE: The easiest way to find it is to use the "Cross Index" in the back of the book. Also, note that the molar mass given is for the anhydrous compound, not the dodecahydrate which you have made.

    •   Work on Section D. This section can be done at any time during the period.

12. Fill a pipet about 1/3 full with 9 M H_2SO_4. (Don't add any more than 1/3 of a pipet or it may be difficult to recover your crystals later.)

    CAUTION: Use care. This solution is very corrosive.

13. Using a straw as a stirrer, add the H_2SO_4 quickly to the liquid in the beaker. Return the beaker to the hot water bath. Stir for at least one minute. The object is to try to break up and redissolve as many of the crystals as possible.

     The chemistry taking place above is very interesting. Under conditions of excess base, aluminum will be present as $Al(OH)_4^-$, which is soluble in water. As the H_2SO_4 is added, the aluminum will first form $Al(OH)_3(s)$. This is the thick white precipitate that is initially observed. But, at the final pH of the solution, most of the $Al(OH)_3$ will redissolve, releasing Al^{3+} into the solution. This is critical, because if Al^{3+} does not redissolve, then alum cannot be formed.

     •   Take a moment to record what you saw.

14. Empty the water from the Styrofoam coffee cup and fill it with ice (2/3) and water (1/3) to make an ice bath.

     NOTE: You *must* use 2/3 ice in order to ensure the bath will be cold enough for the length of time required. If the bath is not cold enough, the crystals *will* dissolve and you will lose your product. Hence, the term ice bath.

15. Place the beaker with liquid into the ice bath to cool it. Cool for around 15–20 minutes. If you do not have crystals in 20 minutes, then check with your TA.

     •   While it's cooling, take care of items such as those described under step 11.

16. Back to the ice bath. A good crop of crystals should now be forming. If crystals are not forming, add a seed crystal or two to start the crystallization.

17. Now you have the problems of removing the liquid (which is very acidic), washing the crystals, and drying them. Steps 19 through 23 describe one method.

18. Combine roughly equal amounts of ethanol and distilled water (about 3 to 5 mL each) in a vial from your drawer. Cap the vial and chill this solution in the ice water bath.

19. Set up the vacuum filtration apparatus. Your instructor will demonstrate how to use it. Make sure you place one of the disposable filter pieces (kept in the front of the room) on top of the plastic filter which is built into the Hirsch funnel.

20. Gently pour the liquid and the crystals into the Hirsh funnel. Use a slim straw spatula to scrape as many of the crystals as possible out of the beaker.

21. Transfer any remaining crystals from the beaker by adding small amounts of the chilled ethanol/water solution and swirling to suspend the crystals.

22. After all the crystals have been transferred, rinse the crystals by adding the chilled ethanol/water solution a little at a time—i.e., add a little to the crystals in the funnel, wait until it has been sucked through, then add some more.

23. Finally, rinse the crystals in the funnel with a squirt of ethanol directly from the squirt bottle.

24. Transfer the crystals to a clean, preweighed weighing boat. They will still be a little damp at this point. Break them up with a spatula, so that they will air dry more quickly. While they are air drying, complete Section D, if you have not already done so.

25. Look at the crystals through your hand lens.

   • Can you see any definite shape to them?

   • If you can, draw a picture of it in your notebook.

26. Weigh your crystals. Save them because you are going to use them in other experiments. The overall equation for the synthesis of alum is

$$2Al(s) + 2KOH + 4H_2SO_4 + 22H_2O \rightarrow 2[KAl(SO_4)_2 \bullet 12H_2O] + 3H_2$$

Questions: Q2.   (a) What is the advantage of using a 50:50 mixture of ethanol and water to rinse the crystals, as opposed to distilled water, or pure ethanol? HINT: Consider the solubilities of the substances involved.

(b) Why switch to pure ethanol in the last step?

Q3. Write two chemical reactions that describe what happened in step 13.

Q4. In several places you were advised not to add too much liquid or "it may be difficult to recover your crystals later." Explain this advice.

Q5. Calculate and record the theoretical yield and the % experimental yield.

$$\% \text{ experimental yield} = \frac{\text{grams of alum obtained in experiment}}{\text{grams of alum theoretically produced}} \times 100$$

The atomic weights of K, Al, S, O, and H can be found on the back cover of this lab manual.

Section B.   Qualitative Analysis of an Alum Sample

Goals: *(1) To carry out a qualitative analysis of the potassium aluminum sulfate* $(KAl(SO_4)_2 \bullet 12H_2O)$ *that you synthesized in Section A. (2) To confirm the presence of* SO_4^{2-}, K^+, Al^{3+}, *and water.*

NOTE: Use your plastic sheet as a reaction surface and do this experiment against a black background.

Experimental Steps: ***Check the pH of your sample.***

1. Use a straw spatula to transfer a few crystals (about 5 mg) to your plastic reaction surface. Add 3 drops of water to the crystals. Stir gently until the crystals dissolve.

2. Use a small piece of indicator paper to check the pH of the resulting solution.

Check for the presence of sulfate.

3.   Now add 1 drop of 0.5 M $BaCl_2$ (barium chloride) to the solution.

The change is the result of the following chemical reaction:

$$KAl(SO_4)_2(aq) + 2BaCl_2(aq) \rightarrow 2BaSO_4(s) + KAlCl_4\ (aq)$$

One of the products of this reaction ($BaSO_4$) is not soluble in water and precipitates as a solid. This is a good test for the sulfate ion $SO_4{}^{2-}$, since sulfate is one of the few anions that will form a precipitate with barium.

Check for the presence of potassium and water.

4.   A really good test for potassium is a flame test. Push a stainless steel pin into a small cork. Hold the pin head in the flame of a Bunsen burner to volatilize impurities from your fingers.

   •   What kind of impurities do you have on your fingers?

5.   This step is tricky: Get the pin head red hot, remove it, and quickly touch it to a small cluster of crystals. Several should stick. Don't melt any plastic!

6.   Slowly bring the pin (plus crystals) toward the flame and watch carefully. Hold the crystals in the flame for at least 5 seconds (until the solid glows).

   •   Carefully observe the alum's behavior as it is heated. HINT: Alum is a hydrate. Note carefully what you see and hear.

   •   Record what colors you saw in the flame as the crystals on the pin were heated by the flame.

   NOTE: The flame color from the hot solid is characteristic of the group IA element, potassium. You may want to refer to the chemistry of flame colors discussed in the chapter in this book on spectroscopy (Experiment 2).

   At the high temperature of the flame (about 1000°C), potassium is volatilized and gives a bluish color in the flame. After a few seconds sulfur dioxide is driven off, and the remaining oxides start to glow.

7.   Remove and hold the cork until the pin cools.

8.   Place the pin, with adhering solid, onto the plastic sheet (against a black background).

9.   Add 2 drops of water to the solid adhering to the pin and stir.

10.   Now add 1 drop of 0.5 M $BaCl_2$ to see if sulfate is present in the burned sample.

Check for the presence of aluminum ions.

11.   Prepare a fresh alum/water solution using the procedure in Step 1.

12.   Dilute 1 drop of 1.5 M KOH tenfold (using the methods developed in the Small-Scale Technique laboratory—Experiment 3) to produce a small amount of 0.15 M KOH.

13.   While stirring, add 1 drop of the 0.15 M KOH to the dissolved alum.

NOTE: The wispy gelatinous precipitate is aluminum hydroxide, which is used extensively as an antacid in various pharmaceuticals.

14.   Now add 1 drop of 1.5 M KOH to the precipitate. Stir.

Under conditions of excess base, it is possible to force a fourth OH^- onto the aluminum ion, forming $Al(OH)_4^-$, which is soluble in water.

Questions:

Q6.   Give a chemical explanation of the result of step 2. (Hint: See the Background Chemistry section in Experiment 7.)

Q7.   Why is the result of the reaction with $BaCl_2$ in step 10 different from the reaction in step 3?

Q8.   What experimental observation would be evidence that the crystals contain water in the structure?

Q9.   Write out chemical reactions that express the results of steps 13 and 14.

Q10. Summarize (in a table) all of the evidence that you have obtained in this section which indicates that you have made $KAl(SO_4)_2 \cdot 12H_2O$.

Section C.   Melting Point Determination

Goal: *To determine the melting point of the potassium aluminum sulfate ($KAl(SO_4)_2 \cdot 12H_2O$) that you synthesized in Section A.*

Discussion: A melting point determination is often taken to help confirm the identity and purity of a compound. Check the Merck Index to see what temperature alum should melt at. Impurities will tend to lower the melting point and broaden the range of melting.

Experimental Steps: 1.   Obtain an open-ended capillary tube from the front of the room. Tap the open end onto your pile of alum crystals. Some should lodge in the open end of the tube.

2.   Drop the tube, closed end down, down a straw held vertically against the benchtop. This should drive the crystals to the bottom of the closed end of the tube.

3.   Locate a Melt-Temp unit in the room. Make sure the temperature is at least 10–15 °C below the expected melting point before inserting a sample. These units can hold up to three capillary tubes at one time. Try to have at least two people's samples in for each run.

4.   Slowly increase the temperature. Note the temperatures at which (a) melting is first noticed, and (b) the melting of a given sample is complete. This constitutes the "melting point range," and it is reported with a hyphen between the two values —e.g., 250–253 °C. (Note: If your sample does not melt by 110 °C, then you have not synthesized the correct compound. Stop heating, and see your instructor.)

5.   Turn the heat down to allow the unit to cool.

Question: Q11. Report your melting point range. Compare it with a literature value, as well as with a neighbor's value. Comment on your results.

| Section D. | A Practical Use for the Reaction of Aluminum with a Base |

Goal: *To examine the composition and investigate the chemical action of a commercially available drain-opening product.*

Discussion: Most of the products sold commercially as drain cleaners contain strong bases that can react with and dissolve away the combination of insoluble grease, soap, and hair that causes blockage of sink, bath, and shower drains. One of these products, Crystal Drano, is very interesting because it is formulated with aluminum metal, solid sodium hydroxide, bleach, and an iron salt.

CAUTION: Drano is very caustic and corrosive, and extreme care must be used when handling it—*never* allow it to touch the skin.

Experimental Steps:
1. Use a *dry* clean straw spatula to obtain a representative sample of Crystal Drano. Make sure you have at least one piece of each type of substance in it. (A sample in a glass jar should be at your arm's reach station. This is for viewing purposes only. Take your sample directly from the Crystal Drano container.) Place the sample on your plastic surface.

2. Carefully observe the sample with your hand lens.

   • How many individual morphological forms (shapes) can you see?

   • Make a rough drawing.

   • Do you see anything changing with time?

3. Add a few drops of water from a pipet.

   • Make careful observations for the next few minutes.

4. Read the side directions-for-use panel on the can of Crystal Drano. The directions caution to "remove any standing water" and to "make sure water in drain is cool."

Questions:
Q12. Why would these two instructions (step 4) be important when using this product?

Q13. From what type of material do you think the Crystal Drano container is made?

Q14. Give some reasons why you think that this combination of ingredients is particularly effective in removing blockages.

Q15. Give a chemical explanation of your observations made in step 3. Include a chemical reaction. Hint: See Discussion above.

Experiment 5

Instruments

What They Do and What They Don't

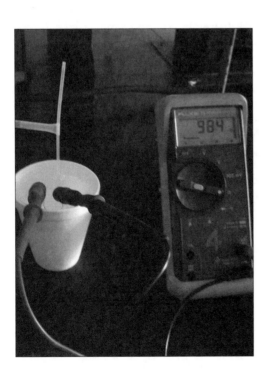

Introduction

"Instrument, n. [L. instrumentum, a tool or tools, implement, stock in trade, furniture, dress, from instruere, to furnish, equip; in, in, and struere, to pile up, arrange.]

1. (a) a thing by means of which something is done; means; (b) a person used by another to bring something about.

2. a tool or implement, especially one used for delicate work or for scientific or artistic purposes."

—*Webster's New Universal Unabridged Dictionary*

Much of the research carried out in modern science is done by means of instruments. This is as true in chemistry as it is in high-energy physics. Many of these instruments are expensive, sophisticated, extremely accurate, and require a Ph.D. (and a team of dedicated technicians) to operate. The advent of microelectronics, lasers, and computers has revolutionized the design, application, and accuracy of instruments of all types.

Unfortunately, many of these developments have tended to obscure the link between the scientific principles of the experiment and the output from the instrument. For the well-experienced scientist or engineer, this is generally not a problem, however for a student who is just getting started in science, the instrument can become an intimidating "black box," spewing forth a mass of meaningless output signals. In an attempt to circumvent some of these problems, we have adopted a different approach to the use of instrumentation in your chemistry course. The general idea is to design, and wherever possible allow you to construct, simple and small working versions of the expensive, commercially available machines. You will find that these simple versions are in the original research papers in the literature. It is perhaps important at this point to note that simple and small does not mean trivial. If you build your own scientific instrument,

- You know how it works.

- You know when it isn't working.

- You can fix it when it breaks.

- You can play with it however you please.

- You know what it can do and what it can't.

- You don't need a Ph.D. to do it!

Eventually, as you progress through the scientific world, you will surely be introduced to the sophisticated versions. When this happens, remember that you really know how "it" works. Read the instruction manuals carefully so that you can find out where the buttons are.

The basic principle of most scientific instruments is that there is a sensor of some type that can probe the system under investigation and that is connected to a measuring device of some type. A simple, classical example is the instrument that has been used for many centuries to measure the amount of "hotness" or "coldness" of a system, i.e., the thermometer. The sensor in this instrument is usually a liquid like mercury or alcohol that expands or contracts as it is heated or cooled by the environment. The key to the thermometer being a meter is, of course, the choice of some type of measuring scale to be attached to it. Unfortunately, throughout the more than three hundred years of development, many different scales have been attached to many different designs of the thermometer. Even today there are at least four or five scales commonly used throughout the world. It is proving an extraordinarily difficult task to choose one as a standardized system (hence, the temperature conversion questions on your freshman chemistry test!). It is worth emphasizing that, even if one particular scale were chosen, the choice would be arbitrary. Of course, every thermometer that is manufactured (no matter what the scale) must somehow be calibrated against some better thermometer, and so on. In this series of experiments, you will have the opportunity to investigate several very different instruments that are used to measure that strange property called temperature.

Background Chemistry

All matter has electrical characteristics. Atoms are composed of negatively charged electrons and positively charged protons. Electrons are responsible for the chemical properties of solids that form the basis for modern electronics. Solids can be divided into three types: conductors, semiconductors, and insulators, depending on how well the material conducts electricity. Metals are excellent *conductors* of electricity because there are many free electrons that can be easily pushed through the macroscopic structure. Most nonmetallic elements and compounds contain strongly bound electrons that are fixed in bonding positions close to the original atoms and are not free to move. These substances do not conduct electricity and are called *insulators*. *Semiconductor* substances have an intermediate electrical conductivity that can be controlled to any desired level during the manufacture of the substance. Combinations of all of these types of materials in extraordinarily thin microlayers and regions can be arranged in carefully designed circuits to control the flow of charge in microelectronic devices.

The flow of charge through a substance is called an *electric current*. Current may flow in only one direction—in which case it is called *direct current (DC)*—or in both directions, which is termed *alternating current (AC)*. The fundamental law that quantitatively describes the flow of direct current is called Ohm's law,

$$V = IR$$

where V is the voltage, I is the current, and R is the resistance. *Voltage (V)* (sometimes called potential) is the electrical pressure or force that pushes charge through the conductor. A good analogy to describe current is to think of it as water flowing through a pipe. The voltage is then the water pressure that is pushing the water through the pipe. The *current (I)* is the quantity of electrons passing a point in one second and is measured in amperes (A). One ampere is 6.25×10^{18} electrons passing a point in one second. All conductors tend to resist the flow of charge to some extent. A conductor has a resistance (R) of 1 ohm (Ω) if a voltage of 1 volt (V) will force a current of 1 ampere (A) through it. Another useful term is that of power (P), which is the work performed by all electrical current measured in watts (W). The power of a direct current is voltage multiplied by current:

$$P = VI$$

An *electronic circuit* is any arrangement of electrical materials that will allow a current to flow. The most basic circuit for direct current flow has a power source (e.g., a battery), a resistor, and conducting connectors, and is represented in the circuit diagram of Figure 5.1. Resistors play a very important role in the design of circuits for scientific instruments because they limit the flow of current and because they exhibit a temperature dependence. This latter property can be extremely useful in designing sensitive temperature sensors. Resistors come in all shapes, sizes, and types, several of which you will be using in this series of experiments. One very common type is the *carbon film resistor*, which is made by depositing a carbon film on a small ceramic cylinder. The length of the carbon film between the leads controls the resistance of this device. Resistors, such as the one pictured in Figure 5.2, are often color-coded to indicate the value of resistance, as shown in Table 5.1. The color bands numbered in Figure 5.2 correspond to the band numbers in Table 5.1.

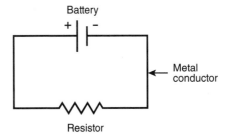

Figure 5.1 A basic DC circuit.

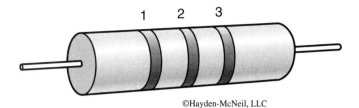

©Hayden-McNeil, LLC

Figure 5.2 Resistor with color bands.

Table 5.1 Resistance Values (Ω) from Color Bands

Band Color	Band 1	Band 2	Band 3 (Multiplier)
Black	0	0	1
Brown	1	1	10^1
Red	2	2	10^2
Orange	3	3	10^3
Yellow	4	4	10^4
Green	5	5	10^5
Blue	6	6	10^6
Violet	7	7	10^7
Grey	8	8	10^8
White	9	9	none

So, for example, a resistor with brown, green, and orange bands would have a resistance of 15 × 10^3 ohms. Sometimes there is a fourth band that gives the accuracy of the resistance value—e.g., gold is ± 5%, silver ± 10%, and none is ± 20%.

You will also be using a relatively uncommon resistor that is a semiconductor silicon temperature sensor. This sensor, shown in Figure 5.3, is a microdevice manufactured from n-type silicon with a doping level of about 10^{15} cm^{-3}.

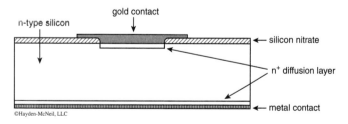

©Hayden-McNeil, LLC

Figure 5.3 Semiconductor temperature sensor.

Between about −50 °C and 150 °C, this device has a positive temperature coefficient of resistance due to a fall in the charge carrier mobility with rising temperature. Solid state electronic temperature sensors of this type are rapidly displacing the traditional mercury-in-glass thermometers in many scientific instruments.

Quantitative measurement of voltage, current, and resistance is most conveniently made with an instrument called a *digital multimeter*. You will be using this basic electronic instrument in conjunction with a number of sensors or probes that can be used to monitor physical and chemical properties of a system during an experiment. One of the key features of these modern multimeters is that they have a huge (10 MΩ) built-in resistance, which means that the meter requires only a very small flow of charge to make a measurement. A measurement can therefore be made *without* perturbing the chemistry of the experiment. Digital multimeters are themselves rather sophisticated examples of microelectronic circuitry; it is not necessary for you to understand the intricacies of this instrument. However, if you wish to examine the insides or obtain more information about how the meter works, check with your instructor who will organize it for you.

One of the main objectives of this series of experiments is to allow you to explore the applications and limitations of radically different types of instrumentation for the measurement of temperature. One of the first instruments for sensing different degrees of hot and cold was called an air thermoscope. The device was simply a bulb (containing air) that was attached to a long, thin stem. The stem was partially filled with liquid and was dipped into liquid in a container. Expansion or contraction of the air in the bulb due to temperature changes led to a rise or fall in the liquid level in the stem of the thermoscope. Eventually, it was realized that by marking the stem with a graduated scale and by adopting uniform methods of construction, the thermoscope could be a quantitative instrument of temperature measurement. The basis for the gas thermometer described above is the principle that the volume of a gas is directly proportional to the temperature of the gas at constant pressure and amount of gas.

This principle is known as Charles' law:

$$V = \text{constant} \times T$$

For 1 mole of an ideal gas at 1 atmosphere, the plot of volume versus temperature is shown in Figure 5.4.

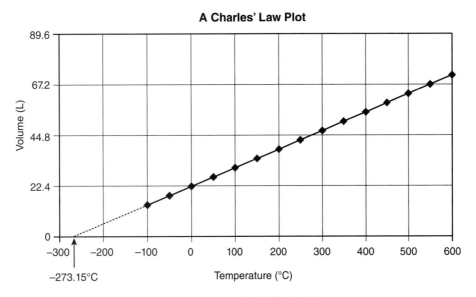

Figure 5.4 A graph of Charles' law.

Note that the volume of the gas becomes zero at −273.15 °C. This temperature is called *absolute zero*, the lowest possible temperature. The British physicist Lord Kelvin realized that it would be very useful to define a temperature scale that has absolute zero as the zero point. The Kelvin temperature scale is related to the Celsius scale in that zero K is −273.15 °C. You will have the opportunity to construct and calibrate a rather novel polyethylene gas thermometer in this sequence of experiments.

Additional Reading

1. Mims, F.M., III., *Getting Started in Electronics*, Radio Shack®, 1987. Written for, and obtainable at, Radio Shack®, it is without doubt the best introduction written for the beginner in electronics. Clear, interesting, and funny.

2. Middleton, W.E.K., *A History of the Thermometer and Its Use in Meterology*, The John Hopkins Press, Baltimore, MD, 1966.

3. *Silicon Temperature Sensors*, Amperex Electronic Corporation, Technical Sheet, 1988.

4. *Instruction Manual for Fluke 75 and 77 Multimeter*, John Fluke Mfg. Co., Inc., Everett, WA, 1983.

Sample Quiz Questions

1. What are some of the advantages of building your own scientific instrument?

2. Convert 40 °C to °F.

3. Solids can be divided into three types depending on how well they conduct electricity. What are the three types?

4. What is Ohm's law?

5. Give the name of one unit of current.

6. What does a gold band on a resistor mean?

7. Give a value in °C for absolute zero.

8. Convert 57 °C to K.

9. What is the principle of an air thermoscope?

10. Give a definition of direct current (DC).

Laboratory Experiments

Flowchart of the Experiments

Section A.	**Basic Electronics**

Section B.	**The Operation of a Digital/Analog Multimeter as a Measurement Instrument**

Section C.	**A Semiconductor Silicon Temperature Sensor System**

Section D.	**The Construction and Calibration of a Gas Thermometer**

Section E.	**A Modified Range Gas Thermometer**

Section F.	**Your Grade for This Experiment**

Requires one four-hour class period to complete.

Section A.   Basic Electronics

Goal:

To use Ohm's law to calculate current, resistance, and voltage in simple electronic circuits.

Discussion:

First, an important word about the direction of an electrical current. If you look at a battery you will see that one terminal is marked positive (+) and the other negative (–). Engineers and solid state designers generally say that *positive current* flows from the positive to the negative terminal. This is the traditional convention that was developed by Benjamin Franklin. It is now known that electrical current is the flow of electrons through a conductor or semiconductor. Since electrons are negatively charged, they move from a negatively charged region to a positively charged region. Throughout these and subsequent experiments, "current flow" means "electron flow."

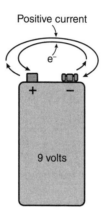

Questions:

Q1.   An interesting question for you. You need to jump-start your car or truck. You are given a set of jumper cables and you've found a second vehicle with a good battery. The two batteries are pictured below. How do you connect them in order to start your car rather than destroying both batteries?

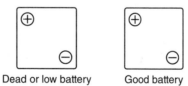

Q2.   Which way will electrons flow in the following circuit?

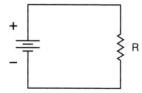

Q3.   For the previous circuit calculate the following:

(a)   What is the resistance if the voltage is 9.26 V and the current is 0.50 A?

(b)   How many mA of current will flow if the resistance is 10 kΩ and the voltage 1.5 V?

(c)   What will happen to the direction of electron flow if the resistor is reversed?

(d)   Is the circuit a DC or an AC circuit?

Section B. The Operation of a Digital/Analog Multimeter as a Measurement Instrument

Goal: *To operate a digital multimeter (DMM) as a measurement instrument in electronic circuits.*

Discussion: There are a large number of digital multimeters (DMM) on the market. For this series of experiments and all the others in this book, the instrumental requirements are very simple. The meter should have a high internal impedance (similar to resistance), be rugged and portable, and have suitable range selection controls. You will be working with an excellent instrument—the Fluke 75 multimeter. The face of the meter is shown below.

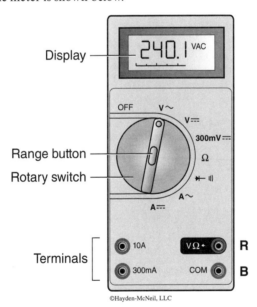

©Hayden-McNeil, LLC

Experimental Steps: 1.   Turn the instrument on by rotating the switch from the off position to the function you wish to measure.

The meter will display all segments, do a self-test, chirp, and is then ready to use.

Function Symbols	
V~	voltage, alternating
V....	voltage, direct
300 mV....	voltage, in mV, for below 300 mV
Ω	resistance
▸⊢ ᵓ)))	diode test and continuity beeper
A~	current, alternating
A....	current, direct

NOTE: A "O.L." reading means "over limit"—i.e., the reading is too high for the multimeter to measure.

Voltage Measurements

1.   Measure the *voltage* as follows (refer to the illustration below).

2.   Connect the test leads as shown. R represents *red lead*, B represents *black lead*.

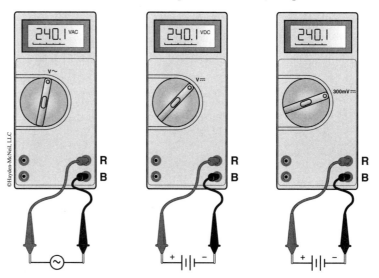

3.   Measure the voltage of the battery that is assigned to you using each of the three settings, using needle probes.

•   Note what the meter reads and which lead is on which battery terminal.

NOTE: The red position (and lead) is the positive terminal of the DMM and the black position is the negative terminal of the DMM.

This means that electrons are coming into the black lead and out of the red lead when you have a positive direct voltage reading.

•   Which of the above settings is most appropriate for measuring your battery's voltage? Why?

4.   Switch the leads and note any change in reading.

5.   Look at the analog scale that is just below the digital reading and relate the analog reading to the digital reading.

6.   Press the range button that is in the center of the rotary switch.

7.   Remeasure the battery voltage.

8.   Continue to press the range button, observing what happens to the voltage reading as you cycle through the ranges.

   •   What happens when you press the range button?

   NOTE: Autorange is automatically the most sensitive range for all measurements.

   It is particularly useful to have the meter set on Autorange when you are making measurements that occur on a boundary between two scales, for example, readings that fall between 1 MΩ and 999 kΩ.

   To get back to Autorange, either switch the meter off and then switch it back on, or press the range button for 1 second; the meter will chirp and go to Autorange.

9.   Using the needle probes, measure and record the voltage of the electrical outlet at your station.

   •   What must you set differently on the DMM to measure this voltage when compared to measuring the voltage of the battery?

Resistance Measurements

Resistance measurements are made by switching the rotary switch to the Ω (omega) symbol. The units of *resistance*, indicated by Ω, kΩ, or MΩ, are shown in the display.

1.   Obtain a carbon filament resistor from Reagent Central and connect the test leads as shown (refer to illustration below).

Remember, R represents *red lead*, B represents *black lead*.

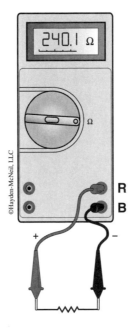

2. From your knowledge of resistor color coding (see Table 5.1 in the Background Chemistry section), find the resistance of the resistor.

   • Record the resistance value in correct units.

3. Connect the DMM to the resistor and measure the resistance using the meter in Autorange.

   • Is the resistor within tolerance?

   • Is the resistance of a resistor temperature-dependent?

   NOTE: If you have a high-value resistor, greater than 50 kΩ, you might try holding it between your fingers to raise the temperature while measuring the resistance.

Making a Resistor

NOTE: One simple way of making a resistor is by drawing a line with a soft lead (2B) pencil.

1. In your notebook (paper must be "non-glossy") draw a line about 12 cm long with a pencil and ruler.

2. Draw over the line about 10 times, pressing firmly and evenly.

   You have now probably laid down enough carbon to have a planar resistor.

3. Mark the line off in 1 cm intervals.

4. Set up the meter for resistance measurement (on Autorange). Press one needle probe firmly at one end of the line and the other probe exactly 1 cm away.

   • Record the resistance.

5. Keeping the one needle probe in place while moving the other, repeat the measurement at 1 cm intervals up to about 9 cm. Try to get at least 5 readings. Don't worry about instability of the measurements; just press the probe, record the resistance, move the probe, etc. You are mostly interested in getting a feel for the trend in resistance as a function of distance rather than in getting numbers accurate to the ohm.

   NOTE: It is important to keep the initial probe position the same each time.

   • Make a graph of resistance versus distance.

   • What factors play a part in controlling the resistance of the line?

   NOTE: If you have too much difficulty with the measurements on the lead pencil line, connect two or more of the carbon filament resistors in series and measure the total resistance of the resistors. Measure the individual resistance of each resistor.

Current Measurement

1. Set up a circuit containing the resistor, battery, and meter and measure the current in the circuit as shown below:

   NOTE: It is possible to wrap one resistor lead around the negative terminal of the battery.

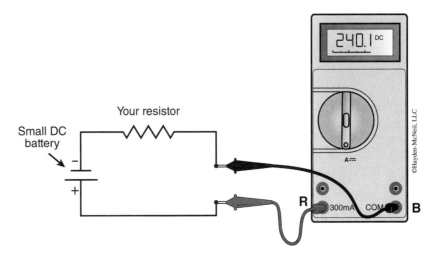

   NOTE: The measurement of current is carried out with the meter in series and with the red lead plugged into the current input. If you are using the 300 mA connection (as shown above), then the current readings will be in units of milliamps.

   You should now be reasonably familiar with the use of a digital/analog multimeter in making various measurements.

Questions:

Q4. Why is it important that the digital multimeter have a high internal resistance when it is on the voltage setting, i.e., what does the high internal resistance prevent?

Q5. What does your graph of resistance versus distance (step 5, under "Making a Resistor") tell you about resistors placed *in series* with each other?

Q6. Use Ohm's law to calculate the current for the measurement in step 1 under "Current Measurment." Do the measured and calculated current agree? If not, why not?

Section C.   A Semiconductor Silicon Temperature Sensor System

Goals:

(1) To explore some of the sensor characteristics of a temperature-sensitive semiconductor device. (2) To compare it with a classical liquid-in-glass thermometer. (3) To plot appropriate calibration curves from manufacturer-supplied data in order to be able to convert resistance measurements into temperature.

Experimental Steps:

1. Obtain a silicon temperature sensor from your instructor. **If the sensor is already mounted in a straw holder, skip to step 5.**

   NOTE: Please be careful with the device. The semiconductor junction is packaged in glass and is somewhat fragile.

The sensor dimensions are:

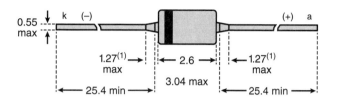

Dimensions in mm

Package material: glass
the sensor must operate in the forward
biased condition for proper performance.

mm	inch
.55	.022
1.27	.050
1.6	.063
2.6	.102
3.04	.120
25.4	1.000

(1) Lead diameter in this zone uncontrolled.

The sensor may already be bent into a U-configuration for ease of use.

NOTE: The film-stripped pictures below illustrate steps 2 through 4.

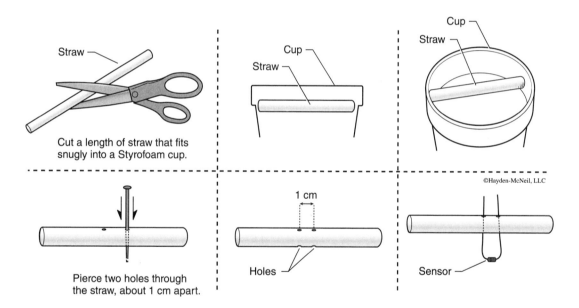

©Hayden-McNeil, LLC

Straw

Cut a length of straw that fits snugly into a Styrofoam cup.

Cup
Straw

Cup
Straw

Pierce two holes through the straw, about 1 cm apart.

1 cm

Holes

Sensor

2.   Make a sensor support by cutting a straw so that the straw will fit snugly by friction into a Styrofoam cup.

3.   Place the straw piece on your notebook and pierce holes about 1 cm apart through the straw.

4.   Now gently push the sensor through the straw holes. The sensor should stay in the support by friction.

5.   Place the straw into a Styrofoam cup.

6. Connect the device to your DMM. The manufacturer recommends that they be used in the "forward-biased" mode (the black DMM lead connected to the black ring (negative) side of the sensor). But, in our experience, both orientations give similar results. So if a black ring is not visible, then connect the sensor in whatever direction is most convenient.

The manufacturer (Amperex—a North American Philips Co.) has supplied the following calibration information for this device.

T_A °C	Resistance Ω		T_A °C	Resistance Ω
−55	495		50	1206
−50	520		60	1295
−40	572		70	1387
−30	627		80	1483
−20	687		90	1583
−10	750		100	1687
0	817		110	1794
10	887		120	1905
20	961		125	1962
25	1000		130	2020
30	1039		140	2138
40	1121		150	2260

Temperature versus resistance values (KTY8₃)

7. Turn the DMM to resistance measurement.

8. Try to get a feel for the response time of the sensor by breathing on it or holding it between the thumb and finger and letting go.

NOTE: In the electronics industry the thermal time constant is the time the sensor needs to reach 63.2% of the total temperature difference.

9. Switch the DMM off.

Question: Q7. Make a brief list of what you consider to be the basic differences between this temperature sensor and a typical mercury-in-glass thermometer.

Homework: HW1. Use a computer to plot a full-scale graph of resistance versus temperature for the range 10 °C to 60 °C, and to determine the best straight line through the points. (Any computer graphing program may be used. Instructions for how to do this using Excel are given in your course packet.) Attach this graph to your notebook when it is completed.

HW2. Make yourself a table of resistance versus temperature in 1 °C intervals from 18 °C to 35 °C by using the equation from Homework 1 (above) to convert resistance values to temperatures.

Attach this table to the graph so that you have easy access to it.

Section D.   The Construction and Calibration of a Gas Thermometer

Goal: To construct and calibrate a simple gas thermometer based on the expansion or contraction of humid air. To do this you will need to position a plug of water so that it resides at the end of a thin-stem pipet when the bulb of the pipet is immersed in hot water in a Styrofoam cup. As the hot water is cooled to room temperature, the plug of water will move down the pipet stem. You will be able to correlate the distance the plug moves with the temperature changes of the water in the cup, thereby creating a gas thermometer.

Discussion: Calibration is accomplished with the sensor-DMM system developed in the last experiment. Although the gas thermometer is basically a simple instrument, it is experimentally tricky to calibrate and use. You will need to be careful, thoughtful, and patient to get good results.

Experimental Steps:

1. Construct a straw clamp and stand system as instructed in Section A of Experiment 4, "The Use and Abuse of Aluminum."

2. Obtain two Styrofoam cups.

3. Fill one cup with ice and the other cup with warm tap water (approximately 30 °C).

   NOTE: Use ice and small volumes of hot water to obtain water of the correct temperature. You can measure the temperature of the water by placing the sensor (which is attached to the support) into the water in the cup.

4. Obtain a new, clean, thin-stem pipet (un-stretched). If necessary, trim the stem so that the thin-stem part (not including the bulb) is exactly 11.0 cm long. If the stem is already less than 11.0 cm, measure the length of the stem and use your measurement in the calculations for Question 1.

5. Place the thin-stem pipet into the 30 °C water, with the bulb down and completely immersed in the water.

6. Hold the pipet in the water for *at least a minute* so that the air inside the bulb will expand and reach thermal equilibrium.

7. Quickly remove the pipet and immediately turn it over and place the thin-stem end into the 30 °C water.

8. Allow a small plug (about 0.5–1 cm) of water to be sucked up into the thin stem. *Do not depress the bulb when you place the thin-stem end in the water; just allow the water to be drawn into the stem.* This will occur naturally as the pipet cools. When the plug has been sucked up, remove the thin-stem pipet from the water immediately.

   NOTE: The indicator plug in the thin stem is now self-calibrated to be positioned right at the top of the stem at the upper working temperature.

For illustrations of the apparatus and procedures discussed in steps 9, 10, and 11, refer to the pictures below.

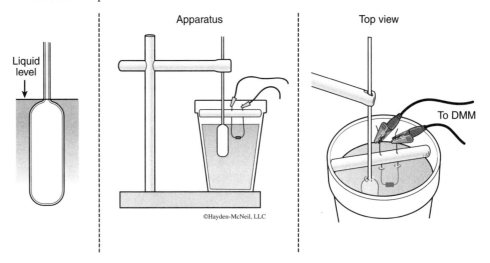

9. Lift the thin-stem pipet by the *stem* and carefully place the thin-stem part into the straw clamp.

10. Slide the clamp down so that the bulb of the pipet is just completely immersed (as shown in the first picture above) in the 30 °C water. If the plug looks like it is going to shoot out the tip, add cold water to the Styrofoam cup to reduce the temperature and draw the plug back into the stem. Stir. Wait until the plug stabilizes at some position (preferably near the tip) in the stem.

11. Adjust the sensor support so that the sensor is in the water alongside the bulb of the pipet.

   • Read the resistance of the sensor by means of the DMM and measure the distance of the plug (in cm, to an estimated 0.5 mm) from the tip of the thin stem.

12. Make four more readings of distance from the tip of the thin stem as a function of resistance (temperature). For each reading, add cold water to the cup, and stir to equalize the temperature in the cup. *Set up your calibration so that the plug travels in roughly equally spaced distances over the entire length of the stem for the five total readings.*

Homework: HW3.   Prepare a plot of distance versus temperature as follows:

   (a) Subtract the plug distances from 11.0 cm to obtain the height of the plug above the bulb at each temperature.

   (b) Plot height of the plug above the bulb versus absolute temperature (K). You can obtain the temperature (in °C) from your accurate resistance versus temperature graph that you prepared earlier.

   (c) Calculate the slope (include units!). Then, using the equation of the best-fit line and length of the thin stem, calculate the "range" (°C or K) of your gas thermometer.

HW4.   How does your graph of distance versus absolute temperature compare with Figure 5.4 in the Background Chemistry section? Which of the gas laws have you verified in this experiment?

HW5.   Compare and contrast the characteristics of the gas thermometer and the semiconductor temperature sensor. Your comparison should include a brief discussion of cost, possible applications, range, flexibility, ease of use, response time, etc.

Section E.   A Modified Gas Thermometer

Goal: *To add water to your thermometer, and explore how this affects its performance.*

Discussion: This is your chance to apply what you have learned—i.e., The exact procedure is up to you!

Experimental Steps: 1.   Take the thin-stem pipet used in the last section and fill the bulb about 3/4 full with water.

2.   Investigate the characteristics of the "modified" gas thermometer.

Homework: HW6.   Draw a calibration graph, as you did in Section D, for the modified gas thermometer.

(a) Calculate the slope (include units!).

(b) How does this slope compare with the value in Section D for that gas thermometer? Does the difference "make sense"? Explain.

(c) Calculate the "range" (°C or K) of your modified gas thermometer.

HW7.   State at least one significant advantage, and one significant disadvantage of the "modified" vs. the "regular" gas thermometer.

Section F.   Your Grade for This Experiment

Your grade for this experiment will be based on two items:

1.   Your answers to homework questions 1 and 2 (Section C), 3, 4, 5, (Section D), and 6 and 7 (Section E). This will be worth a maximum of 50 points.

2.   A quiz, covering material from this experiment, that will be given at the beginning of your next lab period. This quiz will be worth a maximum of 50 points. A good way to prepare for this quiz is by reviewing the questions in each section of this experiment. You will also be responsible for knowing the values of the following SI units: M, k, d, c, m, and μ.

3.   The total of 1 and 2 will be your grade for this experiment.

Experiment 7

Solutions and Reactions

Introduction

"Did you ever stand and shiver
Just because
You were lookin' at a river?"
—Ramblin' Jack Elliott (told to the author
on a plane from Detriot to Denver)

Water is by far the most common and the most important liquid on our planet. It is vital to all living organisms, and it is indispensable to civilization. Water covers most of the earth and through its global cycle—the hydrologic cycle—permeates the atmosphere and the rocks. It shapes the face of the planet as it slowly dissolves and transports the land into the sea. Much of the importance of water lies in its ability to dissolve and suspend so many substances and then transport them to different places. It is indeed the universal solvent for gases, liquids, and solids.

It is probably safe to say that all biochemical reactions in living systems require water as a solvent medium and often use water as a reactant or as a catalyst. For example, the human cardiovascular system is a marvelous multipurpose medium for the exchange and transport of dissolved gases, sugars, suspended organelles, and so on. The oceans, a global example, contain about 3.5% of dissolved inorganic solids, mostly in the form of hydrated cations and anions. Millions of species have evolved to make this salty solution the perfect medium for life. The billions of tiny bubbles continuously trapped in the crashing waves burst and fling microscopic droplets of sea solution into the atmosphere. The droplets evaporate, leaving solid particles that are so small that they remain in the air for long periods of time. These marine aerosols play a large part in controlling the weather because they act as cloud condensation nuclei, catalyzing the formation of the natural precipitates: rain, snow, and hail. The vast global ocean currents transport everything ranging from microscopic plankton to carbon dioxide and air pollutants, such as fluorocarbons, from one hemisphere to the other. At every scale, from the microscopic to the macroscopic, the solvent and fluid properties of water are essential to the removal of the toxic wastes generated by cells, organisms, people, factories, and cities.

Of equal importance are the substances that are not very soluble in water. In many biological systems, the fluid bag of cells is supported by a skeletal structure whose composition can vary from silicates in Radiolaria (tiny sea creatures) to calcium hydroxyphosphate in humans. The transport of hydrated calcium and phosphate ions in the complex system of bone and teeth formation is a marvel of solution chemistry. The survival of birds depends upon a fragile shell composed of tiny calcite crystals laid down on a light network of protein collagen. When things go awry and substances precipitate in the wrong places, serious health problems can occur. Cholesterol plaques in the bloodstream can end the flow of life. Kidney, gall, and bladder stones and calcified deposits in the joints can cause severe pain. Microscopic silica, asbestos, and smoke particles of all kinds injure lung cells and can cause cancer and death. Much is now known about the solution chemistry of these complex biological processes, but there is still much to be learned. We are living in the modern era of microelectronics and photonics* in which the control of the flow of electrons and photons in water-insoluble solids is the basis for our communication and manufacturing machines. It is intriguing to speculate that the study of the chemistry and flow of ions in aqueous solution may lead to a revolution in the understanding of communication and evolution in living systems. Microionics may rival microelectronics in importance in the scientific future. In this series of experiments, you have the opportunity to study the fascinating chemistry of dissolution, reaction, and precipitation in aqueous solution.

*The use of laser light in communication systems, sometimes termed optronics.

Background Chemistry

A homogeneous mixture of two or more substances is called a *solution*. Usually, the substance that is present in a smaller amount is called the *solute*, and the substance present in the larger amount is called the *solvent*. Solutions may be gaseous (e.g., air), liquid (e.g., blood), and solid (e.g., steel).

Solutions are the places where chemical and biological reactions happen. Solutions are also the means by which substances are transported from one place to another. Liquid solutions are particularly important in geological, environmental, biological, and chemical systems; the universal solvent for these solutions is water. The solution is the medium that brings reactants close together long enough to allow new associations and bonds to form. Products appear as bond formation moves toward completion. The solvent almost always plays an active role in all of these processes, especially when water is the solvent. The solvent must first dissolve the substances that are eventually going to react. This deceptively simple process, called *dissolution*, also involves the breaking of bonds and the formation of new associations. The solubility of a substance reflects how easily the solvent can make these changes occur. The *solubility* of a substance is, in fact, defined as the concentration of solute in a saturated solution at a specified temperature. The reverse of dissolution is the "coming out" of solution in which the product(s) of a reaction exceed the solubility and form a new phase that could be a gas, liquid, or solid. Again, the solvent often plays an active part in this process.

At the molecular level these dynamic aqueous solution processes can be pictured as shown in Figure 7.1.

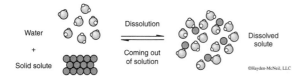

Figure 7.1 Dynamic aqueous solution processes.

Where ⬤ are solute and � are water molecules. The extent to which each of these processes happens can be described in terms of three major interactions:

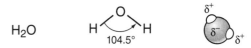

- Solute–solute interactions
- Solute–water interactions
- Water–water interactions

If the solute–solute interaction is dominant, then solute will come out of solution and two phases will form. Which phase goes up (perhaps a gas) and which phase goes down (perhaps a solid) depends on external forces, such as gravity. If the water–water interaction is dominant, then the solute will be "squeezed out" of the solution and form another phase. In between these extremes, water–solute interactions can assure a stable, homogeneous solution.

Water is an excellent solvent for many ionic and polar covalent compounds because the water molecule is a polar covalent molecule. Each H_2O molecule has a small negative charge on the oxygen atom and a small positive charge on the hydrogen atoms. (Refer to Figure 7.2 for illustration.)

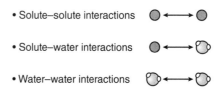

Figure 7.2 Three representations of the water molecule.

This permanent dipole (two poles, a positive one and a negative one) is due to the electronegativity of the oxygen atom. The electrons in the covalent bonds between O and H are pulled slightly towards the O atom, creating the dipole. In liquid water (and ice), the water molecules are fairly close together and attract each other, forming weak bonds called hydrogen bonds, which are pictured in Figure 7.3.

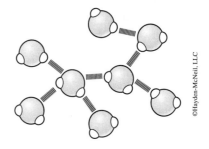

Figure 7.3 Hydrogen bonding in liquid water.

Although these hydrogen bonds are weak, they are responsible for many of the interesting and unusual properties of water, including some of its versatile solvent properties. Solutes that interact with the charges on the water molecule are generally soluble, provided that the solute–solute interactions are not very strong. Ammonia (NH_3), for example, is very soluble in water, forming hydrogen bonds in the process, whereas dinitrogen (N_2), a nonpolar molecule, is not (see Figure 7.4).

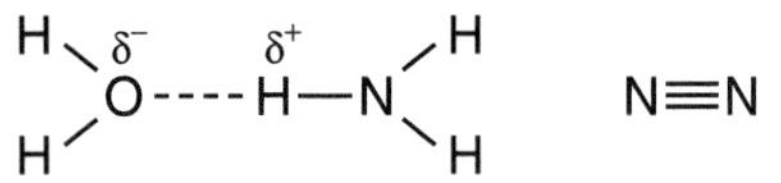

$$H \diagdown \overset{\delta^-}{\underset{\diagup}{O}} \text{----} \overset{\delta^+}{H}\text{---}N \diagup \diagdown H \qquad N \equiv N$$

Figure 7.4 Hydrogen bonding to NH_3 and not to N_2.

Large nonpolar substances, such as gasoline, are not very soluble in water because the long nonpolar hydrocarbon chains disrupt the hydrogen bonding between water molecules. Solvent–solvent interactions dominate, and the gasoline molecules are "squeezed out" of solution and form a separate liquid floating on top of the water, as shown in Figure 7.5.

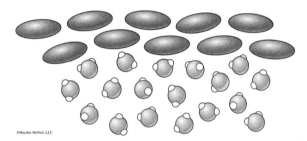
©Hayden-McNeil, LLC

Figure 7.5 Gasoline and water form two layers.

The solubility of solids in water is also governed by the three major interactions discussed earlier. A simple example is the dissolution of sodium nitrate ($NaNO_3$) in water. Solid sodium nitrate has a crystal structure that consists of sodium ions (Na^+) ionically bonded to nitrate ions (NO_3^-). Water is a good solvent for salts such as sodium nitrate because water molecules are able to move in between the cation and anion and screen the charges from each other. When this happens the ionic bond weakens, and the water molecules can then orient around the dissociated (separated) ions with the negative end of the water dipole pointed towards the cation and the positive end pointed towards the anion. The water molecules are bonded quite strongly to the ions by the attraction of unlike charges. All cations and anions dissolved in aqueous solution are surrounded by bound water molecules, and they are said to be *hydrated*. Figure 7.6 illustrates the process of dissolution and hydration.

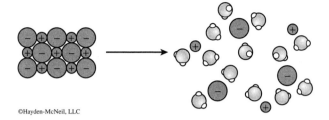
©Hayden-McNeil, LLC

Figure 7.6 Dissolution and hydration of an ionic crystal.

NOTE: Most chemistry texts, including this one, assume that the reader understands that cations and anions in aqueous solution exist as hydrated ions; therefore the formulas for ions are usually written *without* the bonded solvent molecules. The extent to which the dissolution process occurs—i.e., how soluble the salt is—depends on the magnitude of the attraction between ions and water molecules (*hydration energy*) compared with the attraction between ions in the solid salt (*lattice energy*). The battle of forces within the crystal versus those between ions and water molecules is discussed in a later section on precipitation reactions.

The strength of the attraction between ions and water molecule dipoles depends on the charge and the radius of the ion. Small ions with high charge and electronegativity have the greatest attraction for water molecules; conversely, large ions with a single charge have the smallest attraction. If the attraction of the metal ion for the negative end of the water molecule dipole is strong enough, the water molecule may be ripped apart, releasing a hydrogen ion (H^+) that is then hydrated. A good example is the aluminum ion (radius 0.067 nm and a +3 charge), which can react with water as shown below:

$$Al^{3+}(aq) + H_2O(l) \rightleftarrows AlOH^{2+}(aq) + H^+(aq)$$

Compounds that react with water to produce $H^+(aq)$ ions are called *acids*. The aluminum ion is therefore called an *acidic cation*, whereas the sodium ion discussed earlier is called a *nonacidic cation*. This type of reaction can continue with more water molecules to produce hydrated cations containing several hydroxy groups. Eventually, these hydroxy cations can generate insoluble hydroxides—e.g., $Al(OH)_3(s)$—that precipitate from solution.

Anions in aqueous solution also interact with water, except of course in this instance, the positive end of the water dipole is attracted to the anion. If the anion has a small size and high charge, then water molecules are pulled apart and the hydrogen atom bonds to the anion, releasing a hydroxide ion (OH^-). A simple example is the reaction of a carbonate ion (CO_3^{2-}) with water,

$$CO_3^{2-}(aq) + H_2O(l) \rightleftarrows HCO_3^-(aq) + OH^-(aq)$$

which produces a bicarbonate ion (HCO_3^-) and a basic (the opposite of acidic) solution. The carbonate ion is called a *basic anion*, whereas the nitrate ion (NO_3^-) discussed earlier is called a *nonbasic anion*.

The chemistry of ionic solutes in aqueous solution becomes considerably more interesting and complicated when two solutions, each containing a soluble ionic compound, are mixed. Generally, in this situation the resulting solution, at the instant of mixing, contains two different hydrated cations and two different hydrated anions. If strong solute–solute interactions occur between any two of the ions, then a chemical reaction results and a new product is formed. Often the two remaining ions do not interact and remain in solution in the same hydrated state as before the reaction. These unreacted ions are often called *spectator ions*. Chemical reactions in aqueous solution may be divided into four types: precipitation, acid–base, complexation, and redox reactions. A brief discussion of the main characteristics of each of these reaction types follows.

Precipitation Reactions

A *precipitation reaction* is defined as a reaction that produces a new compound that is not soluble in an aqueous solution. Precipitation can be regarded as the reverse of dissolution. The factors mentioned earlier—i.e., hydration energy and lattice energy—play a major role in determining whether an ionic compound will precipitate from solution. Ionic compounds (salts) in which the cation and anion have approximately the same size and the same charge tend to form especially stable crystal structures and precipitate from aqueous solution. Acidic cations—e.g., Al^{3+}—and nonbasic anions—e.g., NO_3^-—give rise to soluble salts because these ions are quite different in size and have much smaller lattice energy than hydration energy. Although these generalizations are useful, it is often difficult to make exact predictions, and it is worthwhile to remember a few simple aqueous solubility rules:

Soluble

- All ammonium (NH_4^+) and Group 1A (Li^+, Na^+, K^+, Rb^+, Cs^+) salts are soluble.

- All nitrates (NO_3^-) and acetates (CH_3COO^-) are soluble.

- Most chlorides (Cl^-), bromides (Br^-), and iodides (I^-) are soluble, except Ag, Hg, and Pb.

- Most sulfates (SO_4^{2-}) are soluble, except Hg, Pb, Ca (slightly soluble), Sr, and Ba.

Insoluble

- Most carbonates (CO_3^{2-}) are insoluble, except when combined with ammonium (NH_4^+) or Group 1A salts.

- Most phosphates (PO_4^{3-}) are insoluble, except when combined with ammonium (NH_4^+) or Group 1A salts.

- Most oxides (O^{2-}) are insoluble, except when combined with ammonium (NH_4^+) or Group 1A salts.

- Most hydroxides (OH^-) are insoluble, except when combined with ammonium (NH_4^+), or Group 1A salts, or Ca, Sr, and Ba (slightly soluble).

- Most sulfides (S^{2-}) are insoluble, except when combined with ammonium (NH_4^+), or Group 1A salts, or Ca, Sr, and Ba.

You will have a chance to apply these rules in this series of experiments.

Acid–Base Reactions

In aqueous solution an acid reacts with a base to give a salt and water. An *acid–base reaction*, sometimes called *neutralization*, is characterized by the formation of covalent, neutral water molecules from hydrated hydrogen ions (H_3O^+) and hydroxide ions (OH^-).

Complexation Reactions

Complexation reactions are closely related to acid–base reactions. Earlier, it was pointed out that some metal cations that have small size and high charge can act as acids—in fact they are called acidic cations. These acidic cations can react with electron-rich species called *ligands* to form *complexes*. A *complex* may be defined as a chemical compound in which there is one or more coordinate-covalent bonds. A *coordinate-covalent bond* is a covalent bond in which the shared pair of electrons is provided by the ligand. A complexation reaction is therefore defined as a reaction in which one or more coordinate-covalent bonds are produced during the formation of product.

Redox Reactions

Redox (an abbreviation of reduction–oxidation) *reactions* are defined as chemical reactions in which electrons are transferred from one species to another. *Oxidation* is defined as loss of electrons; *reduction* is defined as gain of electrons. A transfer of electrons means that the oxidation number of some of the atoms involved in the redox reaction must have changed. The oxidation number is defined by a simple set of rules based on arbitrarily counting electrons:

- The oxidation number of an element in its standard state is zero.

- The sum of the oxidation numbers of all the atoms in a molecule is zero.

- The sum in an ion equals the charge on the ion.

- Oxidation numbers are on a per-atom basis.

- Oxygen usually has an oxidation number of -2 (except in peroxides), and hydrogen has an oxidation number of +1.

- Monatomic ions (e.g., Na^+) have an oxidation number equal to the charge on the ion.

Writing and Interpreting Chemical Equations

Chemical reactions in aqueous solution are described very efficiently by writing a chemical equation in which the component ions of dissolved ionic compounds are written as separate ions—e.g., K^+ and I^- rather than KI. These chemical equations are called ionic equations. Reactions that involve spectator ions can be written in a form in which the spectator ions are deleted (do not appear). These equations are called net ionic equations. The following simple rules should enable you to write most net ionic equations for a reaction:

- Soluble ionic salts are written as separate ions.

- Insoluble compounds are written as complete formula units with the subscript (s).

- Covalent compounds (e.g., CO_2, H_2O) are written as molecules.

The example that follows develops the net ionic equation for a precipitation reaction between silver nitrate solution and hydrochloric acid solution.

Since the two solutes $AgNO_3$ and HCl are obviously soluble and therefore dissolved, we can write the reactants as

$$Ag^+(aq) + NO_3^-(aq) + H^+(aq) + Cl^-(aq)$$

understanding that all the ions are hydrated. In this reaction an off-white precipitate comes out of solution. The precipitate must be either AgCl(s) or HNO_3(s). In this instance it is easy to make the decision because we know that all common inorganic acids such as HNO_3 are soluble in water. The precipitate must be AgCl(s), and the spectator ions are H^+ and NO_3^-. The ionic equation is

$$Ag^+(aq) + NO_3^-(aq) + H^+(aq) + Cl^-(aq) \rightarrow$$
$$AgCl(s) + H^+(aq) + NO_3^-(aq)$$

The net ionic equation is

$$Ag^+(aq) + Cl^-(aq) \rightarrow AgCl(s)$$

The long form of this equation would be

$$AgNO_3(aq) + HCl(aq) \rightarrow AgCl(s) + HNO_3(aq)$$

Not only is the net ionic equation more concise, but it also suggests that any soluble Ag^+ salt and any soluble Cl^- salt would give the same reaction. Hence, many chemical reactions are summarized in this single net ionic equation.

Quiz Outline

Know the solubility rules listed on pg. 7-5 under "Precipitation Reactions."

Be able to answer questions similar to those asked in the sample quiz.

Also know:

- the three interactions that dominate the solubility of a solute in aqueous solution.

- what is meant by an "acidic" vs. a "nonacidic" cation.

- the net ionic equation for the reaction of NaOH solution with HCl solution.

Understand "hydrogen bonding of water" at the level presented in the Background Chemistry section of this experiment.

Know the chart given in Section C of this experiment—i.e., given the name of any of the compounds, be able to list the formula or vice versa.

Know what is meant by the terms "polar molecule" and "nonpolar molecule." Be able to look at some simple molecules and identify which of these two general classes they would fall into.

Note: The first thing you need to do when conducting this experiment is to prepare a set of labeled pipets. To save time, this should be done *before coming to lab*. A set of 16 labels are provided in the Exp. 7 section of your Chem 111 Student Packet. Cut out these labels, and tape them to 16 of the thin-stem pipets in your kit. The labels should be right side up when the stem is facing upward. Cut off all but about an inch of the pipet stem. These 16 short-stem pipets will be filled with the various solutions at the start of lab.

Sample Pre-Laboratory Quiz

1. Give a definition of a solution.

2. Write out the net ionic equation for the reaction of $AgNO_3(aq)$ and $NaCl(aq)$.

3. Indicate next to each of the compounds listed below whether the compound is "soluble" or "insoluble" in water.

    (a) K_2SO_4 (c) $Mg(NO_3)_2$

    (b) $AgCl$ (d) $Ca_3(PO_4)_2$

4. (a) Define "polar molecule." (b) Indicate next to the molecules listed below whether it is "polar" or "nonpolar".

    (a) $O = O$ (b)
    $$Cl - \overset{\displaystyle Cl}{\underset{\displaystyle Cl}{C}} - Cl$$

5. Write out the chemical symbols (and charge if it is an ion) of the substances listed below:

    (a) ammonia   (c) carbonate ion

    (b) silver ion   (d) bicarbonate ion

Laboratory Experiments

Flowchart of the Experiments

| Section A. | Naming and Preparing Solutions |

| Section B. | Solubility and Solutions |

| Section C. | Acidity/Basicity of the Known Solutions |

| Section D. | Solutions and Reactions |

| Section E. | Four Major Types of Chemical Reactions in Aqueous Solution |

| Section F. | A Chemical Reaction Survey: The Ion Reaction Chart |

| Section G. | Identification of Eight Unknowns |

Requires two four-hour class period to complete.

In this two-laboratory-period sequence of experiments, you can investigate a) the chemical factors that control solubility; b) the properties of solutions; c) chemical reactions in aqueous solutions; d) the correlation of chemical phenomenology, nomenclature, and reaction writing; and e) the relationships between chemical reactivity and the periodic chart. You will have ample opportunity to test your understanding of the chemical principles by analyzing the data from several experiments that involve identifying unknown solutions.

CAUTION: Assume that all the chemicals and solutions used in these laboratories are either toxic or corrosive, including those chemicals that are the products of chemical reactions. Even though you are using very small amounts and volumes, exercise caution and follow the appropriate methodologies for cleanup and disposal (discussed in each section). If you get chemicals on any part of your body, wash with cold water and check with your instructor.

Section A.   Naming and Preparing Solutions

Goals:

(1) To write the chemical formula for fourteen solutes. (2) To prepare a rack of 16 known solutions.

Discussion:

All of the solutions needed are at Reagent Central, or your arm's reach station. You and a partner will use these to prepare a rack of 16 solutions in thin stem pipets (according to the instructions given below). Fourteen of these solutions will constitute your "knowns"—i.e., you will study the reactions between these solutions. Two solutions—Universal Indicator (UI) and starch/KI solution—are "indicators." These solutions will be used to help probe what is going on in the solutions and reactions that you will investigate.

Experimental Steps:

1. Have your hand lens, scissors, and tweezers with you.

2. Remove the reaction matrix chart *from your packet* (it will look similar to the chart located at the end of this chapter). Insert the chart between the outer sheet of your plastic reaction surface and the stiff white board (this board helps to keep the surface flat).

3. Both you and your partner should get out a 24-well tray, and the 24-well template for this experiment (the latter is in your Student Packet). On the same page as the template will be a chart of solutions. Set this aside until you get to Question 1. The 24-well tray can be placed over the template to mark which solution should go into which well. One of you will be filling up your 24-well tray with the solutions (as the squirt bottles come around). The other should suck up the solutions from the first partner's well tray (using your labeled pipets, and good transfer technique) and place them into the second rack. When you are done, you should have 16 solutions in thin-stem pipets sitting upright in one of the 24-well trays. These will be shared by you and your partner.

    CAUTION: Make sure you fill each pipet with the correct solution indicated by the label. A mistake in filling the pipets will cause all the chemical reactions to be incorrect.

    These solutions, which were made by the laboratory staff, are *aqueous*—or water-based—solutions. The correct amount of solute was dissolved in distilled water (the solvent), and the resulting solution was diluted with water to a known volume to produce a solution of exactly known *concentration* (which the table in your Student Packet identifies). Before you start exploring chemical reactions, it is necessary to know some of the chemical properties of the *individual* solutions. In order to make a solution in the manner described earlier, you must know something about the *solubility* of the solute in water. Some general principles about the factors controlling solubility and about the nature of solutions were presented in the Background Chemistry section of this chapter. The next section will also consider some general principles of solubility.

Question: Q1.   Let's see how many chemical names you know. Tape the solution chart (that you cut out of your Student Packet earlier) into your notebook. Complete the table by writing in the chemical formula of each solute listed. (Hint: If you are stuck, you can match the formula on the label of the pipet to a name in the table.)

Section B.   Solubility and Solutions

Goal: *To examine some of the general principles governing the solubility of various solutes in water and other solvents.*

Part 1. Molecular Solutes

Discussion: The solubility of molecular substances (i.e., substances held together by covalent bonds) can often be predicted using the "like dissolves like" rule. This means that polar molecules dissolve in polar solvents, and nonpolar molecules dissolve in nonpolar solvents.

Experimental Step: 1.   At your station are the following solvents: ethanol, pentanol, kerosene, and water. Determine by experiments which are polar and which are nonpolar. Think small. It is not necessary to use large amounts.

Questions: Q2.   Based on your experiments, which of the substances tested are polar and which are nonpolar? Briefly describe your experiments, observations, and reasoning.

Q3.   Now take it one step further—rank the four substances from most polar to least polar.

Part 2. Ionic Solutes

Discussion: The solubility of ionic substances (i.e., substances held together by ionic bonds) is more difficult to predict. Many ionic substances ("salts") are soluble in water. But many are not. The solubility of ionic solutes depends primarily on the difference between the stability of the ionic lattice (i.e., how hard it is to pull the ions apart) compared to the stability of the solvated (dissolved) ions. Professionals have cataloged "solubility rules" for ionic substances to make it easier to remember which dissolve in water and which do not. You will have an opportunity to observe and use these generalizations in a later section.

Now, more to the point of the solutions in front of you. Of these solutions, 10 were made by dissolving ionically bonded solids in water and 4 by diluting liquid reagents (HCl(aq), HNO_3(aq), H_2SO_4(l), and NH_3(aq)) with water. The only solute that is not appreciably dissociated upon dissolution in water is ammonia.

Experimental Step: 2.   Use one of your thin-stem pipets to make a small puddle of water (5 to 10 drops) in the test area of your plastic reaction surface. Put a small crystal of KI(s) next to the puddle. Slowly push it into the edge of the puddle and watch it dissolve.

Questions:

Q4. Draw some simple pictures to illustrate *at the atomic level* the dissolution of solid potassium iodide in water that you have just observed.

Q5. A certain ionically bonded solid is added to water and the result is a clear, but *colored,* solution. Is the ionic substance considered soluble in water, or not? Explain your answer.

Q6. Which of the following two gases, ammonia or carbon dioxide, has the greatest solubility in distilled water? Explain your reasoning.

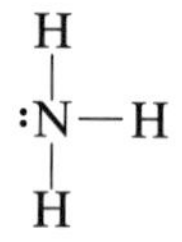

$$\begin{array}{c} H \\ | \\ :N{-}H \\ | \\ H \end{array}$$

$$O{=}C{=}O$$

Ammonia (polar covalent molecule)   Carbon dioxide (nonpolar covalent molecule)

Section C.   Acidity/Basicity of the Known Solutions

Goal: *To learn which of the 14 solutions are acidic/basic/neutral.*

Discussion: You will probably recognize the names of three acids, and at least one base among the list of solutions to be studied. But, you may not know which of the remaining solutions are acidic/basic/neutral. The experiments in this section will enable you to uncover this information.

Experimental Steps: 1. Use the plastic surface with the inserted reaction matrix chart to carry out the following tests: Drop 1 drop of each of the three acids (about 1 cm apart) onto a white background in the *test* area (indicated on the reaction matrix chart) of the plastic sheet.

NOTE: Use the test area to mix solutions until indicated otherwise.

2. To each drop add 1 drop of UI (Universal Indicator).

• Record any color changes. What happens with distilled water and UI?

3. Now test 1 drop of the ammonia solution with UI.

• Note any changes.

4. Try this one: put 1 drop UI *next* to an $NH_3(aq)$ drop—i.e., don't let the drops touch. Add a second drop of UI three or four inches away from the $NH_3(aq)$.

• What do you conclude?

NOTE: Recall that ammonia is a base.

5. Try testing sodium hydroxide solution.

To clean up the waste, add water from a wash bottle to dilute and mix all the drops. Suck the waste liquid up with a large-drop pipet and eject to your waste cup. Wipe with a damp microtowel. This is a general procedure for disposing of all tests.

NOTE: If your waste cup is full, transfer the solution to the appropriately labeled container in front of the room.

The UI test solution gives you a practical way to distinguish between acids and bases. A simple way of writing the dissociation of an acid (e.g., HCl) in aqueous solution is

$$HCl(aq) \rightarrow H^+ (aq) + Cl^-(aq)$$

NOTE: The test solution is responding to the H^+ ions.

Similarly, the dissociation of a base, e.g., NaOH, is written

$$NaOH(aq) \rightarrow Na^+(aq) + OH^-(aq)$$

and the test solution responds to OH^- ions.

The table below is a list of ions and molecules that you will encounter during these experiments.

Cations		Anions		Molecules	
Formula	Name	Formula	Name	Formula	Name
H^+	Hydrogen ion	Cl^-	Chloride ion	H_2O	Water
NH_4^+	Ammonium ion	I^-	Iodide ion	NH_3	Ammonia
Na^+	Sodium ion	OH^-	Hydroxide ion	CO_2	Carbon dioxide
Ag^+	Silver ion	NO_3^-	Nitrate ion	I_2	Iodine
K^+	Potassium ion	HCO_3^-	Bicarbonate ion		
Ba^{2+}	Barium ion	CO_3^{2-}	Carbonate ion		
Pb^{2+}	Lead ion	SO_4^{2-}	Sulfate ion		
Cu^{2+}	Copper (II) ion	PO_4^{3-}	Phosphate ion		
Fe^{3+}	Iron (III) ion				
Al^{3+}	Aluminum ion				

Notice that one of the cations (NH_4^+) and several anions (e.g., NO_3^-) are polyatomic ions—i.e., 2 or more atoms are covalently bonded together in the ion. Water does not break the covalent bonds between the nonmetal atoms of a polyatomic ion, and these ions will generally stay intact in chemical reactions.

6. The remaining 9 untested solutions are solutions of salts as solutes. Salts may be acidic, basic, or neutral. Test each of these solutions with the UI test solution.

    •   Note any color changes.

7. Clean up and dispose of the waste as before.

Questions: Q7.   Define cation, anion, and molecule.

Q8.   Write out chemical equation(s) to explain your results for $Na_2CO_3(aq)$. Hint: See Background Chemistry regarding CO_3^{2-}.

Q9.   One of the most interesting solutes that you are using in this experiment is aqueous ammonia. Let's consider the properties of aqueous ammonia in more detail.

(a) Based on the pH you observed in step 3, write out the reaction of aqueous ammonia with water.

(b) Earlier you were told that "of all the 14 solutes you will be studying, the only one that is NOT appreciably dissociated in water is aqueous ammonia." What does this statement imply about the equilibrium point of the reaction involving aqueous ammonia/ammonium hydroxide?

(c) Use your results and conclusions from (a) and (b) to explain why a complicated name like "aqueous ammonia/ammonium hydroxide" is used for this solution. (Isn't ammonia a gas?)

(d) Use your conclusions from (a), (b), and (c) to explain your observations in step 4.

Section D.   Solutions and Reactions

Goal: *To observe the results of dissolution, diffusion, convection, and reaction of KI and AgNO₃.*

Discussion: The following definitions will help you to understand and explain your observations in this section:

dissolution—the dissolving of a material.

convection—mass transport by moving fluids.

diffusion—the spontaneous decrease in concentration differences due to random molecular motion. Typical diffusion rates (at room temperature and 1 atm pressure) are 3 cm/min for a gas, 0.03 cm/min for a solute in solution, < 0.1 nm/min for particles on the surface of a solid.

Experimental Steps: 1.   Plastic containers of solid, crystalline KI and $AgNO_3$ should be at your arm's reach station. Use a *clean*, dry spatula made from a drinking straw (available at your arm's reach station) to transfer 2 or 3 small crystals of each compound to the plastic surface.

CAUTION: Cut off the end of the straw or clean it before going from one solid to the other!

2.   Push 1 crystal of KI and 1 crystal of $AgNO_3$ together with a straw. Observe with your hand lens. Add 1 drop of water. Stir with a plastic stirrer.

   •   What happens?

3.   Make a pool of water about 1.5 cm in diameter on the plastic by expelling water from a pipet.

4.   Carefully push 1 crystal of KI near one side of the pool, but not in it. Push a crystal of $AgNO_3$ near the other side. The position of the crystals is illustrated below.

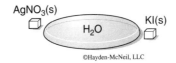

$AgNO_3(s)$ H_2O $KI(s)$

©Hayden-McNeil, LLC

5.   Gently push the $AgNO_3$ crystals onto the edge of the pool. Wait a few seconds. Now do the same with the KI. Use your hand lens to examine the reaction.

6.   Clean up as usual.

Questions: **Q10.**   If the process observed in step 5 above was purely diffusional, then how long would it take for the reactants to reach the center? Is the transport in step 5 primarily diffusional? (See diffusion rates at the beginning of this section.)

Q11.   Draw a series of pictures (i.e., a time sequence) to illustrate at the atomic level what you observed in step 5 above. Include a written description under each picture of what is taking place. You must use the three words defined in the discussion above at least once in your answer. (Refer to the atomic level picture in the background chemistry section if you need help.)

Q12.   Suppose 1 drop of KI *solution* is added to 1 drop of $AgNO_3$ *solution*. How would you expect your observations to differ compared to step 5 above?

Section E.   Four Major Types of Chemical Reactions in Aqueous Solution

Goal: *To investigate the four major types of chemical reactions which occur in aqueous solutions.*

Discussion: In the last section you carried out a chemical reaction between KI and $AgNO_3$ in an aqueous medium. The reaction between these two reactants produced a solid product. In general, products that are not soluble in water and precipitate from solution are called *precipitates*, and the reactions are called *precipitation reactions*. Here we are, back at the principle of solubility again! In order to write the net ionic reaction, you first need to identify the precipitate. For the reaction given above, there are two possible choices.

   •   What are they?

   •   Which one of these is not soluble in water?

   •   Perhaps it's easier to ask which one *is* soluble in water.

Experimental Steps: 1.   Design and conduct an experiment using UI solution to investigate the reaction between HCl and NaOH solutions. This type of reaction is called an *acid–base reaction.*

- Why is an indicator solution necessary in order to follow this reaction?

2.   Now explore the reaction between $CuSO_4$ and NH_3 solutions by dropping drops of NH_3 onto the plastic and adding 1 drop of $CuSO_4$. Stir.

A change has obviously occurred. The full ionic equation is:

$$Cu^{2+}(aq) + SO_4^{2-}(aq) + 4NH_3(aq) \rightarrow Cu(NH_3)_4^{2+}(aq) + SO_4^{2-}(aq)$$

The net ionic equation is:

$$Cu^{2+}(aq) + 4NH_3(aq) \rightarrow Cu(NH_3)_4^{2+}(aq)$$

This is an example of a *complexation reaction.* The deep-blue soluble product $Cu(NH_3)_4^{2+}$ (illustration follows) is a *complex* called tetraaminecopper(II) ion.

Complexes are formed between cations and molecules (or ions) that have unshared pairs of electrons (e.g., NH_3 in the above reaction).

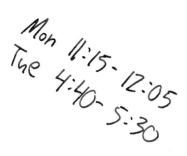

complex ion

The bond between each NH_3 and Cu^{2+} arises from the unshared (or "lone") pair of electrons on the N of NH_3 being shared with Cu^{2+}. What is unusual about this type of covalent bond is that both of the shared electrons come from the same atom. Sometimes these bonds are called coordinate-covalent bonds.

3.   Now add 2 more drops of $CuSO_4$ to the complex ion. Stir.

The net reaction is: $Cu^{2+}(aq) + 2OH^-(aq) \rightarrow Cu(OH)_2(s)$

Now why did that happen? Hint: Limiting reactants.

4.   One more type of reaction. React 1 drop $CuSO_4$ and 1 drop KI. Stir. Ugly.

5.   Now drop 1 drop of starch/KI test solution very close to (but *not* in) the reaction mixture. Wait and watch.

Starch/KI can react with molecular iodine (I_2) to form a blue-black compound. Somehow, the $CuSO_4$/KI solution must have produced I_2.

In KI, I is in the −1 state, so it must have lost electrons, i.e.,

$$2I^-(aq) \rightarrow I_2(aq) + 2 \text{ electrons}$$

If this happened, then something else must have gained electrons, and that is Cu^{2+}:

$$2Cu^{2+}(aq) + 2 \text{ electrons} \rightarrow 2Cu^+(aq)$$

If we add these two reactions together, then we will get the net ionic reaction:

$$2Cu^{2+}(aq) + 2I^-(aq) \rightarrow 2Cu^+(aq) + I_2(aq)$$

This type of reaction is called a *reduction–oxidation* reaction (*redox*) because it is a combination of reduction (gain of electrons by Cu^{2+}) and oxidation (loss of electrons by I^-). *Redox* reactions involve the transfer of electrons from one substance to another, in this example, from I^- to Cu^{2+}.

But how did the I_2 get into the neighboring drop?

6.   Clean up as usual.

Questions: Q13.   Write out the full ionic and the net ionic equation for the reaction between HCl and NaOH solutions. (The net ionic equation is, by the way, the same for most acid–base reactions.)

         Q14.   Write out the full ionic and the net ionic equation for the reaction between $CuSO_4$ and KI solutions.

         Show your answers to Q13 and Q14 to your instructor before moving on.

Section F.   A Chemical Reaction Survey: The Ion Reaction Chart

Goals: *(1) To binary-mix the solutions. (2) To describe and record chemical changes. (3) To write net ionic reactions and identify the type. (4) To name the products of chemical reactions. (5) To correlate reactivity with trends in the periodic table.*

NOTE: Before beginning with step 1, read Section F completely.

Experimental Steps: 1.   Binary-mix the 14 solutions provided in Section A (mix one solution with one other) in a dropwise manner on the rectangles (not the test area) of the plastic reaction surface (with the inserted reaction matrix chart).

NOTE: Each rectangle corresponds to one mixing. The background is white and black. The idea is to put the drops in each rectangle so that they are partially over a black area and partially over a white area. This is because the white background is best for viewing colors, but a black background is best for observing white precipitates.

•   Located in your Student Packet is a version of the reaction chart without the black regions. This should be taped into your notebook and used to record what you see (the phenomenology) in the binary mixing.

•   Devise an accurate code that can be used to describe color changes, precipitate formation, textures of precipitates, gas evolution, etc.

•   Try to think about what you expect to see before you mix each pair of drops.

NOTE: The best way to mix is to drop 1 drop of a solution onto the rectangle. Then add 1 drop of the second solution, stir, add a second, stir.

If you are in doubt about a reaction, feel free to play in the test area. Make sure you understand the arrangement of the reaction chart *before* you start!

Use cotton swabs and microtowels to keep things neat. Don't write on the plastic sheet—it will destroy your flat reaction surface and drops will roll all over the place.

CAUTION: *Drop* the drops—*do not* **touch the solution on the plastic with the tip of the buret or you will contaminate everything!**

2.   When you have finished, leave the mixed solutions on the reaction chart for comparison with the next section.

Section G.   Identification of Eight Unknowns

Goal: To identify eight unknowns by comparison with the reactions of the known solutions.

Discussion: The instructor will give each individual student 8 unknowns. These will be referred to as, "1 of 14," "cation unknown," "anion unknown," and "set of 5."

                       When you think you have solved all of your unknowns, then present your conclusions to your instructor.

Experimental Steps: 1.   One unknown is one of the 14 solutions. Do this one first.

                        2.   Binary-mix the first unknown with the other 14 solutions in the same manner as you mixed the known solutions.

                            •   Compare the results of the reactions of the 14 solutions listed on the reaction matrix chart with the reaction of your unknown. Remember that some time has elapsed and some changes may have occurred—e.g., bubbles may have flown away.

                            •   Identify the unknown solution.

                        3.   Binary-mix the unknown cation solution with the 14 known solutions.

                            NOTE: The second unknown contains a *cation* that is one of the known solution cations, and an anion that may not be associated with one of the known solutions. This is somewhat more difficult than your first unknown. The reason is that this unknown may not completely match up with any of the knowns. Consider the copper sulfate column of reactions. Some of the reactions in this column will be due to Cu^{2+}. Other reactions in this column may be *sulfate* reactions. If your unknown is copper *nitrate*, then you would expect it to match up with the reactions due to Cu^{2+}, but you would not expect it to match up with the sulfate reactions.

                            •   Identify the cation in the second unknown.

                        4.   Binary-mix the unknown anion solution with the 14 known solutions.

NOTE: The third unknown contains an anion that is one of the known solution anions, and a cation that may not be associated with any of the known solutions. This is a similar problem to the one described previously (in step 3).

- Identify the anion in the third unknown.

5. Lastly you should analyze your "set of 5" unknowns. These 5 unknowns are selected from the known solutions. Use any tests you choose to identify your "set of 5" unknowns.

6. Present your conclusions regarding all 8 of your unknowns to your instructor.

Homework:

HW1. In section C, nine salt solutions were tested with Universal Indicator solution (UI). What results were obtained for Na_3PO_4, KI, and $AlCl_3$? Write out net ionic equations to explain your observations for these three solutions.

HW2. (a) Derive a simple set of solubility rules that works for the substances investigated in this experiment. NOTE: This is not as difficult as it looks—e.g., you might begin by counting how many insoluble nitrates you have seen, and so on.

(b) Compare these with those given in the Background Chemistry section of this experiment. Note similarities and differences.

HW3. Write out *full* ionic and *net* ionic equations for 15 of your favorite reactions from today's experiment. (Be sure to include proper subscripts for all substances.) Include at least one example from each of the four major classes of reactions that occur in aqueous solutions. For each reaction, indicate any visible changes that occurred (e.g., color changes, precipitates, etc.), name the product in words (e.g., AgCl = silver chloride), and indicate which of the four classes of reactions the reaction belongs to (e.g., precipitation reaction). Note: "NR," no reaction, is not an acceptable choice for this question.

HW 4. Explain which of the following ions you would expect to be more water soluble: Hg^{2+} or methyl mercury (CH_3Hg^+). More lipid soluble? *Hint: Lipids are the large organic molecules which make up cell membranes.* Based on your assessment of their solubilities, which of these would you expect to be more toxic? (Reasoning is more important here than conclusions.)

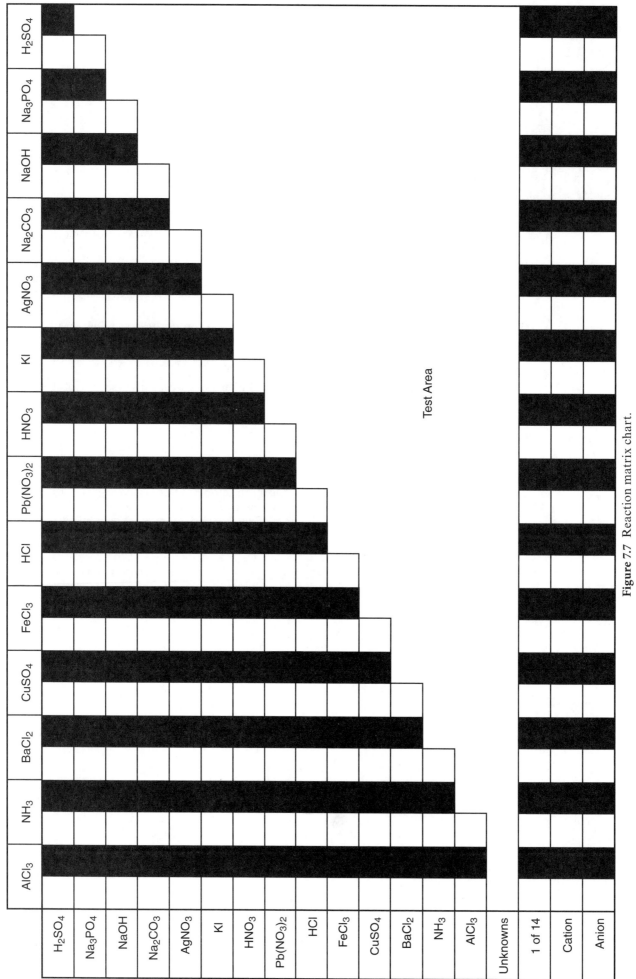

Figure 7.7 Reaction matrix chart.

An Introduction to
Acids and Bases

Introduction

The subject of acids and bases is so enormous that it virtually comprises the whole of chemistry. The definition of an acid or base has evolved continuously throughout the history of chemistry. Acids have been characterized as substances that produce a sour taste on the tongue, whereas bases have a bitter taste. The development of nonsensory (and safer!) definitions began in the 1880s when Swedish chemist Svante Arrhenius developed a theory of ionization in aqueous solutions. He defined an acid as a substance that produced H^+ ions in solution, whereas a base produced OH^- ions. This chemical description stimulated later attempts to generalize the theory so as to include more substances. The Brønsted-Lowry theory (1932), which is still used extensively, defines an acid as a proton donor and a base as a proton acceptor. The Lewis theory emphasizes the electronic characteristics of substances, an acid being defined as an electron acceptor and a base as an electron donor. The most recent theory—the hard and soft acid–base theory (HSAB) or Pearson —is a general empirical system based on thousands of experimental observations. Whatever the definitions, the concept of acids and bases is a very useful classification that is widely applied in almost all areas of science and technology.

The widespread use and enormous industrial production of acids and bases is reflected in the fact that every year, six of the top ten chemicals produced in the United States are acids or bases. Billions of pounds of these compounds are used in an extraordinary variety of applications. Table 8.1 shows some of the major industrial uses of acids and bases. Sulfuric acid is so widely used in industry that its increased or decreased consumption has proved to be a dependable barometer of general business conditions.

The supermarket is full of acids and bases in all kinds of disguises. The detergent aisle is stacked with large cardboard packages of bases—e.g., sodium polyphosphate salts and anionic surfactants, which are the major ingredients in fabric and dishwashing detergents. Drain cleaners and oven cleaners often contain high concentrations of sodium hydroxide (Lye). Window, floor, and brass cleaners almost always contain the base ammonia. And then of course there is the antacid aisle! Typical antacid products for the neutralization of gastric hydrochloric acid contain one or more bases, e.g., aluminum hydroxide, magnesium hydroxide, calcium carbonate, etc. Toilet bowl cleaners and lime deposit removers are highly acidic products.

Acids and bases are present in and often added to many food and beverage products. The "real" taste of cola beverages has more to do with the pleasantly sour taste of phosphoric acid than the other secret ingredients. Jams, jellies, preserves, and sundae and yogurt fruit toppings often contain added malic or citric acid. Gelatin desserts, fruit popsicles, and some types of hard candy all contain acidulants. Acidulants are used for a variety of purposes in the manufacture of products for baking and of baked goods. They are employed, for instance, in the production of baking powders, refrigerated biscuit dough, fruit fillings for pies and cake, angel food cake, rye bread, and frozen pies. Strangely enough, the base sodium hydroxide is used in the production of maraschino cherries and grits!

And now it's raining…guess what?!

Table 8.1

	Name and Formula	Industrial Use
Acid	Sulfuric acid, H_2SO_4	Fertilizers, chemical and petroleum production, steel treatment
	Phosphoric acid, H_3PO_4	Fertilizers, detergents, acid catalyst, acidulant for beverages
	Nitric acid, HNO_3	Fertilizers, explosives, organic chemicals, dyes
Base	Ammonia, NH_3	Manufacture of HNO_3, synthetic fibers, fertilizers, chemicals
	Lime, CaO, $Ca(OH)_2$	Agriculture, water and waste treatment
	Sodium hydroxide, NaOH	Chemicals, alumina, food production
	Sodium carbonate, Na_2CO_3	Chemicals, soaps, glass, textiles, water softening

Background Chemistry

One of the earliest methods of differentiating acids, bases, and salts was by observing their reaction with naturally occurring plant pigments called anthocyanins. Robert Boyle, in his book entitled *Experiments and Considerations Touching Colours* (1664), described an extensive survey of the color changes reproduced by the action of acids, bases, and salts on flower and vegetable extracts. In the pages of the book produced in Figure 8.1, Boyle describes not only the acid–base reactions, but also an ingenious magic writing trick (which is worth trying when you get to the laboratory!).

To decipher Boyle's experiments, read *f*, which is printed in the middle or beginning of words, as *s*.

The modern names for some of the compounds used are:

Spirit of vitriol	Sulfuric acid, H_2SO_4
Juice of limmons	Lemon juice (citric acid)
Spirit of salt	Hydrochloric acid, HCl
Solution of potashes	Potassium carbonate, K_2CO_3
Spirit of vinegar	Acetic acid, CH_3COOH
Spirit of harts-horn	Ammonia, NH_3
Spirit of urine	Ammonia, NH_3

(246)

who have produc'd the like, by Spirit of Vitriol, or juice of Limmons, but have Groundlefsly afcrib'd the Effect to fome Peculiar Quality of thofe two Liquors, whereas, (as we have already intimated) almoft any Acid Salt will turn Syrrup of Violets Red. But to improve the Experiment, let me add what has not (that I know of) been hitherto obferv'd, and has, when we firft fhew'd it them, appear'd fomething ftrange, even to thofe that have been inquifitive into the Nature of Colours; namely, that if inftead of Spirit of Salt, or that of Vinegar, you drop upon the Syrrup of Violets a little Oyl of Tartar *per Deliquium*, or the like quantity of Solution of Potafhes, and rubb them together with your finger, you fhall find the Blew Colour of the Syrrup turn'd in a moment into a perfect Green, and the like may be perform'd by divers other Liquors, as we may have occafion elfewhere to Inform you.

Annotation upon the twentieth Experiment.

The ufe of what we lately deliver'd concerning the way of turning Syrrup of Violets, Red or Green, may be this; That, though it be a far more common and procurable

(247)

Liquor than the Infufion of *Lignum Nephriticum*, it may yet be eafily fubftituted in its Room, when we have a mind to examine, whether or no the Salt predominant in a Liquor or other Body, wherein 'tis Loofe and Abundant, belong to the Tribe of *Acid* Salts or not. For if fuch a Body turn the Syrrup of a Red or Reddifh Purple Colour, it does for the moft part argue the Body (efpecially if it be a diftill'd Liquor) to abound with Acid Salt. But if the Syrrup be made Green, that argues the Predominant Salt to be of a Nature repugnant to that of the Tribe of Acids. For, as I find that either Spirit of Salt, or Oyl of Vitriol, or *Aqua-fortis*, or Spirit of Vinegar, or Juice of Lemmons, or any of the Acid Liquors I have yet had occafion to try, will turn Syrrup of Violets, of a Red, (or at leaft of *Reddifh* Colour, fo I have found, that not only the Volatile Salts of all Animal Subftances I have us'd, as Spirit of Harts-horn, of Urine, of Sal-Armoniack, of Blood, &c. but alfo all the Alcalizate Salts I have imploy'd, as the Solution of Salt of Tartar, of Pot-afhes, of common Wood-afhes, Lime-water, &c. will immediately change the Blew Syrrup, into a perfect Green. And by the fame way (to hint that upon

(248)

the by) I elfewhere fhow you, both the changes that Nature and Time produce, in the more Saline parts of fome Bodies, may be difcover'd, and alfo how ev'n fuch Chymically prepar'd Bodies, as belong not either to the Animal Kingdome, or to the Tribe of *Alcali's*, may have their new and [ ] Nature fuccefsfully Examin'd. In this place I fhall only add, that not alone the Changing the Colour of the Syrrup, requires, that the Changing Body be more ftrong, of the Acid, or other fort of Salt that is Predominant in it, than is requifite for the working upon the Tincture of *Lignum Nephriticum*; but that in this alfo, the Operation of the formerly mention'd Salts upon our Syrrup, differs from their Operation upon our Tinctures, that in this Liquor, if the Caeruleous Colour be *Deftroy'd* by an Acid Salt, it may be *Reftor'd* by one that is either Volatile, or Lixiviate; whereas in Syrrup of Violets, thought one of thefe contrary Salts will *destroy* the Action of the other, yet neither of them will *reftore* the Syrrup to its native Blew; but each of them will Change it into the Colour which it felf doth (if I may fo fpeak) affect, as we fhall have Occafion to fhow in the Notes on the twenty fifth Experiment.

(249)

Experiment XXI

There is a Weed, more known to Plowmen than belov'd by them, *Herbarifts* are whofe Flowers from their *wont to call* Colour are commonly call'd *this Plant* *Blew-bottles*, and *Corn-weed* *Cyanus vul-* from their Growing among *garis minor.* Corn. Thefe Flowers fome Ladies do, upon the account of their Lovely Colour, think worth the being Candied, which when they are, they will long retain fo fair a Colour, as makes them a very fine Sallad in the Winter. But I have try'd, that when they are frefhly gather'd, they will afford a Juice, which when newly exprefs'd, (for in fome cafes 'twill foon enough degenerate) affords a very deep and pleafant Blew. Now, (to draw this to our prefent Scope) by dropping on this frefh Juice, a little Spirit of Salt, (that being the Acid Spirit I had then at hand) it immediately turn'd (as I predicted) into a Red. And if inftead of the Sowr Spirit I mingled with it a little ftrong Solution of an Alcalizate Salt, it did prefently difclofe a lovely Green; the fame Changes being by thofe differing forts of Saline Liquors, producible in this *Natural juice*, that we lately mention'd to

(250)

have happen'd to that *factitious Mixture*, the Syrrup of Violets. And I remember, that finding this Blew Liquor, when frefhly made, to be capable of ferving in a Pen for an Ink of the Colour, I attempted by moiftning one part of a piece of White Paper with the Spirit of Salt I have been mentioning, and another with fome Alcalizate or Volatile Liquor, to draw a Line on the leifurely dry'd Paper, that fhould, e'vn before the Ink was dry, appear partly Blew, partly Red, and partly Green: But though the latter part of the Experiment fucceeded not well, (whether becaufe Volatile Salts are too Fugitive to be retain'd in the Paper, and Alcalizate ones are too Unctuous, or fo apt to draw Moifture from the Air, that they keep the Paper from drying well) yet the former Part fucceeded well enough; the Blew and Red being Confpicuous enough to afford a furprizing Spectacle to thofe, I acquaint not with (what I willingly allow you to call) the *Trick*.

Annotation upon the one and twentieth Experiment.

But left you fhould be tempted to think (*Pyrophilus*) that Volatile or Alcalizate

(251)

Salts change Blews into Green, rather upon the fcore of the eafie Tranfition of the former Colour into the latter, than upon the account of the Texture, wherein moft Vegetables, that afford a Blew, feem, though otherwife differing, to be Allied, I will add, that when I purpofely diffolv'd Blew Vitriol in fair Water, and thereby imbu'd fufficiently that Liquor with that Colour, a Lixiviate Liquor, and a Urinous Salt being Copioufly pour'd upon diftinct Parcels of it, did each of them, though perhaps with fome Difference, turn the Liquor not Green, but of a deep Yellowifh Colour, almoft like that of Yellow Oker, which Colour the Precipitated Corpufcles retain'd, when they had Leifurely fubfided to the Bottom. What this Precipitated Subftance is, it is not needful now to Enquire in the place, and in another, I have fhown you, that notwithftanding its Colour, and its being Obtainable from an Acid *Menftruum* by the help of Salt of Tartar, it is yet far enough from being the true Sulphur of Vitriol.

Experiment XXII

Our next Experiment (*Pyrophilus*) will perhaps feem to be of a contrary Nature

Figure 8.1 Robert Boyle's description of the reactions of acids and bases with some plant pigments.

The use of red cabbage extract as an acid–base indicator was first described by James Watt in 1784 (by the way, he also invented the steam engine). These natural extracts are still used as indicators, but the chemistry is very complicated and was not understood until the work of Dubois in 1978 and Thompson in 1984. Synthetic dyes are now used extensively as acid–base indicators in the field of acid–base chemistry, including acid–base titrations, pH measurements, etc.

Indicators may be used to follow the progress of any acid–base reaction. Consider the reaction that occurs when a solution of the base sodium hydroxide (NaOH) is added to a solution of the acid hydrochloric acid (HCl). The reaction proceeds according to

$$NaOH(aq) + HCl\,(aq) \rightarrow NaCl(aq) + H_2O(l)$$

which may be summarized by the net ionic equation

$$OH^-(aq) + H^+(aq) \rightarrow H_2O(l)$$

This type of reaction is called a *neutralization*. The above chemical equation says that 1 mole of NaOH will react with 1 mole of HCl to produce 1 mole of NaCl (sodium chloride, salt) and 1 mole of H_2O. The ratio 1:1:1:1 is called the *stoichiometry* of the reaction. If the concentration (moles per liter) of one of the reactant solutions is known accurately, then an analysis for an unknown concentration of the other can be carried out by volumetric analysis. *Volumetric analysis* is the process whereby the amount of a substance is determined by measuring the volume of a solution of known concentration (called a standard solution) that reacts with it. The standard solution is usually added by means of a buret to the second solution until all the reactant in the second solution has been consumed. This operation is called a *titration*. The point in the titration when the exact stoichiometric amount of reagent has been added to react with the other reactant in solution is called the *equivalence point*. It is necessary to find some way of determining when this point has occurred. Acid–base color indicators may be used to monitor the progress of a titration. A change in color of the indicator occurs at the end point of the titration, which is usually close to the equivalence point.

In the specific titration introduced at the beginning of the last paragraph, the solution starts off being acidic because HCl is present, and an indicator would show its acid color. At the equivalence point the only substance in solution would be sodium chloride (salt), and the indicator would be in the middle of a

change from its acid color to its base color. Just after the equivalence point, the solution is basic due to a slight excess of NaOH, and the indicator exhibits its basic color. A sharp color change should occur at the end point.

The traditional apparatus that is used to carry out volumetric analysis consists of calibrated pyrex glass pipets and burets. Most of these classical volumetric containers are analog devices in the sense that the measurement of volume is made by estimating the position of a liquid meniscus on a graduated scale. In most of the experiments in this book, the quantitative delivery of incremental volumes of reagent solutions is carried out "digitally" by using plastic pipets. These nontraditional devices can easily be made from commercially available, nonwetted polyethylene pipets. The volume increment is the drop, and total volume is measured by counting and calibration of the pipet. Calibration can be achieved in a number of ways, depending on several factors: (a) how accurate you wish to be, (b) how much time you are willing to spend on the calibration, (c) what type of balance equipment you have access to, and (d) how much money you wish to spend. It is important to point out that the successful use of plastic digital microburets in volumetric analysis requires a fundamental knowledge of the principles of liquid transfer. It is also worth noting that the use of microprocessor-controlled digital liquid transfer devices is quite the norm in industrial, clinical, and pharmaceutical research laboratories.

One of the major experiments in this laboratory is the determination of the calcium carbonate content of eggshells. Most birds produce eggs that have a shell consisting largely of tiny crystals of calcium carbonate laid down on a collagen-protein network. Good shell formation is critical to the survival of the chick embryo and, therefore, the species. The shell not only provides a strong protective covering, but also acts both as a source of calcium and as a respiratory membrane of the embryo. Any environmental factor leading to a decrease in the amount of calcium carbonate in the shell could result in shells too thin and fragile to survive. Unfortunately, there is now firm evidence that halogenated hydrocarbons can upset the delicate mechanism of shell formation.

Birds have evolved extraordinary biochemical processes that enable them to rapidly produce the massive quantities of calcium carbonate required for shell formation. The breeding cycle of birds starts when sex hormones trigger changes in the reproductive organs and promote the storage of a supply of calcium for the eggs. The calcium is stored in the form of new bone growth in the marrow cavities of most of the hen's bones. After ovulation the yolk travels slowly down the oviduct where layers of albumen (egg white) are laid down (four hours) around the yolk, followed by two membranes. Fibrous growths, consisting of a protein-mucopolysaccharide material, appear on the outside of the membrane. This material binds and orients calcium ions so that the ions act as seeds for the later growth of calcium carbonate crystals that form the shell. Over the next five hours, water and salts move through the membranes and into the egg in a process called *plumping*. The main process of shell formation occupies the next 15–16 hours. This process takes place in the shell gland, which has a rich supply of blood containing large amounts of calcium ions bound to a protein called phosvitin and some free calcium ions. The calcium ions react with carbonate ions produced in the shell gland to form calcium carbonate crystals.

The average weight of the shell of a chicken egg is about 5 g. About 2 g of this is calcium. Since shell formation takes 15 hours, the calcium is deposited at the rate of 2000 mg per 15 hours or 133 mg per hour. The *total* calcium content of the blood of a chicken is about 25 mg. This means that every 11 minutes the total amount of calcium circulating in the blood disappears to form calcium carbonate crystals in the shell.

The calcium must come from somewhere or the shell would not form. Food is one source, but it has been shown that it is not the complete answer because the digestive system cannot supply the calcium fast enough. The deficit is made up by the breakdown of the marrow bone growths. The released phosphate is excreted in the urine. These coordinated biochemical processes have been shown to be disrupted by chemicals present in the environment. Chlorinated hydrocarbon pesticides (e.g., DDT and Dieldrin) and polychlorinated and polybrominated biphenyls (PCBs and PBBs which are used as hydraulic fluids, electrical transformer fluids, and plasticizers), have all been found to accumulate in birds. Research has shown that these substances lead to abnormally late breeding in birds, a reduction in the number of eggs, and a dramatic reduction in calcium carbonate content. The latter causes thinning and breakage of the shell—a sure way to kill the fetus. The problem has been found to be general, and a variety of species have been decimated. Peregrine and prairie falcons and other raptor species have almost become extinct on the American continent.

The environmental problems associated with halogenated hydrocarbons were recognized as a result of an incredible amount of research in many disciplines, from agriculture to oology (the study of eggs). Extremely useful information was obtained from chemical research on eggshell thickness and from data on the calcium carbonate content of eggshells. The culmination of this research led to the banning of DDT in the United States (1972) and to reductions in the production of PCBs and PBBs by Monsanto, the sole supplier.

The analytical determination of calcium carbonate in eggshells cannot be carried out simply by titrating the carbonate with acid to the end point because the reaction is too slow. A good way around this problem is to first add an excess of hydrochloric acid to completely dissolve the calcium carbonate and then to titrate the unreacted acid with a standard solution of a soluble base, e.g., sodium hydroxide. This indirect method is sometimes called a *back titration*. The dissolution reaction is

$$CaCO_3(s) + 2HCl(aq) \rightarrow$$
$$CaCl_2(aq) + CO_2(g) + H_2O(l)$$

and the titration reaction is

$$NaOH(aq) + HCl(aq) \rightarrow NaCl(aq) + H_2O(l)$$

The acid–base volumetric analysis can therefore provide a simple, rapid, and inexpensive method of determining the calcium carbonate content of eggshells. This type of analysis is equally useful for determining the calcium carbonate content of seashells.

Quiz Outline

Know the three main definitions of acids/bases (Arrhenius, Brønsted-Lowry, Lewis) given in the Introduction to this experiment.

Be able to answer pre-lab quiz questions similar to those asked in the sample quiz for this experiment.

Also know:

- what is meant by the term "volumetric analysis"

- one major use of sulfuric acid

- the chemist who first differentiated acids, bases, and salts by using color reactions of anthocyanins

- what is meant by the stoichiometry of an acid/base reaction, and an example

- the definition of the equivalence point of a titration

Sample Pre-Laboratory Quiz

1. Explain what is meant by a Brønsted-Lowry acid.

2. Name a supermarket product that contains a base.

3. How many grams of sodium hydroxide does 2.5 mL of 1.00 molar NaOH contain? (The molar mass of NaOH is 40.00 grams/mole.) Note: Watch your significant figures!

4. What types of compounds have been found to interfere with the biological production of calcium carbonate in bird eggshell formation?

5. A student dissolved 7.05×10^{-2} g of powdered eggshell with 20 drops of 2.00 M HCl (pipet calibration factor = 0.036 mL/drop). It then took 11 drops of 1.05 M NaOH to titrate the excess acid. Calculate the % $CaCO_3$ in the eggshell. ($CaCO_3$ = 100.0 g/mole)

Laboratory Experiments

Flowchart of the Experiments

| Section A. | Common Laboratory Acids and Bases: Necessary Facts and Some Questions |

| Section B. | Indicator Color Probes for Acids and Bases |

| Section C. | Acid–Base Titrations; Stoichiometry and Molarity |

| Section D. | Small-drop Pipet Construction |

| Section E. | Standardization of a Solution of NaOH |

| Section E. | Eggshell Analysis |

| Section G. | Acid Concentration in Fruits: Pucker Order |

Requires one four-hour class period to complete.

CAUTION: You will be investigating the chemical reactions of several acids and bases in this sequence of experiments. Regard all of these solutions as being potentially corrosive and dangerous. Even though you will be using very small volumes of these dilute solutions, you should exercise due care when transferring, storing, and reacting solutions. If you spill any of these chemicals, wash with cold water and check with your instructor.

Section A. Common Laboratory Acids and Bases: Necessary Facts and Some Questions

Goal: *To give you some important facts about the common laboratory acids and bases so that you can become familiar with safe procedures for working with these substances.*

Discussion: The common laboratory acids (see the table below) are all very corrosive, highly dangerous liquids when in concentrated form.

	Name	Formula	Formula Weight	Color	Density g mL^{-1}	Percent Weight	Molarity Mol L^{-1}
Common Laboratory Acids (concentrated)	Sulfuric acid	H_2SO_4	98.08	Colorless	1.841	95–98	18.0
	Hydrochloric acid	HCl	36.46	Colorless liquid	1.18	36.5–38	12.0
	Nitric acid	HNO_3	63.01	Colorless liquid	1.503	70.3	16.8
	Acetic acid	CH_3COOH	60.05	Colorless liquid	1.049	99–100	17.5
	Phosphoric acid	H_3PO_4	98.00	Colorless liquid	1.834	85	14.7
Common Laboratory Bases	Sodium hydroxide	NaOH(s)	40.00	White pellets	2.130	—	—
	Potassium hydroxide	KOH(s)	56.11	White pellets	2.044	—	—
	Ammonia (ammonia solution)	NH_3(g) NH_3	17.03 17.03	Colorless gas Colorless liquid	0.000771	28–30 NH_3	14.8
	Sodium carbonate	Na_2CO_3(s)	105.99	White granular powder	2.532	—	—

These chemicals are generally delivered to laboratories in small (5 pint) glass bottles. A typical label from a bottle of acid is shown below.

CHEM-4-U INCORPORATED

Size 9 lb (2.3 L)

For laboratory and manufacturing use only. Not for food, drug or household use.

Hydrochloric Acid

CONTAINS: hydrochloric acid <4% w/w, water balance

DANGER! CORROSIVE: CAUSES SEVERE BURNS—AVOID CONTACT, VAPORS HARMFUL. MAY BE FATAL IF SWALLOWED.

FIRST AID: EYES AND SKIN—Remove contaminated clothing; flush with large amounts of water for 15–20 minutes, lifting eyelids to ensure complete removal. Call a physician at once. INGESTION: If victim is conscious, wash mouth out with water. Do not induce vomiting. Call a physician at once. INHALATION: Move victim to fresh air. If not breathing, give artificial respiration. Call a physician at once.

©Hayden-McNeil, LLC

NOTE: The warnings and instructions on the label should always be followed. Concentrated acids such as these often require dilution with water before use. Dilution should always be carried out by pouring the acid into the water with stirring. It is particularly important that concentrated sulfuric acid be diluted in this way. The dilution process generates an enormous amount of heat, which necessitates that the dilution be carried out in a Pyrex container cooled by an ice bath.

The common laboratory bases are also highly corrosive and dangerous in the pure form. *Sodium and potassium hydroxides are manufactured in the form of 0.5 cm pellets and are extremely hygroscopic*—i.e., the solid attracts water from the atmosphere. This happens to such an extent that in a humid atmosphere, a pellet of the solid turns into a pool of solution in a short time.

Most pure bases are packaged in plastic containers because they dissolve glass. Ammonia is sold as a 30% solution of the gas dissolved in water. This is considered a "concentrated" solution of ammonia. Great care must be exercised when opening and diluting concentrated ammonia solutions. The solution has a very high vapor pressure of NH_3 gas, which has a pungent odor that quickly attacks the eyes and lungs. (You have probably smelled it before, as most glass cleaners contain low concentrations (1–3%) of ammonia.) For these reasons, concentrated ammonia solutions should be diluted in a hood.

Accurately known concentration solutions of the above acids and bases cannot be made by the usual procedure of weighing out the substance, dissolving it in solvent, and then diluting to a known volume. First, a solution of a very approximate concentration is made (with appropriate precautions taken), then further accurate dilution, along with standardization, is required.

Questions: Q1.   When concentrated sulfuric acid is added to water, a tremendous amount of heat is generated. Write out the chemical reaction which generates all of that heat.

                      Q2.   When concentrated hydrochloric acid is added to water, much less heat is generated compared to sulfuric acid. Why? (Hint: Consider the weight percents from the table of common acids.)

                      Q3.   If solid sodium hydroxide is left out on the lab bench, it shortly turns into a puddle. Explain what is going on here.

Section B.   Indicator Color Probes for Acids and Bases

Goal: *To investigate the use of a variety of color indicators as probes for acids and bases.*

Discussion: Most of the reagents for these and subsequent experiments are in dropper bottles at your arm's reach station. The amount of indicator used is qualitative, and therefore indicators can be dispensed directly from the dropper bottles to your reaction container. However, the reactants (HCl and NaOH in this section) need to be added quantitatively. Therefore, these should be transferred from the dropper bottles to a clean and dry 24-well tray, and then delivered with a pipet.

Experimental Steps: 1.   Use a plastic surface with a white background for viewing color changes.

                      2.   First let's investigate one of the oldest color probes known. Drop 1 drop of red cabbage extract into each of several wells of a clean 1×12 well strip.

- Note the color of the extract in your laboratory record. Use your hand lens!

                      3.   Use a small-drop pipet to deliver 1 drop of 0.1 M HCl into one of the wells containing red cabbage extract. Stir with a microstirrer.

- Observe and record any color change by comparison with the extract in the next well.

NOTE: It is worth pointing out here that one of the beauties of small-scale experiments is that comparisons of this type are remarkably easy to do, and subtle differences can often be discerned.

- Does the color change if more acid is added?

                      4.   Now add 1 small drop of 0.1 M NaOH to another well containing red cabbage extract and stir.

- Observe and record the color change.

- Do you think that the probe response is fast?

NOTE: You now have a simple method of distinguishing between acids and bases.

5. A permanent record of these changes can be kept by using red cabbage juice to make some "pH paper." Put 2 or 3 drops of extract onto a piece of chromatography paper, blot off the excess, and put it on a microwipe to dry. Make 3 or 4 pieces approx. 4 cm in length for testing purposes.

    When your homemade pH paper is dry, test it with acid/base/neutral solutions to see if it works. Is it reversible?—i.e., once the indicator has been switched from one color to another, can it be switched back? Tape some samples into your notebook.

6. Repeat steps 1 through 4 using a synthetic indicator probe such as bromothymol blue (BTB).

    • Do you notice any differences compared to the extract?

Questions: Q4. What color would the following solutions give with the red cabbage extract and with BTB?

    (a) A sodium carbonate solution

    (b) An ammonia solution

    (c) Automobile battery fluid

    Q5. In this section you used both a "synthetic" and a "natural" indicator. Which do you think a professional chemist would use? Cite at least two reasons to explain your choice.

Section C.   Acid–Base Titrations; Stoichiometry and Molarity

Goals: *(1) To carry out a series of acid–base titrations using small-drop pipets and synthetic indicator color probes. (2) To determine the stoichiometry of the acid–base reactions by suitable calculations. (3) To determine the molarity of unknown concentration solutions of acids and bases.*

Experimental Steps: 1. Clean a 1 × 12 well strip thoroughly with water and shake out any liquid by slapping the strip against a paper towel held in your hand.

    2. Clean a small-drop pipet by sucking distilled water into it and expelling it several times.

        NOTE: In all quantitative volumetric experiments it is necessary to use the *same small-drop pipet* for all dilutions and for delivering standard and unknown solutions. (Why?)

        NOTE: It is also important to use good transfer and storage technique in order that the concentration of solutions not be changed inadvertently. All these techniques are used in the next steps in this section.

    3. Fill a clean, dry well of a 24-well tray about 3/4 full with 0.1 M HCl. With a clean, small-drop pipet, suck up a little HCl and shake the bulb so that the liquid rinses all of the inside of the bulb. Expel to your waste cup.

    4. Repeat with a little more HCl solution.

    5. Now suck up HCl solution so that the bulb is about 1/2 full.

6. Use good delivery technique to deliver 5 drops of the 0.1 M HCl to each of 10 wells of the 1 × 12 well strip.

7. Add 1 drop BTB indicator to each well.

8. Now use good wash, storage, and transfer techniques to fill the same pipet about 1/2 full of 0.1 M NaOH solution.

9. Carry out a *serial* titration of the HCl in the 1 × 12 well strip. Add 1 drop 0.1 M NaOH to the first well and stir; wipe the stirrer clean; add 2 drops NaOH to the second well; stir; and so on.

    •   Make observations.

Question: Q6. What is the reaction stoichiometry according to your data? Is this reasonable? Explain.

Q7. Write down the overall reaction equation, and the net ionic equation for the reaction.

10. Obtain a sample of the *unknown* concentration HCl solution from your arm's reach station and determine its molarity using the serial titration method. Use 2 drops of the unknown HCl solution per well.

11. Carry out a duplicate analysis of the unknown concentration solution by titrating in a single-well titration rather than in a serial titration.

Questions: Q8. Note the color changes and the number of drops at which the end point occurs for the serial titration of the unknown.

Q9. Show your calculations for the determination of the concentration of your unknown.

Q10. Why was it unnecessary to calibrate your pipet in this section?

Section D.   Small-drop Pipet Construction

Goal: *To construct and calibrate a small-drop pipet for use in Section E.*

Discussion: If you already have a calibrated small-drop pipet, then you may skip over this section.

Experimental Steps: 1. Stretch a thin-stem pipet and cut off the excess to make a small-drop pipet.

    NOTE: You should be familiar with the required techniques for small-drop pipet construction. The detailed instructions are given in the earlier laboratory on small-scale techniques, colorimetry, and spectrophotometry.

2. Calibrate the small-drop pipet as described in Experiment 3.

Section E.   Standardization of a Solution of NaOH

Goal: *To accurately determine the concentration of a solution of NaOH.*

Discussion: As indicated in Q3, solid NaOH in the open air will spontaneously turn into a puddle. As a result of this, it is impossible to accurately weigh sodium hydroxide. So, first a solution of an approximate concentration is made by weighing NaOH. Then this solution is titrated to determine its concentration more accurately. This more accurate determination is called "standardizing" a solution.

Experimental Steps: 1.   Locate the bottle at your Arm's Reach Station containing a solution that is approximately 1 M NaOH.

2.   Titrate this solution with 0.100 M HCl in a single-well titration in a 24-well tray using bromthymol blue as an indicator.

Question: Q11.   Calculate the molarity of the NaOH solution as accurately as possible.

Section F.   Eggshell Analysis

Goal: *To determine the percentage of calcium carbonate in eggshells by dissolving a weighed shell sample in excess hydrochloric acid, and then back titrating unreacted hydrochloric acid with sodium hydroxide.*

Experimental Steps: 1.   Obtain a powdered sample of dry eggshell from near the balances.

2.   Use tweezers to place a clean, dry weighing boat onto the pan of an analytical balance.

3.   Weigh the weighing boat.

   •   Record the weight (preferably to the nearest 0.0001 g).

4.   Use a slim straw spatula located in the front of the room to transfer about 0.050 g of the shell powder to the boat. (Note: Do not use the straws at the arm's reach station, which are too large for this purpose.)

5.   Weigh the shell powder plus weighing boat.

   •   Record the weight.

6.   Carefully transfer the shell powder to a well in the middle of a clean 24-well tray by gently tapping the boat. (Don't worry if some particles of shell stick to the scoop; this will be accounted for in the next step.)

7.   Take the boat back to the balance and reweigh the boat (plus any particles that may be stuck to it).

   •   Calculate the weight of the shell powder delivered to the well.

8.   Add a drop of ethyl alcohol to the shell (it acts as a wetting agent).

9. Use good transfer technique to fill a *calibrated* small-drop pipet with 2.00 M HCl and deliver exactly 30 drops to the shell powder in the well.

    NOTE: Use standard delivery technique to ensure that the drops are all of the same volume!

10. Use a thin-stem pipet to transfer some hot tap water to the spaces in the tray that are around the well containing the reaction mixture.

11. Wait about 10 minutes for the reaction to go to completion. Stir occasionally with a microstirrer and leave the microstirrer in the reaction mixture.

12. When the egg reaction is complete add one or two drops of bromthymol blue to the mixture in the well and stir.

13. Wash the small-drop pipet used to deliver the HCl in Step 9.

14. Use good transfer technique to fill the washed small-drop pipet with the approximately 1 M NaOH solution.

15. Titrate the unreacted HCl in the well with NaOH until an end point is obtained.

    • Note the number of drops of NaOH required.

Calculation of Calcium Carbonate Content of Shell

Overview: You have added more than enough HCl to dissolve the eggshell powder. If you know the total amount of HCl added (determined in step 1 below), then you can subtract the excess HCl (step 2) to determine how much must have reacted with the eggshell (step 3). Lastly, you must consider the equation for the reaction of HCl with $CaCO_3$ to determine how much $CaCO_3$ from the eggshell must have been involved in the reaction (step 4).

Step 1: Calculate the number of moles of HCl added to the eggshell powder in step 9.

This is equal to the number of drops of HCl added, times the volume of one drop (in liters, obtained from the calibration of the small-drop pipet), times the molarity of the HCl.

$$\text{moles HCl} = 30 \text{ drops HCl} \times \frac{x \text{ L}}{1 \text{ drop HCl}} \times \frac{2.00 \text{ mole HCl}}{\text{L}}$$

Step 2: Calculate the number of moles of HCl left over (the excess) after the reaction with eggshell powder is complete.

This is equal to the number of moles of NaOH used in the titration, since one NaOH reacts with one HCl. The number of moles of NaOH used is equal to the number of drops of NaOH used in the titration, times the volume of a drop, times the concentration of the NaOH used.

$$HCl(aq) + NaOH(aq) \rightarrow NaCl(aq) + H_2O(l)$$

Step 3: Subtract the number of moles of excess HCl from the total number of moles of HCl added to determine the number of moles of HCl that must have reacted with the $CaCO_3$ in the eggshell powder.

Step 4: Calculate the amount of $CaCO_3$ that must have been involved in the reaction with HCl.

a. The number of moles of $CaCO_3$ involved is one half the number of moles of HCl, as shown by the reaction stoichiometry given below:

$$CaCO_3(s) + 2\,HCl(aq) \rightarrow CaCl_2(aq) + CO_2(g) + H_2O(l)$$

b. Convert moles to grams by multiplying the moles of $CaCO_3$ times the molar mass of $CaCO_3$ (100 g/mole).

c. Determine the percentage $CaCO_3$ in the eggshell by dividing the grams of $CaCO_3$ by the number of grams of eggshell weighed out, and multiplying times 100.

Questions:

Q12. Show your calculations for the determination of the percentage of calcium carbonate in eggshells.

Q13. Obtain and report at least two duplicate values from neighbors (properly referenced, of course!). Calculate the average and standard deviation.

Q14. Why not just do a "regular" titration?—i.e., what is the advantage of a back titration in this case?

Section G.   Acid Concentration in Fruits: Pucker Order

Goal: *To design and execute an experiment to test the hypothesis that pucker power is proportional to the concentration of organic acids present in fruit.*

Discussion: There is a hypothesis that the pucker-promoting potential of fruits and fruit juices is directly proportional to the concentration of organic acids present in the fruit.

Experimental Steps: Design and execute an experiment to test this hypothesis. Your analysis should include acid–base chemistry and taste-panel sensory-evaluation methodologies. Materials for experimentation are in the front of the room.

NOTE: Samples for taste testing will be kept in a separate corner of the room and will be dispensed by the TA. Do not taste anything other than the samples in this special area.

Check with your instructor before you start this experiment.

Question: Q15. Briefly discuss the design of your experiment, your results, and your conclusions. (Feel free to cite other sections of your notes, if some of this information is clearly explained elsewhere.)

Experiment 9

Halogens and Their Compounds

In honor of Connie Boob, Undergraduate Chemistry's Office Manager, 1996–2012.

Introduction

The chemistry of the halogens and their compounds is extraordinarily rich and complex. Although the free elements are far too reactive to be naturally occurring, all the halogens are manufactured industrially and have a wide variety of uses. Chlorine (Cl_2) ranks in the top ten of industrial chemicals with an annual production of about 20 billion pounds, most of which is generated by the electrolysis of brine (concentrated sodium chloride) by the chloralkali industry. More than 50% of this production of free chlorine is utilized in the manufacture of other chemicals—e.g, dry-cleaning fluids, pharmaceuticals, refrigerants, herbicides, pesticides, and plastics (principally polyvinylchloride, or PVC). Other major uses are as a bleach in the paper and textile industries and as a disinfectant in municipal water supplies and sewage treatment. The use of chlorine for disinfection of water is largely responsible for the almost complete eradication of water-borne diseases—e.g., cholera and hepatitis—that plagued societies for centuries. The active chemical that kills bacteria in disinfection is not chlorine, but hypochlorous acid (HClO), which is formed from the reaction of chlorine gas with water:

$$Cl_2(g) + H_2O \rightarrow HCl + HClO$$

Uncharged hypochlorous acid can then diffuse easily through bacterial cell walls and destroy the enzyme system of the pathogen.

Fluorine (F_2) is industrially produced by electrolysis in a molten salt reaction because the process must be carried out in the absence of water. Fluorine is extremely reactive and very dangerous; the technology to produce, store, transport, and use it originated primarily from the production of fissionable uranium for atomic bombs. Fluorine is used to produce many products that contain carbon–fluorine covalent bonds. The *chlorofluorocarbons*, known by the trade name Freons, are nontoxic, inert, and nonflammable and are extensively used as heat transfer fluids in refrigerators and air conditioners. Unfortunately, there is definite evidence that Freons are not inert in the stratosphere, and it has been shown that photochemical breakdown of these compounds produces chlorine radicals that catalytically destroy ozone. Recently, there has been unprecedented international agreement to phase out the production of chlorofluorocarbons and to carry out research to find substitutes for these fluids. The stability of carbon–fluorine bonds is also utilized in a variety of nonstick coatings, such as Silverstone®. These coatings are fluorocarbon polymers, such as Teflon® (polytetrafluoroethylene), and are extremely inert and resistant to high temperatures.

The *halides*, such as sodium chloride, sodium iodide, and calcium fluoride, are by far the most common halogen compounds found in nature. The oceans contain a remarkably constant concentration of common salt (sodium chloride), with very much smaller concentrations of various bromides and fluorides. It is interesting to note that the salt composition of the ocean is the result of a gigantic, global, acid–base titration between acids that have leaked out of the interior of the earth (e.g., HCl) and bases that have been set free by the weathering of primary rock. The production of common table salt for human consumption was undoubtedly one of the first chemical industries. It has been argued that the earliest roads were made for the transportation of salt and that the earliest cities were established as centers of the salt trade. Sources of salt have even been the object of military campaigns! Sodium chloride is certainly one of the most important electrolytes in body fluids, particularly in blood plasma and interstitial fluid. The addition of small amounts of other halides (e.g., iodide and fluoride) in the human diet is also now very common. Iodide ion is necessary for the production of thyroxine in the thyroid gland, and an insufficiency of iodide ion in the diet leads to a condition known as goiter. To assure the presence of enough iodide ion in the diet, sodium or potassium iodide is often added to table salt. The fluoridation of water is now a relatively common practice. At the very low concentration of one part per million, fluoride ion helps prevent tooth decay without causing discoloration.

One of the most controversial aspects of halogen chemistry is the toxicity problem associated with many of the organic compounds containing carbon–halogen bonds. Halogenated hydrocarbons, such as chloroform, the Freons mentioned earlier, ethylene dibromide in gasoline, DDT, PCBs, and PBBs have all been shown to be toxic in animal systems. Although the complete biochemistry is not yet clear, it seems that the damaging effects are caused as the carbon–halogen bond is broken down in the liver, forming toxic substances. The knowledge of the potential health problems of these halogenated products has led to limits and, in some instances, a complete ban in production of these substances.

It is hoped that you have gained a perspective on the incredible diversity and importance of the chemistry of the halogens and their compounds from this brief introduction. The experiments that follow can only touch the surface of this area of science, but they do represent some of the major principles of halogen chemistry.

Background Chemistry

The elements in the halogen group are all nonmetals that exist at normal temperatures and pressures as diatomic molecules. The trends in properties expected for a family of elements in the periodic table are very evident in the halogens, as can be seen in Table 9.1.

Table 9.1 Some Properties of the Halogens*

Property	Fluorine (F_2)	Chlorine (Cl_2)	Bromine (Br_2)	Iodine (I_2)
Color	Pale yellow	Greenish yellow	Reddish brown	Black
State	Gas	Gas	Liquid	Solid
Melting point (°C)	−220	−101	−73	113
Boiling point (°C)	−188	−34	59	184
Atomic radius (pm)	71	99	114	133
Ionic radius (x^-, pm)	136	181	196	220

*Astatine, the other member of the halogen group, does not appear in Table 9.1 because it is extremely radioactive and has never been obtained in the pure form.

The outstanding characteristic of the halogens is the large number of compounds they form with other elements. In chemical reactions, the halogens readily accept one electron per halogen atom to form singly charged anions (e.g., F^- and Cl^-) or readily share their single, unpaired electron to form covalent bonds. As a result of this strong tendency to attract electrons, the halogens are all strong oxidizing agents. Fluorine (F_2), the first member of the family, is somewhat different from the other halogens primarily because of the small size and very high electronegativity of the fluorine atom. Fluorine is the most reactive of all the nonmetals and is one of the strongest oxidizing agents known. Fluorine cannot be prepared in aqueous solutions because it reacts rapidly with water:

$$2F_2(g) + 2H_2O \rightarrow 4HF + O_2(g)$$

Chlorine, bromine, and iodine all undergo redox reactions with water. For example, chlorine, with an oxidation number of 0, reacts as follows:

$$Cl_2 + H_2O \rightarrow HCl + HClO$$

In this reaction, it can be seen that in one product, HCl, the oxidation number of chlorine is −1, and in the other, HClO, the chlorine has an oxidation number of +1. As a result, a saturated solution of chlorine in water (chlorine water) is about 30% hypochlorous acid (HClO). The disinfectant properties of chlorine when used in water and sewage treatment are due to the presence of the hypochlorous acid, which is also a powerful oxidizing agent. Commercial liquid bleach is made by bubbling chlorine into sodium hydroxide solution:

$$Cl_2 + 2NaOH \rightarrow NaCl + NaOCl + H_2O$$

In the resulting reactions, the active ingredient is sodium hypochlorite (NaOCl).

Iodine has the unique property of reacting with excess iodide in aqueous solution to give the triiodide ion

$$I_2 + I^- \rightleftarrows I_3^-$$

This ion has the very unusual property of reacting with soluble starch to give a blue-black colored complex in which I_3^- and additional I_2 molecules form I_5^- chains:

$$I_3^- + I_2 \rightleftarrows \cdots [I - I - I - I - I]^- \cdots$$

These I_5^- chains just happen to be the right size to fit down the middle of the amylose sugar helix (pictured in Figure 9.1).

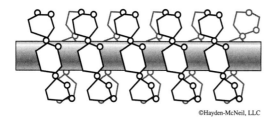

©Hayden-McNeil, LLC

Figure 9.1 Schematic structure of the starch–iodine complex. The amylose sugar chain forms a helix around the nearly linear iodine chain.

The pronounced color of this complex has led to its use as an excellent detection reaction for iodine and for oxidizing agents that can oxidize I^- to I_2.

One of the most common types of reactions of the halogens is the formation of *halides* in which each halogen atom gains one electron to become F^-, Cl^-, Br^-, or I^-. Almost all metals, metalloids, and nonmetals will react with halogens to produce halides. The properties of halides vary tremendously depending on which element enters into combination with the halogen. Alkali metal halides (e.g., sodium chloride) are ionically bonded, white, crystalline solids that are very soluble in water and dissociate to give hydrated ions. Nonmetal halides (e.g., phosphorus trichloride) are generally covalent compounds with polar covalent bonds because of the high electronegativity of the halogen atom. The combination of halogens with carbon produces covalent organic compounds, many of them having properties that make them useful as solvents, refrigerants, anesthetics, pesticides, and plastics.

There are many compounds in which the halogen atoms have a positive oxidation number, the great majority of them in the form of oxyanions and oxyacids. Table 9.2 shows most of the known compounds of this type, together with the nomenclature and some examples of common stable salts.

Table 9.2 Halogen Oxyacids and Their Salts

Oxyacid	Name	Can It Be Isolated?	Oxidation No. of Halogen	Example of Salts
HClO	Hypochlorous acid	No	+1	Hypochlorites (NaClO)
HBrO	Hypobromous acid	No	+1	Hypobromites (not stable)
HIO	Hypoiodous acid	No	+1	Hypoiodites (not stable)
$HClO_2$	Chlorous acid	No	+3	Chlorites (not stable)
$HClO_3$	Chloric acid	No	+5	Chlorates ($KClO_3$)
$HBrO_3$	Bromic acid	No	+5	Bromates ($NaBrO_3$)
HIO_3	Iodic acid	Yes	+5	Iodates (KIO_3)
$HClO_4$	Perchloric acid	Yes	+7	Perchlorates ($LiClO_4$)
$HBrO_4$	Perbromic acid	No	+7	Perbromates ($KBrO_4$)
HIO_4	Periodic acid	Yes	+7	Periodates (KIO_4)

Quiz Outline

Your quiz will NOT cover all of the information below, but it will cover some subset of the information.

Know the names (correctly spelled!) and atomic symbols for the halogens.

Know the electron configurations of the halogens.

Know and understand the trends in properties that the halogen family exhibits (examples are melting point, atomic radius, or electronegativity). Why is there a progression from gas to solid as you go down the column?

Understand why halogens are so reactive.

Be able to balance redox reactions.

What is "brine"?

Know (a) what is observed when a halogen reacts with starch/KI, and (b) what the iodide is converted to by this reaction.

Sample Pre-Laboratory Quiz

1. Draw the Lewis structure for any halogen *molecule*.

2. (a) What are the three types of chemical plants used to produce chlorine?

    (b) Which one is being phased out and why?

3. (a) What is the observed trend in the melting points of the halogens as you go down the periodic chart?

    (b) Why is this trend this way? (i.e., give a chemical explanation for this trend.)

4. To balance redox reactions, you need to make sure that the number of electrons lost by one substance equals the number of electrons gained by another. Given below is a BALANCED redox reaction from Section B of this experiment. Indicate which atoms are losing electrons (and how many), and which atoms are gaining those electrons.

$$NaOCl + 2HCl \rightarrow Cl_2(g) + NaCl + H_2O$$

5. Briefly explain why the halogens are so reactive.

Laboratory Experiments

Flowchart of the Experiments

Section A.	**From Fluorine to Astatine: A Basic Introduction to the Halogens**

Section B.	**The Synthesis and Reactions of Chlorine**

Section C.	**A Small-Scale Pilot Plant for the Manufacture of Chlorine by the Industrial Process**

Section D.	**Electrochemical Writing with a Halogen**

Section E.	**Redox Analysis of Commercial Bleach**

Requires one four-hour class period to complete.

CAUTION: **All of the halogens are very toxic and should be handled with great care—even iodine! Even though you will be working with extraordinarily small amounts of all the materials in this series of experiments, please be careful. If you get any of these chemicals on your skin, wash well with cold water and check with your instructor.**

Section A.   From Fluorine to Astatine: A Basic Introduction to the Halogens

Goal:

To become familiar with some of the structures, properties, and reactions of the halogens (listed in the table below).

Group VIIA		
Symbol	**Name**	**Atomic No.**
F	fluorine	9
Cl	chlorine	17
Br	bromine	35
I	iodine	53
At	astatine	85

Discussion:

This family of elements, collectively called the halogens, represents one of the most typical groups of nonmetallic elements in the periodic chart. The electron configurations of the halogens reveal that each element in this group has 7 valence electrons, one short of an octet. At normal temperatures and pressures, all the halogens form diatomic molecules in which they complete their octet by sharing electrons.

At room temperature and pressure, fluorine and chlorine are gases, bromine is a red-brown liquid, and iodine is a shiny black solid that sublimes readily to give a violet vapor. Astatine is so radioactive that it has never been isolated in the pure form. The longest-lived isotope ($^{210}_{85}$ At) has a half-life of 8.3 hours.

Although the halogens form a family (Group VIIA in the Periodic Chart) with periodic properties, fluorine (F_2), the first member, exhibits some differences from the other elements. These differences are largely due to the small size and high electronegativity of the fluorine atom. F_2 is extraordinarily reactive because of the very strong tendency to grab electrons and become fluoride ion F^-. Fluorine is far too nasty to make in this laboratory, but you can at least write some of its reactions.

If a metal such as sodium is exposed to gaseous fluorine, there is an instantaneous violent reaction that produces a white saltlike product. The reaction is

$$2Na(s) + F_2(g) \rightarrow 2Na^+ + 2F^-$$

This is an example of a redox reaction in which the Na atom has lost an electron in becoming a Na^+ ion:

$$2Na \rightarrow 2Na^+ + 2e^-$$

This part of the reaction is a *loss* of electrons (by Na) and is called *oxidation*. The fluorine atoms in F_2 each gained an electron to become fluoride ions F^-:

$$F_2 + 2e^- \rightarrow 2F^-$$

This gain of electrons by F_2 is called *reduction*. If the two parts, reduction and oxidation, are added up, we obtain the redox reaction

$2Na \rightarrow 2Na^+ + 2e^-$	oxidation
$F_2 + 2e^- \rightarrow 2F^-$	reduction
$2Na + F_2 \rightarrow 2Na^+ + 2F^-$	redox

NOTE: The product is the ionically bonded salt sodium fluoride (NaF).

One more piece of jargon—but a useful one. In the above redox reaction, the chemical species that grabs the electrons (F_2) is called the *oxidizing agent*, and the species that gives the electrons (Na) is called the *reducing agent*. F_2 is one of the most powerful oxidizing agents known.

CAUTION: All the halogens have pungent and irritating odors, and all can cause serious burns to the skin (particularly bromine). They are also highly reactive and form a large number of compounds with other elements. Fluorine is the most reactive and iodine the least.

Question: Q1.   (a) Write a balanced redox equation for the reaction between F_2 and Cl^-. Divide the reaction into two parts and identify the reduction and oxidation half-reactions.

(b) Identify the reducing agent in this reaction.

Section B.   The Synthesis and Reactions of Chlorine

Goals: *(1) To carry out a microscale preparation of chlorine gas ($Cl_2(g)$). (2) To investigate some of its redox reactions.*

Discussion: The solutions you will need for this experiment and the following experiments can be found at Reagent Central. In your packet is a plastic reaction surface that provides a white and a black background for viewing the chemistry. The synthesis of gases will be done in a plastic Petri dish, which acts as a miniature environmental chamber.

The chemical reaction for the synthesis of chlorine gas is the action of dilute acid (hydrochloric acid) on commercial bleach solution (e.g., regular Clorox®). The active ingredient in bleach is sodium hypochlorite (NaOCl), and the inactive ingredient is presumably water. The reaction equation is

$$NaOCl + 2HCl \rightarrow Cl_2(g) + NaCl + H_2O$$

It is worth noting that the misuse of bleach solutions in household situations is common enough to warrant a hazardous chemical warning on the label. The label reads: "Strong oxidizer. Flush drains before and after use. *Do not use or mix with other chemicals*, such as toilet bowl cleaners, rust removers, acid- or ammonia-containing products. To do so will release hazardous gases."

Experimental Steps: **NOTE: DO THIS SECTION UNDER THE HOOD.**

1. Place the Petri dish onto the plastic surface against a white background.

2. Drop 1 drop of diluted bleach solution (already diluted to 50%) into the center of the dish.

3. In a circle around the drop of bleach, drop separately 1 drop of 0.1 M KI (potassium iodide), 1 drop of dye (bromocresol green), 1 drop of phenolphthalein, and 1 drop of starch/0.1 M KI solution. Place these outer drops near the edge of the Petri dish. Since it will take longer for the gas to diffuse to the edge of the Petri dish, it will be easier to see any color changes.

4. Also place in the dish, close to the center, a small circle of filter paper that has been wet with 1 drop of 0.1 M KI and that has had the excess liquid removed by dabbing it with a piece of folded microtowel.

5. Get ready to put the top on. Drop 1 drop of 1 M HCl onto the bleach solution. Quickly put the top on.

    •   Make a picture of which solution is where—it's easy to get them mixed up.

    •   Watch and record what happens.

    •   What happened to the starch/KI solution? Do you remember this reaction from an earlier lab?

    •   Describe carefully the appearance of the filter paper. What must be happening here?

    HINT: Chlorine gas is still present in excess in the dish!

    •   Notice that the bromocresol green indicator initially changes color. However, if you wait a few minutes, the color gradually changes again. Describe these color changes of the dye.

    NOTE: If the bromocresol green does not appear to be changing color twice, add another drop of 1 M HCl to the bleach to generate more Cl_2, then wait a few more minutes.

6. Terminate the reaction by adding 1 drop of 2 M NH_3 directly to the central drop in the dish where the Cl_2 is being generated.

    CAUTION: Do *not* add the NH_3 to any of the other drops.

7. Place the Petri dish onto a black background.

    •   Describe what happens.

NOTE: You have formed an aerosol of ammonium chloride (NH_4Cl) that consists of tiny white particles of the salt settling on the plastic surface.

8.   Flood the dish by adding distilled water from your wash bottle. Swirl to dilute the remaining drops.

9.   Pour the liquid into your waste cup.

10. Wash thoroughly with tap water at the sink.

11. Rinse once with distilled water, and dab dry with a microtowel.

Questions: Q2.   (a) Write out the reduction half-reaction, the oxidation half-reaction, and the overall equation for the redox reaction of chlorine with potassium iodide solution.

                      (b) How do you know from the experiment that this reaction is occurring, i.e., what color changes occurred and what did these color changes indicate?

                      (c) What is the oxidizing agent in this reaction?

                Q3.   From step 5, what do the two changes in the bromocresol green indicate?

                      NOTE: One of the reactions in the bromocresol green is typical of the oxidizing power of chlorine towards organic dyes in general.

                Q4.   In step 5 did you expect the phenolphthalein indicator to change color? Why or why not?

Section C.   A Small-Scale Pilot Plant for the Manufacture of Chlorine by the Industrial Process

Goal: *To construct a small-scale pilot plant for the manufacture of chlorine.*

Discussion: Chlorine is manufactured on a very large scale by the electrolysis of sodium chloride solution (brine). *Electrolysis* is a process in which a redox reaction is made to occur by means of an outside source of electrical energy in the form of direct current. The design of the pilot plant is critical because it is necessary to separate the two products of the electrolysis—chlorine gas and sodium hydroxide—before they can react and disappear.

Experimental Steps: The pilot plant is pictured in the following diagram. Refer to the diagram as you complete each step to ensure that your pilot plant is built properly.

                      NOTE: The design features of the pilot plant have been carefully chosen to duplicate those in the industrial process.

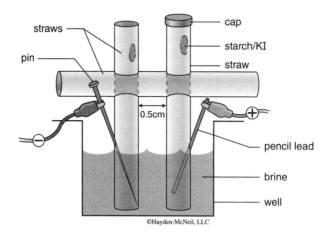

©Hayden-McNeil, LLC

1.   Obtain pins, pencil lead, and a 9-volt battery from Reagent Central.

2.   To construct the plant, cut 3 straw pieces, 1 piece about 8 cm long, and 2 pieces about 6 cm long.

3.   Use a 1/4" punch to make 2 holes about 0.5–0.7 cm apart in the 8 cm straw.

4.   Push the short straws through the holes in the long straw.

5.   Make a hole in one of the 6 cm straws with the pin so that you can insert the pencil lead without breaking it.

6.   Now push the pin into the other 6 cm straw. The pin does not go through the horizontal straw; it is only inserted in the vertical straw.

      NOTE: The pencil lead and pin in the straws is the electrode system. The pin is the cathode, defined as the place where reduction occurs. The pencil lead is the anode, defined as the place where oxidation occurs.

7.   Fill a clean well of a 24-well tray about 3/4 full with brine. Add 3 drops of phenolphthalein to the brine and stir. Place the tray on a white surface.

      NOTE: The brine solution should be colorless before you begin the electrolysis. If not, thoroughly rinse your well plate and the pilot plant, then replace the brine and phenolphthalein solutions with fresh ones.

8.   Dip the electrode system into the brine. **Be sure that the straws are pressed to the bottom of the well in the 24-well tray.**

9.   Clip the alligator clips to the electrodes but do *not* attach the clips to the battery yet.

10.   Place a small drop of starch/KI solution on the wall inside each straw (about 1 cm down).

11.   Place a cap on the anode straw.

NOTE: DO THE REST OF THIS SECTION UNDER THE HOOD.

12.   With the straws pressed to the bottom of the 24-well tray, attach one clip to the battery and touch the other clip to the battery on and off to see what is happening. You only need to generate chlorine gas for 3–4 seconds.

•   Report your observations. Especially note the color changes of the brine and the starch/KI drops.

The part of the redox reaction at the *cathode* is the reduction of water:

$$2H_2O + 2e^- \rightarrow H_2(g) + 2OH^-$$

13.   Terminate by unclipping all clips.

14.   Lay the wires to one side.

NOTE: Try not to get brine on the clips or they will corrode!

15.   Carefully lift off the cap, add 1 drop of NH_3 to it, and put it back on the same straw. This will remove toxic chlorine gas via the following reaction:

$$2NH_3(g) + 3Cl_2(g) \rightarrow N_2(g) + 6HCl(g)$$

16.   Leave the straw for a few minutes and then clean up. Remove the pencil lead, wash it, wipe it with a towel, and retain for the next experiment.

Questions: Q5.   What evidence do you have for the redox reaction? Consider both the color of the starch/KI drops and the color changes in the brine solution when you answer this. What do the color changes indicate?

Q6.   (a) Write the part of the redox reaction that occurs at the anode, and

(b) the part that occurs at the *cathode*.

Q7.   Write the balanced equation for the redox reaction accomplished during this electrolysis.

Q8.   Explain how the products of the electrolysis reaction were kept from reacting with each other. Why was the anode straw capped, but not the cathode straw?

Section D.   Electrochemical Writing with a Halogen

Goal: *To carry out an electrolysis to generate iodine by using a pencil lead as a stylus.*

Discussion: This experiment is an interesting variation on the electrolytic production of a halogen that you just completed.

Experimental Steps: 1.   Obtain a piece of aluminum foil and a piece of filter paper from Reagent Central.

2. Lay the foil down on the plastic surface and place the paper on top of it.

3. Drop 2 or 3 drops of starch/KI solution onto the paper. Let it spread out into the pores of the paper. Drop 2 or 3 drops of phenolphthalein onto the paper.

4. Clip 1 electrical wire to the edge of the foil. Clip the pencil lead to the other wire.

5. Decide how you are going to clip the wires to the battery and which electrode should be connected to the pencil lead, then do so.

    NOTE: You are trying to make iodine at the top of the pencil lead.

6. Make contact between the pencil lead and the paper and write your name.

    •   Observe the results.

    NOTE: For a comparison, try steps 3–6 again with another piece of filter paper. This time switch the battery connections.

7. Unclip the battery.

8. After the papers dry, attach them to your notebook.

Questions: Q9.   Why was the writing on the filter paper blue-purple in the initial experiment—i.e., what did this indicate the presence of? What did the phenolphthalein indicate the presence of?

              Q10.   Write the overall redox reaction and the reduction and the oxidation half-reactions.

              Q11.   In the experiment which produced iodine at the tip of the pencil lead, was the aluminum foil the cathode, or was it the anode? Explain.

Section E.   Redox Analysis of Commercial Bleach

Goal: *To carry out an analysis of a commercial chlorine bleach.*

Discussion: The sodium hypochlorite ($NaOCl$) in bleach is allowed to oxidize I^- to I_2. The I_2 concentration formed in this reaction can be determined by titration with sodium thiosulfate ($Na_2S_2O_3$) solution using starch as an indicator.

Experimental Steps: NOTE: This experiment is a quantitative volumetric analysis and you must be careful to use good wash, rinse, and transfer techniques and the same pipet for the dilutions and titration.

                    1. Clean a pipet and suck some of the 100% (not the 50%) bleach up into the pipet.

                    2. Carry out a 10-fold dilution of the bleach as follows:

                        (a) Drop 2 drops of bleach on the white plastic surface.

                        (b) Wash the pipet several times with water and fill it 1/2 full with distilled water.

                        (c) Add 18 drops of water to the 2 drops of bleach.

3.   Expel the water from the pipet and suck up the diluted bleach solution from the surface. If you like, you can easily assure that it is mixed by expelling and sucking up again.

4.   Drop 1 drop of the diluted bleach solution in 2 places on the plastic. The drops need to be far enough apart so that they won't merge when titrated.

NOTE: You will be doing duplicate titrations.

5.   Expel the diluted bleach solution from the pipet into a waste cup.

6.   Now carry out a "pool" titration on the plastic by adding 1 drop of acetic acid and 2 drops of starch/KI solution to one of the drops of diluted bleach solution on the plastic. Stir and leave the stirrer lying in the pool.

NOTE: If the solution does not remain blue with stirring, add another drop of starch/KI solution.

7.   Wash the pipet thoroughly with water and use good wash and rinse technique to fill it 1/2 full with 0.01 M (record and use the actual molarity from the bottle) $Na_2S_2O_3$ solution.

8.   Titrate the blue-black pool with the 0.01 M $Na_2S_2O_3$ with constant stirring.

NOTE: Don't forget to count drops of titrant as you go!

9.   Repeating from step 6, do the same titration on the duplicate sample.

The chemistry is a little complicated, but it's not too bad. Here are the reactions that occur. First, the bleach oxidizes the I^- to I_2.

$$OCl^- + 2I^- + 2H^+ \rightleftarrows Cl^- + I_2 + H_2O$$

In the presence of I^- (which was deliberately added in excess), triiodide ion I_3^- is formed:

$$I_2 + I^- \rightleftarrows I_3^-$$

The I_3^- then reacts with the starch to form the blue-black complex. The blue-black I_3^- complex is then titrated with sodium thiosulfate, which reduces the I_3^- back to colorless I^-, forming the tetrathionate ion $S_4O_6^{2-}$ as product:

$$I_3^- + 2S_2O_3^{2-} \rightleftarrows S_4O_6^{2-} + 3I^-$$

Questions: Q12.   Using the *average* of your titration results, calculate the sodium hypochlorite concentration in the bleach sample as follows:

First, calculate the molarity of the I_3^- solution. Let's say that it took 12 drops of 0.01 M $Na_2S_2O_3$ to titrate the blue-black I_3^- to a colorless end point. Then the I_3^- molarity is

$$0.010 \text{ M Na}_2\text{S}_2\text{O}_3 \times \frac{12 \text{ drops}}{1 \text{ drop}} \times \frac{1 \text{ mol I}_3^-}{2 \text{ mol Na}_2\text{S}_2\text{O}_3} = 0.060 \text{ M I}_3^-$$

The reason for this last factor is that each I_3^- reacts with two $S_2O_3^{2-}$ ions in the titration reaction. Because the stoichiometry of the reaction is 1 mol NaOCl : 1 mol I_3^-, this is also the molarity of the diluted bleach solution.

You diluted the original bleach by 10 times. The molarity of the original commercial bleach is 10×0.060 M = 0.60 mol NaOCl/L bleach.

The original bleach contains NaOCl, which has a formula weight of 74.5 g mol^{-1}. From your experimental value for the molarity of the commercial bleach solution, calculate the number of grams of NaOCl per liter of bleach. From this, calculate the number of grams of NaOCl per mL of bleach. Finally, use the density of bleach solution (1.097 g bleach/mL bleach) to obtain the weight of NaOCl per gram of bleach solution.

Q13.   Check your bleach sample container to see if you can find the percentage by weight (g NaOCl/100 g bleach solution) of sodium hypochlorite in the commercial sample. Compare the value reported on the bottle to your experimental result.

10

Experiment 10

The Chemistry
of Natural Waters

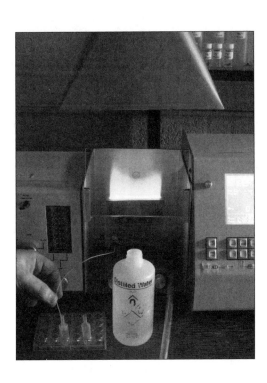

Introduction

The availability of high-quality water is essential to the survival of all living species. On a global scale, the hydrologic cycle ensures the continuous cycle of evaporation, condensation, and precipitation that brings water to the land and moves the winds over the earth. The constant supply of incoming solar energy drives the water cycle at a relatively constant rate although lately it seems that we humans can influence global kinetics, even to the point of changing the climate. The annual amount of relatively pure water precipitating onto the land is therefore quite constant, and it is important to note that almost all of the good-quality water from this precipitation is now being used. About 80 liters of water per person per day is required to sustain a reasonable quality of life. However, the average consumption ranges from 5.4 liters a day in Madagascar (it takes 5 liters simply to survive!) to more than 500 liters a day in the United States. As the world's population doubles over the next 15 years, meeting the challenge of providing quality usable water will be critical to the survival of billions of people.

The quality of water and its suitability for particular uses are almost entirely evaluated on the basis of its chemical and biological composition. The chemical composition of natural water derives from many different sources of solutes, including gases and aerosols from the atmosphere, weathering and erosion of rocks and soils, and solution or precipitation reactions occurring below the land surface and from anthropogenic wastes. Rainwater generally contains dissolved gases and aerosols, man-made pollutants, and particles from sea spray. Seawater, which is about 98% of the total water on Earth, has a remarkably constant composition. The average concentrations of the 10 major dissolved elements or ions in seawater are shown in Table 10.1. Saltiness (NaCl) of seawater precludes its use as drinking water. Other natural waters, such as streams, rivers, lakes, and groundwaters, contain dissolved substances that come mainly from the dissolution of minerals as the water flows over or percolates through various soil and rock strata.

Table 10.1 Some Ion Concentrations in Seawater

Species	Concentration (mg L^{-1})
Cl^-	19,000
Na^+	10,500
SO_4^{2-}	2,700
Mg^{2+}	1,350
Ca^{2+}	410
K^+	390
HCO_3^-	142
Br^-	67
Sr^{2+}	8
SiO_2	6.4

Two of the most important chemical species that come from mineral dissolution are the cations Ca^{2+} and Mg^{2+}. Calcium is the most abundant of the alkaline earth metals and is a major constituent of many common rock minerals. It is an essential element for plants and animals and is a major component in most natural waters. Most of the soluble calcium ion comes from the more soluble sedimentary rocks, such as limestone ($CaCO_3$), dolomite ($CaMg(CO_3)_2$), and gypsum ($CaSO_4 \cdot 2H_2O$), rather than from the very much less soluble igneous rocks. The dissolution of carbonates is dominated by the aqueous chemistry of dissolved carbon dioxide (CO_2). Aqueous solutions of CO_2 are slightly acidic, and calcium carbonate slowly dissolves under these conditions, forming soluble calcium bicarbonate. Magnesium is also a common element and is essential in plant and animal nutrition. Rock sources of magnesium ion include olivine, pyroxenes, the dark-colored micas, and the dolomites.

The presence of the dissolved divalent cations Ca^{2+} and Mg^{2+} (and other polyvalent cations) gives natural waters chemical properties that are often evaluated as *hardness*. Water that contains a large combined concentration of Ca^{2+} and Mg^{2+} are said to be hard, and waters with a low concentration are said to be soft. The terms hard and soft are very old. For example, they are contained in a discourse on water quality by Hippocrates (460–377 BC). The modern concept of hardness pertains to the use of natural waters in washing processes involving soaps and detergents and in the use of waters in industrial boilers and evaporators.

Most soaps are anionic surface-active agents that work by reducing the surface tension of wash water and by weakening chemical bonds between dirt and the surface being cleaned. If the concentration of a divalent cation is high, the soap anion will react with Ca^{2+} and Mg^{2+} to produce an insoluble, greasy scum. The scum precipitates and coats the cleaned surface. Soaps can be precipitated by other ions —e.g., H^+ and all polyvalent cations—but these ions are present in insignificant amounts in waters that are used domestically. The importance of the hardness of water is reflected in the fact that manufacturers of fabric and dishwashing detergents formulate their products with ingredients specifically designed to complex Ca^{2+} and Mg^{2+}. These water-softening ingredients are generally polyphosphates or citrates. Many detergents are also formulated to work well with water, which has a natural hardness of about 6 grains per gallon. (See Section D for a discussion of units.)

The problem in the use of hard water in industrial boilers and evaporators is scale formation. When hard water is heated or evaporated, rocklike deposits consisting largely of calcite crystals ($CaCO_3$) form on the surface of pipes, boiler walls, tubes, and evaporator surfaces. Scale is one of the banes of industry. It narrows pipes, blocks jets and tubes, and is extremely expensive (and sometimes impossible) to remove. The hard layer interferes with heat transfer in boilers, leading to gross energy inefficiencies, and can often lead to metal corrosion and structural weakness. Scale formation causes problems in the utility industry, in beer brewing, in humidifying systems for computer centers, in chicken hatcheries and hog farms, in steel and auto plants—in fact everywhere where large volumes of natural waters are used. Of course, the harder the water, the bigger the problem. A number of industrial processes are in use for removing most of the divalent cations or for slowing down the rate of scale formation. A variety of chemical treatments, such as the addition of lime ($Ca(OH)_2$) or washing soda (Na_2CO_3), are effective in precipitating Ca^{2+} and Mg^{2+} ions as insoluble salts:

$$Ca(HCO_3)_2 + Ca(OH)_2 \rightarrow 2CaCO_3(s) + 2H_2O$$

$$Mg(HCO_3)_2 + 2Ca(OH)_2 \rightarrow$$
$$2CaCO_3(s) + Mg(OH)_2(s) + 2H_2O$$

$$CaSO_4 + Na_2CO_3 \rightarrow CaCO_3(s) + Na_2SO_4$$

The precipitated compounds are removed by settling and/or filtration, and the softened water is fed to the boiler or evaporator. Ion exchange is also a useful, if somewhat expensive, softening technique, particularly for small-scale domestic applications.

The importance and magnitude of the problems associated with the presence of dissolved minerals in natural waters have led to research into rapid and accurate methods of analysis for these ions. Prior to the 1940s, the most commonly used method was a soap titration. This method built many strong arms (as you will see later), but was rather time-consuming and inaccurate. The introduction of ethylenediaminetetraacetic acid (EDTA) as a complexing agent for Ca^{2+} and Mg^{2+}, together with suitable indicators such as eriochrome black T (EBT), revolutionized the analysis of divalent ions in natural waters. It is this method that will allow you to explore the world of the chemistry of natural waters in this series of experiments.

Background Chemistry

The dissolution of many different minerals in water results in natural waters that contain Ca^{2+} and Mg^{2+} ions, with the counter ions being predominantly bicarbonate (HCO_3^-) and sulfate (SO_4^{2-}) ions. The solubility of most minerals is increased by the acidity of aqueous solutions of carbon dioxide (CO_2). In many groundwaters, the acidity may be quite high because of the large amount of CO_2 produced by biological activity:

$$Biological\ activity \rightarrow CO_2 + H_2O \rightleftharpoons H_2CO_3$$
$$H_2CO_3 \rightleftharpoons H^+ + HCO_3^-$$

An example of the dissolution of an igneous rock is the decomposition of anorthite:

$$CaAl_2Si_2O_8(s) + H_2O + 2H^+ \rightleftharpoons$$
$$Al_2Si_2O_5(OH)_4(s) + Ca^{2+}$$

The dissolution of a magnesium-containing rock is exemplified by the decomposition of fosterite into serpentite:

$$5Mg_2SiO_4(s) + 8H^+ + 2H_2O \rightleftharpoons$$
$$Mg_6(OH)_8Si_4O_{10}(s) + 4Mg^{2+} + H_4SiO_4$$

Sedimentary rocks containing calcium and magnesium are most often found in the form of carbonates, which are much more soluble than igneous rocks, particularly in acidic solutions. For example,

$$CaCO_3(s) + H^+ \rightleftharpoons Ca^{2+} + HCO_3^-$$

$$CaMg(CO_3)_2(s) + 2H^+ \rightleftharpoons Ca^{2+} + Mg^{2+} + 2HCO_3^-$$

Many other cations (e.g., Na^+, K^+, Fe^{3+}, and Al^{3+}) are often present in natural water samples, but their concentrations are usually insignificant compared with Ca^{2+} and Mg^{2+}.

One of the simplest methods of finding out what solutes are present in a water sample is to evaporate the solvent (water) and examine the residue of nonvolatile solids that remains. The amount of residue left after the evaporation of a known volume of water is called the *total dissolved solids* (TDS) of the water sample. This type of analysis also allows an assessment to be made of the potential scaling problem of a water sample. Quantitative analysis of a water sample (or the residue from a TDS experiment) for total divalent cation content can be conveniently carried out by means of a complexation titration. The chelating agent, ethylenediaminetetracetic acid (EDTA), is most commonly used in this analysis:

EDTA, $C_{10}H_{16}N_2O_8$

Actually, for practical reasons of solubility, the reagent used in the laboratory is the disodium dihydrate salt of EDTA ($C_{10}H_{14}N_2O_8Na_2 \cdot 2H_2O$). The indicator used in EDTA titrations is often a dye called eriochrome black T (EBT) which has the following structure:

This dye is water soluble because of the negative charge on the sulfonate group ($-SO_3-$) and is intensely colored because of delocalized electrons in the structure. EBT is also an acid–base indicator ($pK_a = 6.3$):

Red form (H_2D^-)   Blue form (HD^{2-})

EBT also forms intensely colored chelates with certain metal ions (e.g., Mg^{2+}), but not with others (e.g., Ca^{2+}). It is necessary to adjust the pH of the solution in the titration so that the blue form predominates.

Chemistry of the Determination of Divalent Cation Concentration (Hardness) by EDTA Titration: A Stepwise Discussion

1. A known volume of the natural water sample is taken, and the pH is adjusted to 10 by means of an NH_3/NH_4 buffer.

2. EBT indicator is added to the solution. At the high pH the indicator is in the HD^{2-} form, which is blue.

3. If Mg^{2+} is present in the water sample, then Mg^{2+} will react with the indicator to form a wine red chelate. Calcium does not react with the indicator. Therefore, at the start of the titration the solution is a wine red color.

4. EDTA solution (of known concentration) is now added to the solution from a pipet. First the EDTA reacts with the Ca^{2+}, forming a colorless chelate. As soon as enough EDTA has been added to chelate all of the Ca^{2+}, then the EDTA begins to react with the magnesium indicator chelate to produce a colorless MgEDTA chelate. As the Mg^{2+} is removed from the indicator, the indicator returns to its blue form.

5. The end point in the titration, which corresponds to the complete reaction of all of the Ca^{2+} and the Mg^{2+} with EDTA, is a definite change from a wine red color to a sky blue color.

The reactions described in steps 1–5 are summarized below:

$$HD^{2-} + Mg^{2+} + Ca^{2+} \longrightarrow MgD^- + H^+ + Ca^{2+} \xrightarrow{\text{EDTA}} CaEDTA + MgEDTA + HD^{2-}$$

Blue	Red	(immediately) (eventually) (last)
		Blue

It should be noted that the titration is difficult, if not impossible, to do if there is little or no Mg^{2+} in the natural water sample. The water sample must contain some Mg^{2+} in order for reaction to occur with the indicator to give a *wine red* color at the start. If there is no Mg^{2+} in the sample, then the color of the solution at the start and end of the titration will be blue—i.e., no end point! Even though most natural water samples contain sufficient Mg^{2+} for the color change to occur, it is important to ensure that the method works for *all* samples. The usual practice is to "spike" the buffer with a small volume of a solution that contains the MgEDTA chelate. As soon as this spiked buffer is added to the water sample, the following reaction occurs, releasing enough Mg^{2+} to produce a wine red color with the indicator:

$$MgEDTA + Ca^{2+} \rightleftarrows CaEDTA + Mg^{2+}$$

Chelation of Ca^{2+} and Mg^{2+} by EDTA has a number of applications in commercial products. Bathroom tub and tile cleaners often contain EDTA in the form of a tetrasodium salt. Stubborn lime and scum deposits dissolve easily in the highly alkaline chelating medium, and the products that are soluble can be flushed away with water. Many salad dressings and other oil-containing products contain CaEDTA as a preservative. The calcium chelate removes any trace iron or copper ions that promote the spoilage of the oil:

$$CaEDTA + Fe^{3+} \rightleftarrows FeEDTA + Ca^{2+} + H^+$$

Cation Exchange Resin

Another very common method of removing divalent cations from water samples is by ion exchange. The ion exchange materials for water softening are cation exchange resins in which monovalent cations (e.g., Na^+ or H^+) are exchanged with divalent cations (e.g., Ca^{2+}). The process may be illustrated as follows for resin containing Na^+ ions:

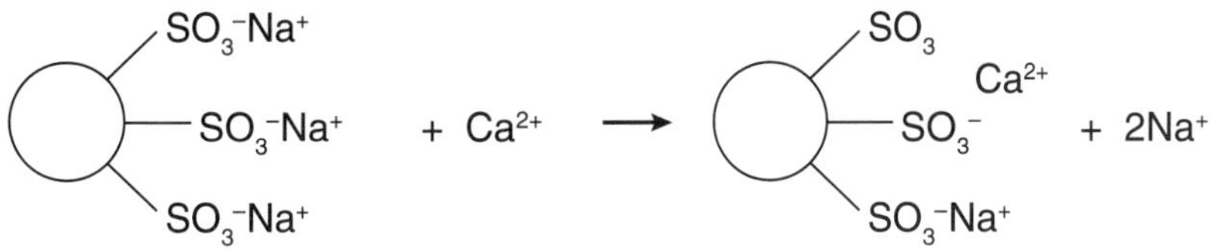

The exchange is usually carried out by percolating the water through a column containing the ion exchange material. Note that the column will need regeneration once all the Na^+ ions have been exchanged. Regeneration is accomplished by reversing the above process. A solution containing a high concentration of salt (NaCl) is pushed through the spent column.

Atomic Absorption Spectrophotometry (AA)

Atomic absorption spectrophotometry (AA) is a useful technique for the determination of metals that are dissolved or suspended in a solution. The metals can be alkalis, alkaline earths, and even transition metals. AA is useful in many areas of chemistry and related fields such as geochemistry, biochemistry, ecology, polymer science, as well as many others.

As you have already learned from Experiment 2, atoms have discrete electronic energy levels which are unique to the specific atom. For example, as you have seen, the emission spectrum of atomic mercury is clearly different from that of atomic hydrogen. In order for the atom of interest to be excited, the energy of light falling incident on the atoms must match the energy separation between two electronic energy levels. As seen in Figure 10.1, absorption will occur if the energy of the incident light, hv, equals ΔE.

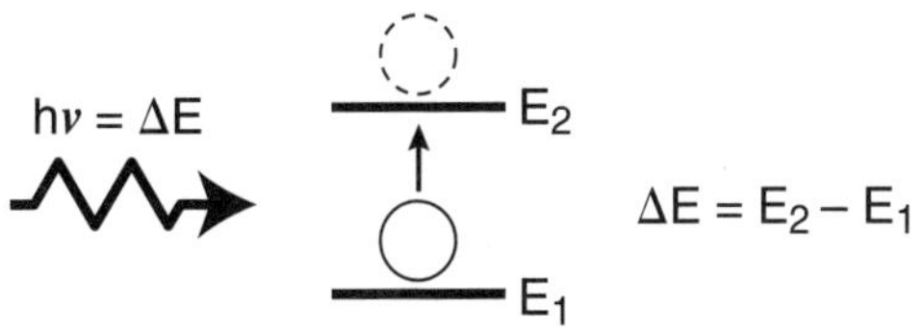

Figure 10.1 Atomic electronic energy levels involved with absorption.

This same principle is used in the operation of atomic absorption spectrophotometry. Monochromatic light having energy corresponding to the ΔE of the atoms of interest is projected through the sample to be analyzed. The atoms in the sample having electronic energy separation ΔE will absorb the light. The amount of absorbance is proportional to the concentration of the metal atoms in the sample. The Beer–Lambert law is, therefore, used to calculate the unknown metal concentration in the sample.

A typical atomic absorption spectrophotometer, similar to the one you will be using, is shown in Figure 10.2. The AA instrument can be broken into three separate and easily identifiable sections.

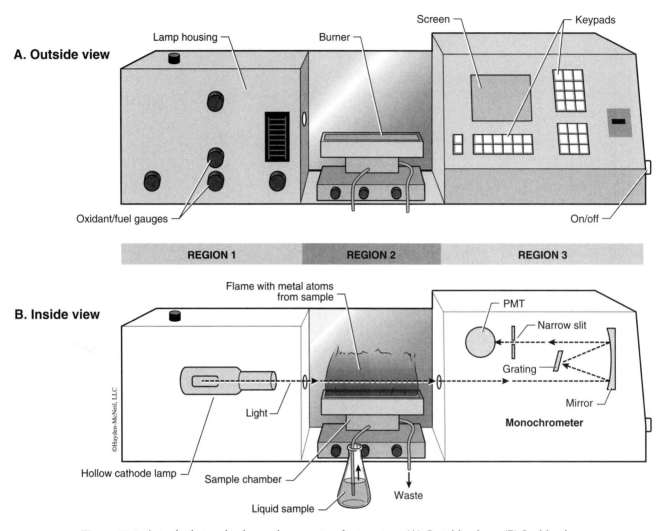

Figure 10.2 A typical atomic absorption spectrophotometer. (A) Outside view, (B) Inside view.

Region 1 comprises the lamp housing and supplies the sources of light. These light sources are what are known as hollow cathode lamps (or HCLs) which emit monochromatic light that corresponds to the ΔE of the element which is to be analyzed. For example, if Mg is the element to be tested in an unknown sample, then the Mg lamp is selected. For this experiment, we will be using the Mg and Ca lamps to determine the amount of Mg and Ca in your water samples. You will be comparing this data with the total divalent cation concentration obtained from the EDTA titrations.

The voltage across the electrodes excites the Mg (or Ca) inside the lamp. When the excited Mg (or Ca) atoms relax, monochromatic light is produced which is equal to the energy separation (ΔE) of the two electronic levels (Figure 10.3). This process is just the opposite of absorption. The emitted monochromatic light will then be absorbed by the Mg (or Ca) atoms in the water sample as shown in Figure 10.1.

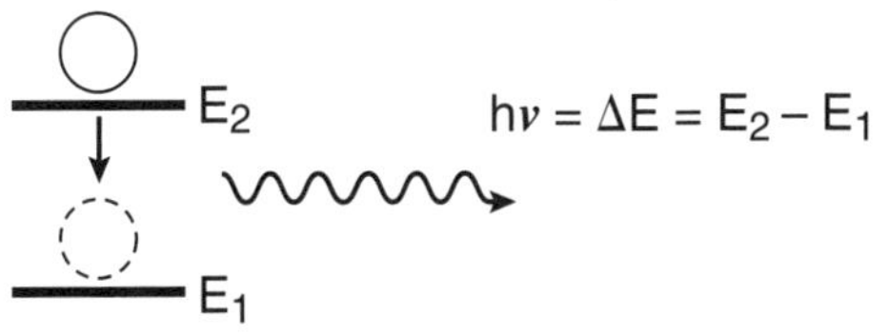

Figure 10.3 Atomic electronic energy levels involved with relaxation.

Region 2 comprises the sample chamber and burner which provides the high temperature flame. The liquid water sample is sucked, or aspirated, into the sample chamber where the sample is converted from a liquid to a fine aerosol which is then introduced into the flame at the burner. The conversion of liquid to aerosol is highly inefficient. Only about 10% of the liquid is converted to the aerosol that reaches the flame. The remaining is emptied out of the sample chamber as waste. The flame is composed of an air-acetylene mixture that reaches approximately 2300 °C. This high temperature is capable of atomizing everything in the liquid sample—the solvent (water) as well as the solvated divalent metal cations (Mg^{2+} and Ca^{2+}).

The light from the hollow cathode lamp passes through the flame where the sample is atomized. The light will be absorbed only if there is a matching energy separation of electronic energy levels (ΔE). To continue with the example, if one is using the Mg (or Ca) lamp, then the only material in the sample having the corresponding energy separation in electronic energy levels is Mg (or Ca). Therefore, only the Mg (or Ca) atoms in the sample will absorb the light produced from the Mg (or Ca) lamp.

Region 3 contains three components: a monochrometer, a detector, and an internal computer system. A grating in the monochrometer is adjusted so that only the wavelength of light corresponding to the ΔE of the metal of interest is allowed to pass through a narrow slit, thus blocking all other wavelengths of light. In other words, the grating is adjusted so that only the light produced from the lamp due to the excited metal emission is allowed to pass through the monochrometer.

This light then continues on to fall incident on the detector which is a photomultiplier tube (PMT). Since the metal atoms absorb some of the light passing through the flame from the lamp, a decrease in the initial signal is detected by the PMT. This decrease is proportional to the concentration of the metal in the sample. The transmitted intensity, I_t, of the lamp through the flame is governed by the Beer–Lambert law that you learned from Experiment 3:

$$I_t = I_o(10^{-abc})$$

where I_o is the intensity of the initial light source. The other variables have their usual meanings.

The concentration of a metal in a sample solution is determined by a calibration graph. First, the AA operator prepares a set of metal solutions of known concentrations. Then these are analyzed by AA and the absorbance of each solution is recorded. These values are used to construct a calibration graph such as the one shown in Figure 10.4. In order to check the accuracy and reproducibility of the instrument, the standards are reanalyzed to see how closely they match the correct values. These are referred to as "Check Standards." You will receive the most recent calibration and check standard values when you visit the Instrument Room.

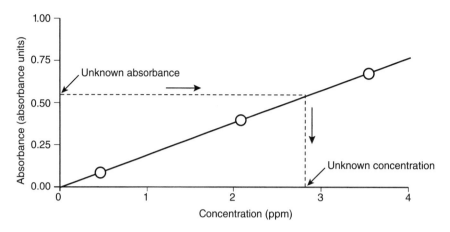

Figure 10.4 Typical calibration graph for AA analysis.

Often the calibrated data will be linear. The absorbance of the sample of unknown metal concentration is recorded, and by interpolation, its concentration is determined (see Figure 10.4). For accurate data, it is preferred that the standard solutions surround the unknown sample solution in terms of absorbance (or concentration) since the most accurate region of the calibration graph is between the maximum and minimum standard points. The calibration data will be given to you on the day of the experiment.

The AAs have been calibrated for Ca concentrations in the 0–50 mg/L range and Mg concentrations in the 0–30 mg/L range. Most drinking water samples will fall in these ranges. If your samples have Ca or Mg concentrations higher than these values (e.g., sea water) then you will need to dilute your samples before analysis. This is because reliable data is obtained only if the absorbances of the sample solutions are below one absorbance unit. Above one absorbance unit, most of the light is being absorbed at that particular wavelength. In other words, there is little light transmitted for the PMT to detect.

At the AA, the sample is aspirated into the burner by placing the aspirator (a small-diameter, white plastic tube) into the sample as shown in Figure 10.5.

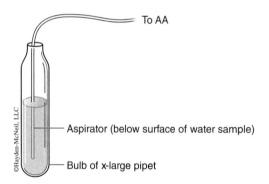

Figure 10.5 Insertion of the aspirator into the sample solutions.

When the flame is lit, the aspirator is initially placed into a beaker of distilled water to keep the burner from overheating. To run your water samples, it is important that the end of the aspirator be below the surface of the liquid. The computer will already be programmed so that both the light absorbance value and the concentration of the metal content will be displayed on the screen.

Additional Reading

1. *Chemistry: The Central Science*, T. L. Brown, H. E. LeMay, Jr. and B. E. Bursten, Prentice Hall, 10th Ed. Section 18.6 discusses natural waters and the Closer Look Box talks about water softening.

2. *Chemistry: The Molecular Science,* J. W. Moore, C. L. Stanitski, and P. C. Jurs, Harcourt College Publishers, Orlando, 2002. Section 15.11 discusses natural water and water hardness.

3. *The Water Encyclopedia*, 2nd Ed., Frits vander Leeden, Fred L. Troise, David Keith Todd, published by Lewis Publishers, Chelsea, Michigan, 1990. Not only does this book have a lot of information about water quality and hardness, but it also lists typical values of hardness for water from cities all over Pennsylvania and the United States.

Quiz Outline

Know the following information from the Introduction and Background sections of this experiment:

- an example of a sedimentary rock containing Ca^{2+}

- what is meant by the hardness of water

- why scale formation is the bane of industry

- a common method of softening water

- why some salad dressings contain EDTA-chelated calcium

Understand what is meant by the phrase "Total Dissolved Solids" or "TDS," and the difference between what this type of analysis tells you compared to a "Divalent Cation Analysis."

Understand what the equation below is telling you:

$$HD^{2-} + Mg^{2+} + Ca^{2+} \longrightarrow MgD^- + H^+ + Ca^{2+} \xrightarrow{EDTA} CaEDTA + MgEDTA + HD^{2-}$$

Blue		Red	(immediately)	(eventually)	(last)
					Blue

Understand what happens when a hard water sample is treated with a "cation exchange resin" and why you would want to do this.

Be able to explain in a short paragraph how an AA analysis is carried out, and the principles behind how it works.

Know that AA is normally used to analyze water for metals.

Be able to draw a rough picture of the instrument and label the most important parts.

What is the "Beer–Lambert Law," and what is its significance in AA?

What is the purpose of the "standards" that are run as part of an AA analysis?

What is the problem with analyzing a sample whose absorbance *exceeds* 1 absorbance unit? What will be done in this experiment to compensate for this problem?

REMINDER: You will need to bring your water sample. It should be in a clean container that has been rinsed with some of the sample prior to the final filling. Approximately 5 to 10 mL will be needed for the analysis.

Sample Pre-Laboratory Quiz

1. The equations below are the basis for a "divalent cation analysis." (a) Is this type of analysis possible for a sample that contains only Mg^{2+} (i.e., no Ca^{2+})? (b) Explain your answer.

$$HD^{2-} + Mg^{2+} + Ca^{2+} \longrightarrow MgD^- + H^+ + Ca^{2+} \xrightarrow{\text{EDTA}} CaEDTA + MgEDTA + HD^{2-}$$

2. A student did a divalent cation analysis of a particular mineral water sample, and calculated a hardness of 305 parts per million (ppm). But, the label on the mineral water bottle gave a TDS of 510 ppm. Does this make sense? Explain. ("Experimental error" is *not* the answer.)

3. Briefly explain how an Atomic Absorption (AA) analysis is carried out, and the principles behind how it works.

4. Label the four arrows shown in the figure below.

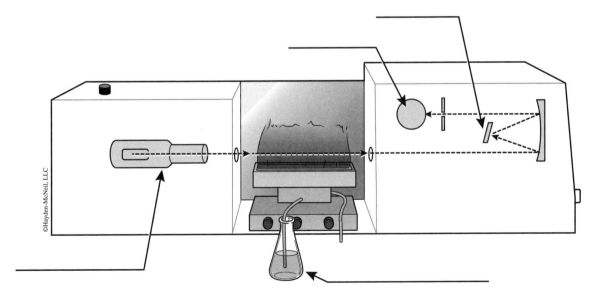

Laboratory Experiments

Flowchart of the Experiments

| Section A. | Determination of Water Hardness by Atomic Absorption Spectroscopy (AA) |

| Section B. | Evaporation of Your Water Sample to Give Total Dissolved Solids |

| Section C. | Divalent Cation Analysis by EDTA Titration |

| Section D. | Determination of the Hardness of Your Water Sample |

| Section E. | Water Softening with a Commercial Water-Conditioning Agent |

| Section F. | Divalent Cation Removal by Ion Exchange |

| Section G. | Important Ways of Reporting the Hardness of Water |

Requires one four-hour class period to complete.

Section A.	Determination of Water Hardness by Atomic Absorption Spectroscopy (AA)

Goals: *(1) To use Atomic Absorption spectroscopy (AA) to determine the hardness of your water sample. (2) To compare the results from this analysis to the information obtained from the EDTA titrations and TDS determinations.*

Discussion: Atomic Absorption spectroscopy (AA) is a sensitive, element-specific method for the analysis of metals. The steps below describe how to prepare your samples for AA analysis.

Experimental Steps:

1. Visually examine your water sample. Is it cloudy, and/or are there any particles visible? If there are, then your sample will need to be filtered before analysis. Check with your instructor regarding what filtration equipment is available. If your water is completely clear, then proceed to step 2.

2. Obtain two extra large pipets from the front of the room. Cut off the stems of each pipet near the base where it is attached to the bulb. Fill both bulbs with some of your water sample (filtered, if necessary). The bulbs should be at least two-thirds full. One bulb will be used for the Ca analysis, the other for the Mg analysis. A 24-well tray should be used as a sample holder. This will leave your hands free for operating the AA.

3. At the appropriate time (your instructor will tell you when this is), take your samples to the instrumental analysis room where you will be given the procedure for using the AA. Until then, set your samples aside and proceed with Section B, etc.

Question: HW1. Determine the hardness of your sample due to calcium and magnesium. This will require a number of steps:

(a) Calibration graphs of light absorbance vs. metal ion concentration must be made, using data supplied by the instrument operator. These graphs will enable you to determine the amount of Ca and Mg in your sample. These graphs should be done at home on a computer and taped into your lab notebook.

(b) These Ca and Mg values must be converted into their "equivalent concentration of $CaCO_3$," which is the "hardness" of the sample—i.e., the actual mass of Ca and Mg in the water is not exactly the same as the "hardness" of that water sample. (See Section G part B for further details.)

(c) The hardness due to the Ca and Mg (determined in step b) must be added together to give a total hardness value. This value should be similar to the hardness determined by EDTA titration (Section D).

Section B.	Evaporation of Your Water Sample to Give Total Dissolved Solids

Goal:
To make a qualitative measurement of the Total Dissolved Solids (TDS) in your water sample.

Discussion:
A TDS determination is complementary to the other water analysis methods used in this experiment—i.e., its value is related to hardness, but it is not identical to the hardness of a sample. For example, a water sample with a high TDS would most likely be "hard" water. But, if all of the dissolved solids were NaCl then the sample would have a hardness of zero.

Experimental Steps:

1. Obtain a small piece of aluminum foil (approx. 2 cm × 2 cm).

2. Place it on the table shiny side up and smooth it with your fingers.

3. Using tweezers, place the foil shiny side up onto a hot plate set on a low or medium setting.

4. Drop 1 drop of your undiluted water sample onto the foil. About 0.5 cm away, place a drop of distilled water. About 0.5 cm away from the previous two drops, add a drop of 1×10^{-3} M Ca^{2+}.

   • Note where each water sample is located on the foil.

5. Allow the water to evaporate. If it spits and splashes, the hot plate is too hot and you should turn it down.

6. After the water has evaporated, use the tweezers to remove the foil from the hot plate.

   Describe and record what you see.

   The white solids that remain after evaporation of the water are the nonvolatile salts that were originally in solution in the water sample. The amount of nonvolatile salts in a certain volume of a water sample is called the *total dissolved solids* (TDS).

Question: Q1.

(a) Compare the TDS of the water samples that you placed on the foil.

(b) Which salts are likely to be present in the white solid residue on the foil?

Attach the foil to your notebook.

Section C.   Divalent Cation Analysis by EDTA Titration

Goal: *To investigate the chemistry of the complexation reactions of ethylenediaminetetraacetic acid (EDTA) with solutions of Ca^{2+} and Mg^{2+} of known concentrations.*

Discussion: The purpose of this section is to practice with solutions of calcium and magnesium of known concentrations (each at 1×10^{-3} M). You will see what the color changes look like, and see how closely you are able to determine the concentrations of these solutions. If all goes well in this section, then you can proceed to Section D in which you will substitute your water sample in place of the 1×10^{-3} M solutions of calcium and magnesium, and determine the hardness of your water sample.

All of the titrations in this section should be carried out in a *serial* manner in 1×12 well strips. It is important to note that cleanliness is critical to achieving good results. Sources of Ca^{2+} ions, Mg^{2+} ions, etc., are ubiquitous. *Make sure that all your apparatus is well washed with DISTILLED water.*

In this experiment you will be doing quantitative volumetric analysis. Therefore, it is necessary to use good wash, rinse, and transfer techniques and the *same* pipet for all solutions, except the buffer and the indicator. The exact volumes of the buffer and the indicator should not affect the titration end point.

Experimental Steps: **PART I: The Effect of the Buffer and the Effect of Mg^{2+}(aq)**

The indicator to be used is eriochrome black T (EBT). EBT can undergo a color change due to pH change or due to a reaction with Mg^{2+}. Test these two color changes as follows:

1.   Clean out a 1×12 well and add 1 drop of EBT to each of the first three wells.

    • Note the color.

2.   Add 1 drop of NH_3/NH_4Cl buffer to only well 2 and well 3. Stir.

    NOTE: There are two buffers; be sure to use the correct one.

    • Note the color.

3.   Now add 1 drop of 10^{-3} M Mg^{2+} solution to the EBT/buffer solution in well 3. Stir.

    • Record what you see.

    NOTE: From this point on, all of the solutions to be analyzed will be buffered, so that any color change will be due to either the addition of Mg^{2+} to the indicator or the removal of Mg^{2+} from it—in other words, in all of your titrations, all of the wells should be either the color you observe in well 2 or the color you observe in well 3.

Mg
54.83   P 2 50   83.43

Mg
57.68   49.7

w Mg
6353   5483

p. Mg
5590   52 50

PART II: Practice Titrations with Known Amounts of Ca^{2+}(aq) and Mg^{2+}(aq)

Now let's try some "serial" titrations. This is similar to a series of regular titrations in which each titration is stopped at a different point.

1. Clean a 1×12 well strip with distilled water.

2. Using a small-drop pipet, add one drop of the 1×10^{-3} M Ca^{2+} solution to each of the 12 wells.

3. Add one drop of the EBT indicator to each well.

4. Add one drop of the $NH_3/NH_4Cl/MgEDTA$ buffer to each well.

5. Now, titrate serially with the EDTA solution—i.e., add 1 drop of the 2×10^{-4} M EDTA to the first well, 2 drops to the second well, 3 drops to the third well, etc. Stir the solution in each well after the addition of the EDTA. When you are done, you have a "snapshot" of each step of the titration. The first blue well is the point where you have excess EDTA. This is considered the end point, even though it is obviously slightly past the end point.

Question: Q2. Calculate the concentration of the original Ca^{2+} solution. Do your results agree with the value on the label of the solution tested?

We know that the moles of EDTA are equal to the moles of divalent cations, but in this case, only Ca^{2+} is present. So,

moles of EDTA = moles of Ca^{2+}

$$M_{EDTA} \, V_{EDTA} = M_{Ca}{}^{2+} \, V_{Ca}{}^{2+}$$

Since volume appears on both sides of the equation, the volume units cancel out—i.e., it doesn't matter what volume units you use...so let's use drops.

Experimental Steps: 6. Clean out your 1×12 well strip with distilled water.

7. Repeat the titration done in steps 2–5. Except in this case, add one drop of the 10^{-3} M Ca^{2+} solution *and* one drop of the 10^{-3} M Mg^{2+} solution to each well.

- Record your observations.

Questions: Q3. Calculate the concentration of the combined Ca^{2+} and Mg^{2+} mixture. Do your results make sense?

Q4. What is the accuracy of this method according to your results?

Section D.   Determination of the Hardness of Your Water Sample

Goal: *To determine the total divalent cation concentration (hardness) of your water sample by EDTA titration.*

Experimental Steps: 1. Using the method in Section C, part II, determine the hardness of your water sample.

2. Carry out a duplicate analysis on the same water sample.

Questions: Q5.   A student observed that all 12 wells were pink after titrating her sample. What does this imply?

Q6.   Calculate the hardness in molarity, ppm, and grains per gallon. (See Section G, part A for calculation information.)

Q7.   What is the precision of your measurements? How much will the hardness value change if you are off by one well?

NOTE: If your sample has a hardness of zero, then your sample EBT buffer mixture will be blue, even before any EDTA is added.

Section E.   Water Softening with a Commercial Water-Conditioning Agent

Goal: *To investigate the softening of water—i.e., the removal of hardness by commercial water-conditioning products.*

Discussion: If your water sample is extremely soft, then you may use the 1×10^{-3} M Ca^{2+} sample used in Section C, part II for this section.

Experimental Steps: 1.   Wash a vial and cap thoroughly with distilled water.

2.   Add your water sample to the vial to about 1 cm in height.

3.   Add about 20 mg of a selected commercial conditioning product to the vial by means of a straw spatula. Shake until the powder dissolves.

Question: Q8.   (a)   Using the $NH_3/NH_4Cl/MgEDTA$ buffer, determine the hardness for your treated water sample by EDTA titration.

(b)   Compare the results from this titration with the results from the titration where no softening agent was added.

(c)   Record any information about the active ingredients from the product package.

Section F.   Divalent Cation Removal by Ion Exchange

Goal: *To investigate the use of cation exchange resins in the removal of Ca^{2+} and Mg^{2+} from hard water samples.*

Discussion: If your water sample is extremely soft, then you may use the 1×10^{-3} M Ca^{2+} sample used in Section C, part II for this section.

Experimental Steps: 1.   Wash one of your 8 mL vials and pop cap thoroughly with distilled water.

2.   Transfer a small amount of cation exchange resin into the vial using a straw spatula —approximately enough to just cover the bottom of the vial.

3.   Add your water sample to the vial to about 1 cm in height.

4.   Replace the cap and shake gently for about a minute.

5.   Set the vial down and allow the resin to settle.

6.   Remove some of the supernatant liquid using a clean pipet and being careful not to suck up any resin beads.

7.   Test 1 drop of the liquid in the vial with wide-range pH paper. Also test the pH of your water sample for comparison purposes.

Questions: Q9.   (a) Using the $NH_3/NH_4Cl/MgEDTA$ buffer, determine the hardness for your treated water sample by EDTA titration.

(b) Compare the results from this titration with the results from the titration where no softening agent was added.

Q10.   What cation replaced the polyvalent cations in the solution?

Q11.   Give a brief description of the chemistry of this exchange process.

There is a container in the front of the room for used ion exchange resin. Please make sure yours ends up in it. We will recycle it as much as possible.

HW2.   (a) What is the result of the AA determination of hardness of your water sample?

(b) What is the result of the EDTA determination of hardness of your water sample?

(c) Explain why there might be differences in these two results.

Section G.   Important Ways of Reporting the Hardness of Water

Goal: *To be able to calculate and report the hardness of water in various units.*

Discussion: The divalent cation concentration of water is often referred to as the *hardness* of water—less of a mouthful and more tactile! There are several ways of quantitatively expressing the hardness of water that are used extensively by engineers and technicians in the water industry. The two most common units are *parts per million* (ppm) and *grains per gallon*. Separate determinations for the individual $[Ca^{2+}]$ and $[Mg^{2+}]$ ions are not usually made. The combined total concentration of Ca^{2+}, Mg^{2+}, and any other polyvalent cations is what is determined by an EDTA titration.

Hardness is therefore a property of water that is imparted by several different cations, all of which are included in the single EDTA analysis. In this situation, it turns out to be very convenient to express hardness in terms of an "equivalent concentration of calcium carbonate $(CaCO_3)$"—i.e., hardness is calculated by determining the concentration of $CaCO_3$ that would be required to yield the same EDTA titration result. This serves the purpose of defining a single quantity which represents the effect of many ions.

Sample Calculations: *A.   Converting a molar concentration of divalent cations into a hardness value, in units of either ppm or grains per gallon.*

1.   Conversion to units of ppm

EDTA titrations will give a hardness value in terms of molarity of divalent cations. To convert this to units of ppm, we must know the mass of the solute. The definition of hardness requires us to treat this solute as if it were all $CaCO_3$, so we will use the molar mass of $CaCO_3$, which is 100.0 g. So, suppose your water sample has a hardness measured by EDTA of 1×10^{-3} M divalent cations. This will correspond to a concentration of:

$$\frac{1 \times 10^{-3}\,\text{moles CaCO}_3}{1\,\text{liter of solution}} \times \frac{100.0\,\text{g CaCO}_3}{1\,\text{mole CaCO}_3} \times \frac{1000\,\text{mg CaCO}_3}{1\,\text{g CaCO}_3} = \frac{100\,\text{mg CaCo}_3}{1\,\text{liter of solution}}$$

or 100 ppm*

*Note: The density of dilute aqueous solutions is very close to 1 g/mL, and therefore 1 mg of solute/1 liter of solution is equivalent to 1 mg of solute per 10^{+6} mg of solution—i.e., 1 mg/L is equivalent to 1 ppm for dilute aqueous solutions.

2.   Conversion to units of grains per gallon

Surprisingly, hardness is often reported in Henry VIII units of grains per gallon, rather than in metric units. Given below is an example of how to calculate hardness in these units.

1 grain = weight of an average grain of wheat = 64.7 mg

Since,

1 gallon = 3.785 liters,

Then,

$$\frac{1\,\text{grain CaCO}_3}{\text{gallon water}} = 17.1\,\text{ppm}$$

Thus, the 10^{-3} M water sample has a hardness of

$$100\,\text{pm} \times \frac{1\,\text{grain per gallon}}{17.1\,\text{ppm}}$$

= 5.8 grains per gallon

3.   Your turn

   •   Convert 2.5×10^{-3} M Ca^{2+} concentration into ppm and grains per gallon hardness. (answer = 250 ppm, 14.6 grains per gallon)

   •   What is the factor that will allow you to convert molarity of divalent cations directly into ppm hardness?

B.   *Converting a metal ion concentration in ppm to a hardness value in ppm.*

A related calculation is the conversion from ppm of a particular divalent cation into ppm hardness. This type of calculation must be performed if you are going to compare the Ca and Mg measurements made by AA to the EDTA determined hardness values.

In these cases, you must multiply the ppm of the divalent cation times the ratio of the molar mass of $CaCO_3$ to the molar mass of the divalent metal ion of interest. For example, if a particular water sample had a Ca^{2+} concentration of 1 ppm, then the hardness of that sample would be equal to:

$$1 \text{ ppm Ca}^{2+} \times \left[\frac{\frac{100 \text{ g CaCO}_3}{1 \text{ mole}}}{\frac{40.0 \text{ g Ca}^{2+}}{1 \text{ mole}}} \right] = 2.5 \text{ ppm CaCO}_3 = 2.5 \text{ ppm hardness}$$

Similarly, if a particular sample had a Mg^{2+} concentration of 1 ppm, then the hardness of that sample would be equal to:

$$1 \text{ ppm Mg}^{2+} \times \left[\frac{\frac{100 \text{ g CaCO}_3}{1 \text{ mole}}}{\frac{24.3 \text{ g Mg}^{2+}}{1 \text{ mole}}} \right] = 4.12 \text{ ppm CaCO}_3 = 4.12 \text{ ppm hardness}$$

Experiment 11

Synthesis and Quantitation of Acetylsalicylic Acid (Aspirin)

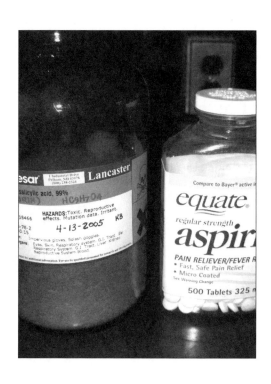

Synthesis and Quantitation of Acetylsalicylic Acid (Aspirin)

Matthew Szapacs, Mary Jo Bojan, and Joseph Keiser, August 2005

Introduction

Aspirin is a substance commonly found in medicine cabinets around the world. It is one of the least expensive and most useful drugs. The role that chemists have played in its development is a fascinating study of how the drug industry works.

The precursor to modern day aspirin was found in the bark of willow trees and used by people for thousands of years to alleviate pain. It was commonly brewed into a tea to soothe the sufferer. In the mid-1800s, the active ingredient (the chemical responsible for the pain relief), salicylic acid, was isolated and by 1870 methods had been developed to produce it on a wide-scale basis. The structure of salicylic acid is shown in the figure below.

A white powder, it could be taken orally, but it had an unfortunate side effect. Salicylic acid is a relatively strong acid (pH of a saturated aqueous solution = 2.4) and causes irritation to the mouth, esophagus, and stomach. In the late 1890s, a young chemist at Bayer named Felix Hoffman sought to improve this drug. His father suffered from rheumatoid arthritis, and the side effects of salicylic acid were preventing him from obtaining relief from the swelling and inflammation of the disease. Felix attempted to modify salicylic acid to make it less acidic and more soluble in stomach acids by replacing the alcohol functional group with an ester. This involved a simple condensation reaction between an acid and an alcohol. In the example below, acetic anhydride reacts with the OH group on salicylic acid to produce acetyl salicylic acid.

Salicylic Acid	Acetic Anhydride	Acetylsalicylic Acid (Aspirin)	Acetic Acid
$C_7H_6O_3$ (s)	$C_4H_6O_3$ (l)	$C_9H_8O_4$ (s)	$C_2H_4O_2$ (l)

This new compound proved to be immensely successful. It retained the pain-relieving and fever-reducing properties of salicylic acid, but was not as irritating to the stomach. When Hoffman revealed his work to his supervisors at Bayer, the company began to produce and market this new drug giving it the trade name Aspirin. Bayer aspirin is still a well-known name, even though the patent has long since run out, and aspirin is available under many trade names and in generic form.

Aspirin is a mild analgesic (pain reliever) that works by blocking the synthesis of prostaglandins, a group of compounds produced in the body. These compounds can act directly on the heat-regulating centers of the central nervous system (producing fever) and constrict blood vessels which increases the body temperature (because less heat can escape from the tissues into the blood). Prostaglandins also increase the permeability of capillaries, allowing water to pass out of the capillaries and into the nearby tissues causing swelling and pain. Thus, by lowering the concentration of these compounds, aspirin reduces pain, fever, and inflammation. Other analgesics include acetaminophen (Tylenol) and ibuprofen (Advil and Nuprin).

Acetaminophen   Ibuprofen

Aspirin can be hydrolyzed to form salicylic acid. Hydrolysis is a reaction that causes the dissociation of water and results in the replacement of an organic functional group with a hydroxide. The hydrolysis of an ester results in the formation of an alcohol and a carboxylic acid. When an O—C bond is broken the –H and –OH of the dissociated water adds to the two molecules where the bond was broken.

Acetylsalicylic Acid (Aspirin)   Water   Salicylic Acid   Acetic Acid
$C_9H_8O_4$ $C_7H_6O_3$ $C_2H_4O_2$

In this experiment, the hydrolysis will be done using an aqueous base (thus simulating the alkaline conditions of the digestive tract where this reaction occurs in the body). Under these conditions, the salicylate dianion will be produced. Hydrolysis of an ester done in basic solution is called saponification. (It is the reaction by which soaps are made.)

Aspirin

In the second part of the experiment, the amount of hydrolyzed aspirin in a solution will be determined quantitatively using a spectrophotometric technique. The spectrophotometers you will be using produce and detect visible light (light in the 400–750 nm range). For this method to work, it is necessary to produce a colored compound (a compound that will absorb light in the visible region). This can be done by adding a solution of Fe^{3+}(aq) to the hydrolyzed aspirin. At an appropriate pH, a 1:1 complex of Fe^{3+} to hydrolyzed acid forms. This complex absorbs light of 520 nm, and therefore appears to be pink/purple in color.

Spectrophotometric Methods

When a beam of light of a selected wavelength strikes an absorbing medium of known dimensions (such as a sample tube in a spectrophotometer), part of the incident light is transmitted to a detector and part of it is lost by reflection, refraction, and scattering. If the same beam of light is passed through a "blank" medium (one which contains all but the absorbing solute), we still obtain loss in transmitted intensity due to reflection, refraction, and scattering, but no loss in intensity due to solute molecules that absorb radiation. Hence the difference in the intensity of light transmitted by the "blank" and the sample gives the absorption by the solute.

Beer's Law

When a beam of monochromatic radiation passes through a population of absorbing species, the radiant power of the beam is progressively decreased as part of its energy is absorbed by the species. This diminution in power is dependent on the concentration of the absorbed substance as well as the length of the path traversed by the incident beam. These relationships are expressed in Beer's Law.

$$A = abc$$

A = absorbance, a = absorptivity or extinction coefficient (measure of how strongly a particular substance absorbs light.), b = path length (cm), c = concentration (moles/L)

So it can be seen that absorbance, A, is directly (linearly) proportional to the concentration, c.

Quantitative Analysis

1. The procedure involves selection of an appropriate wavelength (nanometers) corresponding to an absorption peak for the absorbing species obtained after scanning a wide wavelength range and recording the absorption at small nanometer intervals. The change in absorbance per unit change in concentration is greatest at this wavelength.

2. Variables that affect the absorption of a substance must be considered. These are the nature of the solvent, pH, temperature, and presence of interfering species. All affect absorption.

3. The relationship between absorbance and concentration is examined with the help of a set of calibration standards. The standards must cover a reasonable concentration range over which a linear plot of absorbance vs. concentration is obtained. This line should pass through the origin. The unknown concentration to be analyzed can then be estimated by simple extrapolation from such a standard calibration graph.

The Spectronic 20 is a direct-reading, single-beam spectrophotometer that can be used to study absorbance in the range of 350–750 nm. The scale is scribed to read transmittance and absorbance.

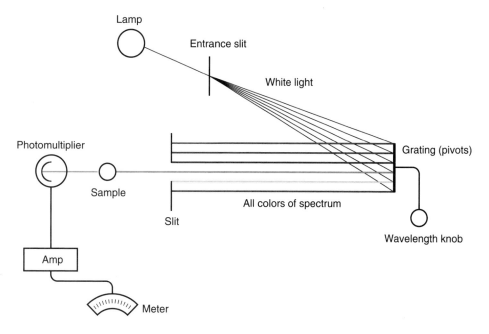

In this instrument the white light of the tungsten lamp is reflected and dispersed (separated into various wavelengths) by the diffraction grating. The different wavelengths, or colors, leave the grating at different angles and thus are spread out in space as they arrive at the exit slit. The grating can be pivoted about an axis so that a particular wavelength is selected and focused on the exit slit. This light then passes through the sample to the phototube and is detected.

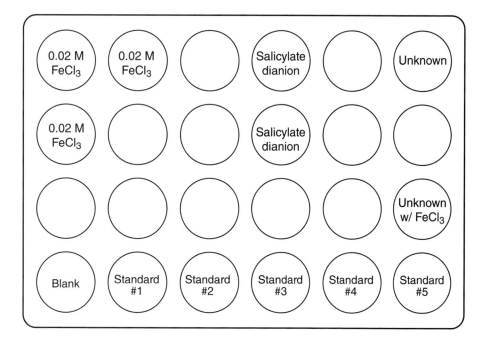

A full-size version of this 24-well template will be provided.

Sample Pre-Laboratory Quiz

1. What is Beer's law?

2. What organic functional groups are on aspirin?

3. What is a catalyst?

4. Draw a color wheel and use it to illustrate complementary colors. (See Exp. #3, *Chemtrek*.)

5. A student weighs out 0.3966 g of salicylic acid and uses it to synthesize aspirin. 0.3224 g of aspirin are recovered. What is the % yield of aspirin?

Laboratory Experiments

Flowchart of the Experiments

Section A.	Synthesis of Acetylsalicylic Acid (Aspirin)

Section B.	Compare Pure Aspirin with Your Sample

Section C.	Formation of a Colored Complex from Aspirin

Section D.	Preparation of Calibration Standards (can be done in pairs)

Section E.	Spectrophotometric Determination of Aspirin (can be done in pairs)

Requires one four-hour class period to complete.

Experimental

Note: There is a 24-well template for this experiment. It will help you to organize your solutions in this experiment. See page 5 in the introduction.

Section A.   Synthesis of Acetylsalicylic Acid (Aspirin)

Salicylic Acid	Acetic Anhydride	Acetylsalicylic Acid (Aspirin)	Acetic Acid
$C_7H_6O_3$ (s)	$C_4H_6O_3$ (l)	$C_9H_8O_4$ (s)	$C_2H_4O_2$ (l)

Discussion: In this experiment you will be synthesizing Aspirin from salicylic acid and acetic anhydride. (Acetic anhydride is the result of two molecules of acetic acid combining to form the anhydride and water.)

Questions: Q1.   What is a lacrimator?

Experimental Steps: 1.   Weigh 0.40 g salicylic acid in a clean, dry, screw-top vial (record exact weight). Note: You do not need the top for this experiment.

2.   Fill a Styrofoam cup from your drawer with boiling water (obtain from coffee urn in the front of the room) to make a hot water bath for the reaction. Set it near the hood by your workspace. Have a clamp ready to hold your vial in the hot water bath once all of the reagents have been added.

The next two steps should be done in the hood in the front of the room where the acetic anhydride and sulfuric acid are kept. Then the reaction container may be moved to the hot water bath near your workspace.

3.   *Slowly add* 0.800 mL (density = 1.082 g/mL) acetic anhydride to the salicylic acid in your vial using an air displacement pipet. (Do this directly in front of the hood; acetic anhydride is a lacrimator) **Note:** If you do not feel confident regarding the use of an air displacement pipet ask your TA for help or read the description on page 11.

4.   Add 1 drop of concentrated sulfuric acid (H_2SO_4) to the reaction mixture using a glass pipet. Gently swirl the screw-top vial until the contents are well mixed.

5.   Take the vial to your workspace, clamp it to a ring stand located by the hood vent near your workspace, and lower into your hot water bath.

6.   Let the vial sit in the hot water bath 15–20 minutes.

Q2.   Is salicylic acid or acetic anhydride the limiting reactant in this reaction?

Q3.   What do you think sulfuric acid does in the reaction above? (**Hint:** Why might you need to add only 1 drop?)

While you are waiting for the reaction to progress, make an ice bath and place a clean 8 mL pop-top vial full of distilled water into the ice bath to cool. (You can also go on to Section C and beyond.)

7.   After 20 minutes *slowly add* approximately 2 mL of cold distilled water to the reaction mixture to decompose the remaining acetic anhydride. (**Caution:** If water is added to the reaction mixture too fast, the reaction will foam over.)

8.   Cool the reaction mixture in an ice bath for 10–15 minutes. (Aspirin should crystallize; you may need to cool your reaction mixture longer to achieve crystallization.)

9.   Setup the vacuum filtration apparatus. See your instructor if you are not sure how to set up or use the apparatus. Make sure you place one piece of the disposable filter paper (kept in the front of the room) on top of the plastic filter which is built into the Hirsch funnel.

10.   Add 5 mL of cold water to the crystals and stir to break up any lumps.

11.   Gently pour the liquid and the crystals into the Hirsch funnel. Use a straw spatula to scrape as many of the crystals as possible out of the screw-top vial.

12.   Transfer any remaining crystals from the screw-top vial by adding small amounts of chilled water to the screw-top vial and swirl to suspend crystals.

13.   After all the crystals have been transferred to the filtration apparatus, rinse the crystals by adding a small amount of chilled water and stir the crystals in the funnel.

14.   Let the crystals air dry in the funnel for 5 minutes by continuing to pull a vacuum on the filtration apparatus.

15.   Transfer the crystals to a clean, preweighed weighing boat. The crystals may still be a little damp at this point. Break them up with a spatula so that they will air dry more quickly.

16.   Weigh crystals.

Q4.   Calculate the percent yield of aspirin from the above reaction. Show your work.

Purity Check

To check the purity of your aspirin sample, place a spatula tip full of your synthesized aspirin (~0.01 g) in a clean, dry, screw-top vial. Add ~1 mL of 95% ethanol to completely dissolve the aspirin. 2 drops of 0.02 M $FeCl_3$ can then be added to the mixture. If the solution turns purple there is salicylic acid impurity still left in your sample.

Q5.   (a) Why do you see a purple color if you have salicylic acid left in your product?

       (b) Why do you not see a purple color if you have pure aspirin? (Hint: What functional groups participate in the formation of the color-causing iron complex according to the introduction?)

Section B.   Compare Pure Aspirin with Your Sample

Experimental Steps: 1.   Qualitatively test the solubility of pure aspirin and compare it with the solubility of your synthesized aspirin. Are the pure aspirin or synthesized aspirin more soluble in ethanol or water? Check your results with the solubility of pure aspirin as listed in the Merck index.

2.   Also compare the behavior of pure aspirin heated in a melting-point capillary with the behavior of your sample heated in a similar manner.

Questions: Q6.   (a) Did the solubilities of the pure aspirin and your synthesized aspirin differ? Compare them to the solubility given in the literature.

(b) Were the samples more soluble in water or ethanol? If so, why do you think this is the case?

Q7.   (a) What was the melting point range of your aspirin sample?

(b) What is the melting point range of the commercial sample?

(c) What is the literature value for the melting point of aspirin?

(d) What does this tell you about your sample?

Section C.   Formation of a Colored Complex from Aspirin

Discussion: Another way to analyze for the presence of aspirin is to convert it into a colored compound, and then quantitatively measure the intensity of the colored compound using a spectrophotometer. To obtain a colored compound, aspirin is first reacted with sodium hydroxide as shown in the reaction below. This produces a dianion with a structure similar to that of salicylic acid which is called the salicylate dianion.

| Acetylsalicylic Acid (Aspirin) $C_9H_8O_4$ (s) | Sodium hydroxide (aq) | Salicylate dianion $C_7H_4O_3^{2-}$ (aq) | Acetic acid $C_2H_4O_2$ (l) |

The salicylate dianion is colorless, but when reacted ("complexed") with iron (III) it forms a colored compound. We do not have time for you to produce the salicylate dianion from your aspirin, so a solution of this compound has been prepared for you by the stockroom. You will conduct the reaction of the salicylate dianion with iron (III).

Questions: Q8.   What does the term hydrolyzed mean?

Q9.   Draw the structure of the salicylate dianion. (**Hint:** Which atoms will most easily leave the salicylic acid molecule in the presence of a base?)

Section D.   Preparation of Calibration Standards (can be done in pairs)

Discussion:

In this section you will be using the 0.1 mg/mL salicylate dianion (also referred to as "hydrolyzed aspirin") to make an iron (III) salicylate dianion complex. This compound can then be analyzed to determine the amount of hydrolyzed aspirin in an unknown mixture.

The following dilutions are best prepared in a 24-well tray (refer to the 24-well tray template on page 6). You will be using several different solutions in this experiment, and if you label the pipet tips provided at your workstation, then you can minimize cross contamination. The fine point marker in your kit can be used to mark the upper outside section of the pipet tip. For the section below you only need four pipet tips—one for the distilled water, one for 0.1 mg/mL salicylate dianion solution (hydrolyzed aspirin), one for the unknown dianion solution, and one for the 0.02 M $FeCl_3$.

Before making the solutions, take a few moments to become familiar with the features of the air pipet and practice using it with distilled water. You can check your technique by weighing the amount of distilled water pipetted at various volume settings.

Features of Air Displacement Pipet

Dial: Used to set volume

(a) Put black lever in unlock position.

(b) Turn wheel on top of pipet to set the volume. Volume is given in microliters (μL).

$$500\ \mu L = 0.5\ mL$$

(c) Flip black lever back to lock.

To make solutions:

• Place tip on bottom of pipet, (to eject tip, push white lever near thumb on side of pipet).

• Place pipet tip into solution and press down on wheel to the FIRST stop. Slowly release, allowing fluid to be drawn in.

• To eject fluid, press down on wheel to first stop, then press to second stop to eject the last drop.

Using an air displacement pipet, prepare the following solutions:

Table 11.1 Making Standard Curve

	Amount 0.1 mg/mL hydrolyzed aspirin (mL)	Amount DI H_2O (mL)	Amount 0.02 M $FeCl_3$ (mL)
Blank	0	0.5	0.5
Standard 1	0.1	0.4	0.5
Standard 2	0.2	0.3	0.5
Standard 3	0.3	0.2	0.5
Standard 4	0.4	0.1	0.5
Standard 5	0.5	0	0.5
	Amount of 0.1 mg/mL Excedrin (mL)		
Unknown	0.5	0	0.5

Questions: Q10.   What is the importance of preparing a "blank"?

Q11.   Calculate the concentrations of hydrolyzed aspirin in the solutions above in mg/L. Be sure to show at least one sample calculation.

Note: For dilute aqueous solutions, mg/L is equivalent to "ppm" (parts per million).

Section E.   Spectrophotometric Determination of Aspirin (Can be done in Pairs)

Experimental Steps: 1.   Set the wavelength on the Spec 20 to 520 nm.

Questions: Q12.   (a) What is the color of the salicylate dianion iron (III) complex?

(b) What is the color of 520 nm light?

(c) Does the use of 520 nm light make sense in light of the color of the salicylate dianion iron (III) complex? Explain. (Hint: Refer to the background reading of Experiment 3.)

Q13.   Which of the standard solutions most closely matches the color of the unknown solution? (**Hint:** Look at the wells in your 24-well tray where you prepared each solution.)

2.   Make sure there is nothing in the sample compartment of the spectrophotometer. With no sample in the sample compartment and the lid shut, adjust the "zero control" knob (left knob) to read 0% T. (When there is no cuvette in the instrument, a shutter closes, and therefore no light should be reaching the detector.) Wipe and clean the outside of the cuvette containing the blank with a microwipe and place it in the black plastic cuvette holder. Then place the entire assembly into the sample compartment. The fully exposed side of the cuvette should face to the right. Shut the lid. Adjust the "light control" knob (the knob on the right) until the indicator reading is 100% T (Absorbance = 0). What you have just done is calibrate the instrument to show infinite absorbance when the beam is blocked, and zero absorbance for the blank.

At this point, you should switch back and forth between no sample (with the lid closed) and the blank sample and verify that the needle moves reproducibly between 0% T and 100% T. If it does not, please check with your TA.

Q14.   What is the role of each of the three knobs on the Spectronic 20?

3.   Next, remove the blank from the sample compartment and replace it with the cuvette containing standard #1. Measure the absorbance to 3 significant figures using the best estimate for the final place. Record this in your notebook. Repeat with standard #2 through standard #5.

Your spectrophotometer scale can also be read in "% transmittance", and sometimes this scale is easier to read. If your measurements are recorded in % Transmittance (%T), then this must be converted to Absorbance (A) for your graph. A = −log (%T/100).

Q15.   What trend do you observe in the absorption vs. concentration results of your standard solutions?

Q16.   What is the absorption law that governs this phenomenon? Explain.

Q17.   Plot a graph of absorbance versus concentration (mg/L) for the various aspirin standards *on the sheet of graph paper provided*. Do this plot in pencil. This plot is your "standard calibration curve." (Note: Each person should make his or her own graph.) Show your finished calibration curve to your TA before continuing. Attach this plot to your answer sheet.

4.   Now measure the absorbance value for your unknown aspirin sample. From the absorbance values of the unknown solution, determine its concentration by interpolation from the standard calibration curve.

Q18.   Indicate on the calibration graph the interpolation used to determine the concentration of hydrolyzed aspirin in your hydrolyzed Excedrin solution. Record the concentration you calculated based on the equation for your best-fit line on your answer sheet.

Q19.   What is the percentage of aspirin in Excedrin? (Hint: The percent aspirin in the unknown can be determined by comparing the concentration of the unknown to the result from standard #5.)

Q20.   Does this agree with the amount of aspirin in Excedrin according to the label on the bottle? Remember to use the amount of aspirin listed on label and divide by the total weight of the tablet (~ 675 mg).

13

Kinetic Blues

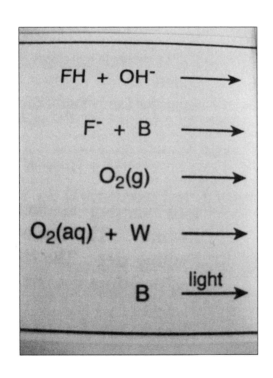

"Equilibrium is when all of the fast things have happened and all of the slow things have not."

—Quote attributed to Richard Feynman

Introduction

There are two fundamentally different ways of studying chemical reactions: thermodynamics and kinetics. The *thermodynamic* approach is static and involves the study of the initial and final states of a chemical system. Thermodynamics tells us nothing about the dynamics of a chemical reaction. One of the most useful things to know about a chemical reaction is the rate at which products are formed from reactants. Chemical *kinetics* is the study of the various factors that control the rates of reactions and the study of mechanisms by which reactants become products. The speeds of chemical reactions can vary tremendously, from extremely fast—e.g., in explosions and acid–base reactions—to very slow, which is seen in the geochemical weathering of rocks. These very fast or very slow reactions are difficult to study experimentally. However, even these extreme kinetics are beginning to yield to sophisticated techniques. Great progress has been made in many scientific fields—e.g., molecular biology, medicine, and atmospheric chemistry—due to a knowledge of the fundamental reaction dynamics.

The *rate* of a chemical reaction tells us how the concentration of a reactant or product changes over time. Kinetic studies of a chemical reaction almost always start with experimental measurements made in the laboratory. Various hypotheses are then proposed in an attempt to explain the experimental data. This approach clearly shows that the rate of a chemical reaction generally depends on the following factors:

- The temperature of the system

- The concentrations of the various chemical species present in the system

- The presence of catalysts

- The rate at which reactants can mix or diffuse together

Usually, the experimental investigations are designed to produce quantitative information about all of the above factors. This information can be used to predict how the rate of the reaction will change when the reaction conditions are varied. Kinetic data are also of great interest because it provides the most general and powerful method of determining the mechanism of a reaction. A *mechanism* is defined as all of the actual elementary steps involving molecules

that take place simultaneously or consecutively and that added together give the observed, overall reaction.

Generally, it is extremely difficult to identify the exact mechanism of a chemical reaction. Often, the two major sources of difficulty are the extraordinarily fast rate of many elementary steps and the problem of identifying transient chemical species. The most useful approach to identifying a mechanism is to invent plausible schemes that seem to be consistent with the kinetic data. These schemes can then be tested in more sophisticated experiments that are specifically designed to probe for certain steps or individual species. It must always be kept in mind that the suggested schemes are merely that—suggestions!

The application of the principles of kinetic analysis is best discussed by studying a well-known reaction. Consider the reaction between nitric oxide (NO) and dioxygen (O_2) to produce brown nitrogen dioxide (NO_2):

$$2NO(g) + O_2(g) \rightarrow 2NO_2(g)$$

Known concentrations of the two reactants NO and O_2 are pumped into a thermostatted reaction container kept at a known temperature. The rate of the reaction is determined either by measuring the decrease in the concentration of NO or O_2 or by measuring the increase in concentration of the product NO_2 over time.

A convenient way of studying the effect of concentration on reaction rate is to determine the initial rate (at the start of the reaction) as a function of the initial concentration of one reagent while keeping the concentration of all other reactants constant. The results from a series of experiments carried out in this way, at some known constant temperature, are expressed in the form of a *rate law*. The rate law for the above reaction is experimentally found to be

$$\text{Rate} = k\,[NO]^2[O_2]$$

where the proportionality constant k is called the *rate constant*. The experimentally determined exponents for the concentration of each species— i.e., 2 for [NO] and 1 for [O_2]—describe the *order* of the reaction for that reactant. The reaction is said to be second order in NO, first order in O_2, and is third order overall. It is important to emphasize that these experimentally determined orders have nothing to do with the stoichiometry of the balanced equation for the reaction. The fact that this reaction is second order in NO and first order in O_2 and that these orders are the same numbers as the coefficients in the reaction is entirely fortuitous! The fact that the reaction is second order in NO simply means that a doubling of the NO concentration will result in a four-fold increase in the reaction rate, provided that the O_2 concentration and the temperature are kept constant. Once the rate law is known and the rate constant k has been measured (at a particular temperature), then the rate of reaction for any concentration of reactants can be calculated.

The rates of most simple chemical reactions increase as the temperature rises. This rate change occurs because an increase in temperature increases the fraction of molecules having high kinetic energies, and these very energetic molecules are the ones most likely to react upon collision. The expression that relates the dependence of the rate constant of a reaction on temperature was first introduced by Arrhenius (a Swedish chemist) and is called the *Arrhenius equation*:

$$k = Ae^{-\frac{E_a}{RT}}$$

where E_a is the activation energy of the reaction (in kJ mol^{-1}), R is the gas constant (8.31 $JK^{-1}mol^{-1}$), T is the absolute temperature (K), e is the base in natural logarithms, and A is the frequency factor. The Arrhenius equation can be expressed in a more convenient form by taking the natural logarithm of both sides,

$$\ln k = \ln A - \frac{E_a}{RT}$$

and converting to base 10 logarithms:

$$2.3\log_{10}k = 2.3\log_{10}A - \frac{E_a}{RT}$$

and dividing by 2.30 gives:

$$\log_{10}K = \log_{10}A - \frac{E_a}{2.30RT}$$

The activation energy E_a is the minimum amount of energy required for the reaction to occur. Molecules that do not acquire this energy will not react. The potential energy profile of a reaction shows that the activation energy represents an energy barrier that must be overcome in order for products to be formed. Potential energy profiles for exothermic and endothermic reactions are shown in Figure 13.1.

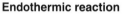

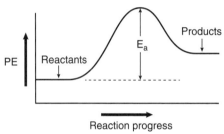

Figure 13.1 Potential energy profiles for exothermic and endothermic reactions.

The activation energy for a reaction can be determined experimentally by carrying out the reaction at different temperatures and by measuring the rate constant at each temperature. A plot of $\log_{10} k$ versus $1/T$ has a slope of $-E_a/2.30R$; hence, E_a can be calculated.

Different types of chemical reactions have dramatically different activation energies, depending on the stability of the reactant molecules. The gas phase reaction

$$2NO(g) + O_2(g) \rightarrow 2NO_2(g)$$

discussed earlier, is very interesting and rather atypical. This reaction *slows down* as the temperature increases! Application of the Arrhenius equation to this reaction would give the strange result of a negative value for the activation energy. The reasons for this apparent anomaly have been much debated, and the consensus is that the mechanism for this reaction involves an elementary step that is very sensitive to temperature increases.

The determination of the rate law and the temperature dependence of a chemical reaction represents the starting point for possible mechanistic interpretations of the reaction. The overall third-order kinetics for the reaction

$$2NO(g) + O_2(g) \rightarrow 2NO_2(g)$$

originally led scientists to speculate that this reaction involved the simultaneous collision of two NO molecules and one O_2 molecule, i.e., a termolecular collision. Termolecular collisions are statistically rare, and this fact did not seem to be consistent with the large value for the rate constant. A much more plausible mechanism is the suggestion that the formation of NO_2 occurs by a two-step process, the first of which involves the fast dimerization of NO,

$$2NO(g) \rightleftarrows N_2O_2(g) \text{ dimerization}$$

followed by a slower reaction between the dimer and O_2:

$$N_2O_2(g) + O_2(g) \rightarrow 2NO_2(g)$$

The slowest reaction in any sequence of reactions determines the rate of the overall reaction and is called the *rate-determining step*. The rate of the slow second reaction is

$$\text{Rate } NO_2 \text{ formation} = k[O_2][N_2O_2]$$

Now, for the fast equilibrium reaction, the equilibrium constant K_{eq} is

$$K_{eq} = \frac{[N_2O_2]}{[NO]^2}$$

and, rearranging,

$$[N_2O_2] = K_{eq}[NO]^2$$

Substituting $[N_2O_2]$ back into the rate law for NO_2 formation results in

$$\text{Rate } NO_2 \text{ formation} = k \, K_{eq} \, [NO]^2[O_2]$$

This last rate law is identical with the experimentally determined rate law, giving support for the suggested two-step mechanism. Further evidence for the two-step mechanism is the unusual temperature dependence reported earlier. The interpretation of the slowdown of the overall reaction with increasing temperature is that the dimer N_2O_2 is unstable at higher temperatures. Another way of saying this is that the equilibrium constant K_{eq} for the dimerization reaction decreases with increasing temperature.

It is important to emphasize that a proposed mechanism is simply a reasonable model that is apparently consistent with the experimental kinetic data. Often, several plausible mechanistic routes for a reaction are possible, and the determination of the "true" mechanism then requires many more experimental investigations.

Background Chemistry

The goal in this series of experiments is to investigate the chemical kinetics of "The System" reactions. One of the most interesting aspects of the chemistry of "The System" is that the chemical kinetics have never been quantitatively studied, in spite of the fact that the phenomenon has been known for a long time.

The blue dye used in "The System" is called methylene blue, and it has the following structure:

$C_{16}H_{18}N_3SCl \cdot 3H_2O$

338.88 g mol^{-1}

(The correct chemical name is a real mouthful: phenothiazin-5-ium, 3, 7-bisdimethylamino chloride trihydrate.) Methylene blue was first synthesized by Caro in 1876 and was used as a fabric dye because of its beautiful deep blue color. By 1890 the dye was found to be an invaluable biological staining reagent, as well as a very useful indicator of biochemical reduction. The action of alkaline glucose solutions on methylene blue was also discovered in about 1890 and was successfully used as a method of sugar analysis. The use of methylene blue as a catalyst in the oxidation of sugars by air was first recorded by H. A. Spoehr in a research paper in the *Journal of the American Chemical Society* in 1924. Spoehr reported that methylene blue is reduced by alkaline glucose solutions and that when air is drawn through such a colorless solution, the blue color again appears, and carbon dioxide is formed. He abandoned the study of methylene blue as a catalyst because he thought he had discovered a much better catalyst, sodium ferro-pyrophosphate.

The general redox properties of methylene blue also appear to be involved in many other very useful applications of the dye. Methylene blue was one of the first anthelmintics (worming agent) and was one of the first reported antimalarial drugs. Modified derivatives of the dye form a very large class of animal tranquilizers, e.g., chlorpromazine. Methylene blue is still used in the treatment of nitrate intoxication of cattle. Hundreds of other uses for this remarkable dye have appeared in the research literature over the past 50 years. One of the most interesting applications of

"The System" reactions is reported in some recent Japanese patents. Various chemical formulations of methylene blue and reducing agents, e.g., glucose, are being used as oxygen color indicators for packaged foods. These formulations (in the colorless form) are coated or printed onto plastic packaging materials used as containers for foods that are packed under vacuum or under nitrogen. The formulation turns blue if oxygen leaks into the package.

The sugar used in "The System" solution is fructose, commonly known as fruit sugar. Fructose has the structure

$C_6H_{12}O_6$

180.2 g mol^{-1}

and occurs in a large number of fruits and honey and as the sole sugar in bull and human semen. Fructose is extremely soluble in water and, in fact, is rather difficult to obtain in the pure anhydrous crystalline form. As soon as solid fructose is dissolved in water, the molecule undergoes various rearrangements, e.g., mutarotation and enolization. In alkaline solution, such as in "The System" solution, the changes are very complicated and not very well understood. The simplest approach is to assume that an acid–base reaction can occur between sodium hydroxide and fructose, giving rise to an anion of some type. The anion is then capable of acting as a reducing agent towards the methylene blue dye. It is interesting to note that all the reducing sugars—e.g., glucose, mannose, lactose, etc.—appear to work in a similar manner in "The System," although there are definite differences in the various rates of reactions.

"The System" offers a fascinating, novel series of reactions for the study of chemical kinetics and for the interpretation of mechanistic routes for reactions. In the field of chemical kinetics, it is the experimental facts that form the entire basis for the mechanistic possibilities. In this series of experiments, there are many opportunities for individual contributions and suggestions, and there are many new interpretations to be discovered. Please don't hesitate to discuss with your instructor any ideas and new possibilities you think of during the laboratory.

Additional Reading

1. Campbell, J.A., "Kinetics—Early and Often," *J. Chem. Ed.* 40, 1963, p. 578. An excellent discussion of the catalytic oxidation of glucose in alkaline solution.

2. Spoehr, H.A., "The Oxidation of Carbohydrates with Air," *J. Am. Chem. Soc.* 46, 1924, p. 1494. This is the original reference in which the methylene blue oxidation of sugars is described.

3. Clark, W.M., Cohen, B., Gibbs, H.D., "Studies on Oxidation–Reduction, VIII. Methylene Blue," *Public Health Reports* 40, 1925, p. 1131.

Quiz Outline

Your quiz will NOT cover all of the information below, but it will cover some subset of the information given below.

Be able to list the four major factors that determine the rate of a reaction.

Be able to explain how the energy of activation for a reaction is determined.

Be able to explain how the rate law for a reaction is determined.

Be able to determine the order of reaction for a rate law, e.g., for the reaction $2A + B \rightarrow 3C$, the rate law is rate = $[A][B]^2$. What is the overall order of the reaction? What is the order with respect to the individual reactants?

Be able to determine what will happen to the rate if the concentrations are changed, e.g., for the reaction $2A + B \rightarrow 3C$, the rate law is rate = $[A][B]^2$. What will happen to the rate if the concentration of A is kept the same and the concentration of B is tripled?

Be able to define the mechanism of a reaction and the term "rate-determining step."

Be able to list a practical use of methylene blue.

Be able to draw potential energy diagrams for a fast endothermic reaction and a slow exothermic reaction.

Sample Pre-Laboratory Quiz

1. What are the major factors that determine the rate of a chemical reaction?

2. For the reaction $2A + B \rightarrow C$, the rate law is rate = $k[A]^1[B]^1$. What is the overall order of the reaction?

3. In the above reaction, what will happen to the rate if the concentration of A is kept the same and the concentration of B is tripled?

4. How is the energy of activation for a reaction determined?

5. Give a definition for the rate–determining step.

6. Draw two potential energy profiles—one representing a fast, endothermic reaction, and the other representing a slow, exothermic reaction.

Laboratory Experiments

Flowchart of the Experiments

Section A.	**Experimental Evidence: An Overview of "The System"**

Section B.	**A Possible Reaction Mechanism, the Rate-Determining Step, and the Rate Law for the Overall Reaction for "The System"**

Section C.	**Determination of the Order of Reaction for Fructose and Hydroxide Ion**

Section D.	**Determination of the Energy of Activation**

Requires one four-hour class period to complete.

NOTE: Set out a cup of water so that it can come to room temperature. You will need this in Section C.

Section A.   Experimental Evidence: An Overview of "The System"

Goals: (1) To assemble "The System" by mixing fructose, sodium hydroxide, and methylene blue solutions. (2) To carry out experimental investigations on "The System" that could lead to the formulation of a reasonable reaction mechanism for the oxidation of fructose by methylene blue.

Discussion: The reagents for this sequence of experiments are 0.2 M fructose, 0.5 M sodium hydroxide (NaOH), and 0.02 wt % methylene blue (MB) in 50% by volume ethanol/ water. Record the actual concentrations from the bottles. You will find these reagents at the arm's reach stations. Fill cells in your 24-well plate with these solutions, then use large-drop pipets to deliver drops. Assume that the drop volume is approximately the same. It is important, however, to use a consistent delivery technique throughout. You will need a watch or clock with the capability of timing events in seconds. View the solutions against a white background.

Experimental Steps: 1.   Clean an 8 mL pop-cap vial. This is best done by using a large-drop pipet filled with distilled water. Suck up any waste liquid and expel to a waste cup.

2.   Deliver 5 drops 0.2 M fructose, 5 drops 0.5 M NaOH, and 3 drops methylene blue (MB) to the vial. Stir with a microstirrer.

   •   Watch carefully and time from the stirring until something happens. Use your hand lens.

   •   Describe what you see in your lab manual.

3.   Place the cap onto the vial. Give the vial one sharp shake.

   •   How long does it take for the solution to become colored?

   •   How long does it take for the solution to lose its color?

   •   What do you see at the interface between the solution and the air?

4.   Give the vial several sharp shakes.

   •   Does the solution become more intensely colored the more you shake it?

5.   Investigate the effect of heat and cold on the reactions. To do this, prepare a cold (perhaps an ice bath) and a warm (about 40–50 °C) water bath.

6.   If "The System" shows signs of deterioration, clean the vial and prepare another solution (as in Step 2).

7.   Shake the vial vigorously and while the solution is blue, place it in the intense light from an overhead projector (or in bright sunshine).

   •   Describe what happens.

   •   Will the system still cycle?

Section B.	A Possible Reaction Mechanism, the Rate-Determining Step, and the Rate Law for the Overall Reaction for "The System"

Goals:
(1) To examine a possible reaction mechanism for the oxidation of fructose by methylene blue. (2) To be able to choose the rate-determining step in the proposed mechanism and determine the rate law for the overall reaction.

Discussion:
A review of the evidence from the last section indicates that there are five fundamental processes occurring in "The System."

1. Initially, the fructose reacts with sodium hydroxide to produce some unknown anion. This reaction can be regarded as an acid–base reaction between the weak acid fructose and the strong base sodium hydroxide.

2. The unknown anion reacts with blue methylene blue to produce colorless methylene white and some unknown colorless products.

3. Vigorous shaking of "The System" results in air mixing with, and dissolving in, the colorless solution.

4. Dissolved gas, probably dioxygen (O_2) from air, oxidizes methylene white back to methylene blue. The solution may then cycle through the deblueing process, over and over again, provided that fructose, base, and dissolved dioxygen are present in "The System."

5. Intense light, in the presence of base, changes blue methylene blue into some other, much redder substance.

   The processes described above can be incorporated into a more concise reaction scheme by giving symbols to the various ingredients and by writing reasonable chemical reactions for each process. Let

   • FH = fructose

   • F^- = an anion formed by the reaction of base with fructose

   • OH^- = sodium hydroxide, a strong base

   • B = the blue form of methylene blue

   • W = the colorless form called methylene white

   • $O_2(g)$ = gaseous dioxygen in air

   • $O_2(aq)$ = dioxygen dissolved in the solution

   • P = product(s) formed in the overall scheme

   • R = reddish-purple substance formed by the action of intense light on methylene blue

The following scheme is a possible reaction mechanism for "The System." At this point, it is important to note that the scheme does not include any kinetic information.

$$FH + OH^- \longrightarrow F^- + H_2O$$

$$F^- + B \longrightarrow W + P$$

$$O_2(g) \longrightarrow O_2(aq)$$

$$O_2(aq) + W \longrightarrow B$$

$$B \xrightarrow{\text{light}} R$$

Overall reaction: $FH + OH^- + O_2(g) \longrightarrow P + H_2O$

The overall reaction, the oxidation of fructose by atmospheric oxygen catalyzed by methylene blue in aqueous alkaline solution, was obtained by adding up all the reactions in the mechanism, canceling species common to both sides.

The next step is to consider the relative rates of these reactions to determine which is the slowest, and therefore rate-determining step in the mechanism. Consider the kinetic information obtained thus far from observation of "The System":

The last reaction in the mechanism,

$$B \xrightarrow{\text{light}} R$$

which involves the photochemical destruction of the blue species, is apparently far too slow in ordinary room light to have any effect on the overall reaction. Therefore, it was left out of the overall reaction.

The initial reaction in the mechanism, a typically fast acid–base reaction, requires some time to come to equilibrium.

$$FH + OH^- \rightleftharpoons F^- + H_2O$$

Once the sequence is allowed to set up, then the initial time period does not matter. Consequently, this reaction is not the limiting step in the overall reaction.

There are three remaining reactions to consider in choosing the rate-determining step. From your experimentation in Section A, you probably observed that upon shaking, "The System" turned blue fairly quickly. So, the dissolving of oxygen in water,

$$O_2(g) \rightarrow O_2(aq)$$

and the reaction to form the blue form of methylene blue

$$O_2(aq) + W \rightarrow B$$

must be fairly rapid reactions. However, the deblueing process,

$$F^- + B \rightarrow W + P$$

took varying amounts of time, depending on the temperature of "The System." The deblueing reaction must be the slowest, and therefore rate–limiting step. The rate limiting step determines the overall rate of reaction, and therefore the rate law for the overall reaction.

The rate law for the deblueing reaction is

$$\text{rate} = \frac{-d[B]}{dt} = k[B][F^-]$$

where k is the rate constant for the deblueing reaction and [B], [F⁻] are the molar concentrations of B and F⁻, respectively.

Since F⁻ is part of an equilibrium reaction,

$$FH + OH^- \rightleftharpoons F^- + H_2O$$

for which we can write an equilibrium constant:

$$K_{eq} = \frac{[F^-]}{[FH][OH^-]}$$

Thus

$$[F^-] = K_{eq}[FH][OH^-]$$

And substituting for [F⁻] in the above rate law,

$$\text{Rate} = \frac{-d[B]}{dt} = kK_{eq}[B][FH][OH^-]$$

Then combining the constants k and K_{eq}, the final rate law for the rate-determining step and, therefore, the overall reaction is

$$\text{Rate} = \frac{-d[B]}{dt} = k_f[B][FH][OH^-]$$

The interesting conclusion is that the rate is first order in methylene blue, fructose, and hydroxide ion and zero order in oxygen.

Question: Q1.   (a) What is a catalyst?

(b) One defining feature of a catalyst is that it is consumed in one step of a reaction mechanism, but is produced in another so that it does not appear in the overall reaction. Based on the mechanism given on page 13-12, cite one substance that could be a catalyst.

Section C.   Determination of the Order of Reaction for Fructose and Hydroxide Ion

---

Goal:

To determine the order of reaction for fructose and for hydroxide ion in the rate-determining step of the catalytic oxidation of fructose by atmospheric oxygen.

Experimental Steps:

1. Make sure that the large-drop pipets are filled with the appropriate reagents.

   NOTE: You will need 0.5 M NaOH, 0.2 M fructose (use concentrations from bottles in calculations), and 0.02 wt % MB solutions.

2. Fill a Styrofoam cup almost to the top with water that is equilibrated at room temperature.

   NOTE: Do not adjust the temperature of the water bath once you begin the experiment. To study the effects of concentration on rate, the temperature must be constant.

3. Using large-drop pipets, prepare a solution by delivering 10 drops of 0.5 M NaOH, 10 drops of 0.2 M fructose, and 5 drops MB to a clean, dry 8 mL pop-cap vial. Shake the vial, then float it on its side in the Styrofoam cup. Wait until the solution deblues and comes to thermal equilibrium with the water in the cup.

   NOTE: Make sure that you have a watch ready.

4. Once the solution has reached equilibrium, pluck the vial from the water and shake it vigorously until the solution reaches a steady-state blue color. Place the vial back on its side in the cup and begin timing.

   - Record the deblueing time in the table in step 8.

   - Monitor the temperature of the water and be careful to maintain a constant temperature.

   NOTE: As you observed in Section A, there is often a faint blue color at the interface between the air and water. Consequently, your solution may not appear entirely colorless even after "deblueing" has occurred. Just be careful to time to the same shade of faint blue at the interface in every trial.

5. Repeat step 4 two more times (for a total of three trials on this solution).

6. Empty the vial, rinse it with distilled water, and shake it dry.

7. Repeat steps 3 through 6, this time using a mixed solution containing 5 drops 0.2 M fructose, 5 drops distilled water, 10 drops 0.5 M NaOH, and 5 drops MB solution.

8. Repeat steps 3 through 6, this time using a mixed solution containing 10 drops 0.2 M fructose, 5 drops distilled water, 5 drops 0.5 M NaOH, and 5 drops MB solution.

Exp. #	Mixed Solution	[Fructose]	[OH⁻]	Deblueing Time (sec)			Average Time (sec)	Rate of deblueing (1/sec)
				run 1	run 2	run 3		
1	Step 3							
2	Step 7							
3	Step 8							

Using the data in the table, consider how to calculate the order of reaction with respect to fructose:

The concentration of fructose and OH⁻ (in mol L⁻¹) is easily calculated from the dilution. (Remember, the total volume is 25 drops in each instance.) Rate is inversely proportional to time. If the deblueing reaction took 55 seconds, then the rate = 1/55 = 0.018 s⁻¹.

The rate law for the deblueing reaction is

$$\text{Rate of deblueing} = k_f \times [\text{fructose}]^a \times [B]^b \times [OH^-]^c$$

where a, b, and c are the experimental orders of reaction with respect to fructose, methylene blue, and hydroxide. What we wish to do is find a, b, and c from the experimental rate and concentration data in the above table. The rate of deblueing in Experiment 1 is

$$\text{Rate 1} = k_f \times [\text{fructose}]_1^a \times [B]^b \times [OH^-]_1^c$$

The rate of deblueing in Experiment 2 is

$$\text{Rate 2} = k_f \times [\text{fructose}]_2^a \times [B]^b \times [OH^-]_2^c$$

Dividing the rates,

$$\frac{\text{Rate 1}}{\text{Rate 2}} = \frac{K_f}{K_f} \times \frac{[\text{fructose}]_1^a}{[\text{fructose}]_2^a} \times \frac{[B]^b}{[B]^b} \times \frac{[OH^-]_1^c}{[OH^-]_2^c}$$

and since in all three experiments the

$$\frac{\text{Rate 1}}{\text{Rate 2}} = \frac{[\text{fructose}]_1}{[\text{fructose}]_2}$$

and putting in the values for rate 1, rate 2, [fructose]₁, and [fructose]₂, the order of reaction with respect to fructose, "a", can be obtained.

$$\frac{\text{Rate 1}}{\text{Rate 2}} = \left(\frac{[\text{fructose}]_1}{[\text{fructose}]_2}\right)^a$$

Questions: Q2.   Calculate the order of reaction for fructose using the data from experiments 1 and 2 (from the table in step 8). Report your answer to the correct number of significant figures.

Q3.   Calculate the order of reaction for OH⁻ using the data from experiments 1 and 3 (from the table in step 8). Report your answer to the correct number of significant figures.

Q4.   Compare the experimentally obtained orders of reaction with those deduced for the proposed mechanism (see Section B). Name three experimental sources of error that can contribute to differences between your experimentally obtained orders and the postulated orders of reaction.

Section D.   Determination of the Energy of Activation

Goal: *To quantitatively examine the effect of temperature on the rate of the deblueing reaction.*

Discussion: The temperature dependence data can be used to plot an Arrhenius graph from which the energy of activation for the catalytic oxidation of fructose can be calculated.

Experimental Steps: 1.   Construct a constant temperature reaction apparatus from a Styrofoam cup and a temperature sensor as shown below.

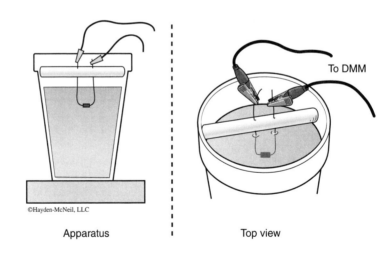

©Hayden-McNeil, LLC

Apparatus   Top view

2.   Prepare a table of data as follows:

Si Temp. Sensor (Ω)	Bath Temp (°C)	Bath Temp (K)	$\frac{1}{T}$ (K^{-1})	Deblueing Time (sec)		Average Time (sec)	Rate (1/sec)	Log$_{10}$ Rate
				Run 1	Run 2			

3.   Fill the Styrofoam cup almost full with warm water (at a temperature of about 30 °C).

4.   Make sure that the temperature measurement system (sensor and DMM or thermometer) is working and that the sensor is actually in the water.

NOTE: See Experiment 5 for the details of temperature measurement using sensor and DMM.

5.   Fill another cup with ice.

NOTE: You will be using the ice to change the temperature of the water in the constant-temperature bath.

6.   In a clean, dry 8 mL pop-cap vial, prepare a solution containing 10 drops 0.2 M fructose, 10 drops 0.5 M NaOH, and 5 drops MB solution.

7.   Shake the vial, then float it on its side in the Styrofoam cup. Wait a few minutes until the solution deblues and comes to thermal equilibrium with the water in the cup.

NOTE: Make sure that you have a watch ready.

8.   Once the solution has reached equilibrium, pluck the vial from the water and shake it vigorously until the solution reaches a steady-state blue color. Place the vial back on its side in the cup and begin timing the deblueing reaction.

• Record the time in the table in step 2.

9.   Repeat the measurement (step 8).

• Record the temperature of the bath as well as the deblueing time for the duplicate measurement.

NOTE: Timing the deblueing reaction in the above experiment may have been difficult because the reaction was so fast.

10.   Cool the water in the bath about 5 °C (for the Si temperature sensor 10Ω/1 °C) by adding ice and stirring with a straw. When the solution in the vial has come to thermal equilibrium with the water in the cup, repeat the duplicate measurements of deblueing time at this new temperature.

• Record the two deblueing times and the temperature.

11.   Continue by successively cooling the bath another 5 °C and repeating duplicate measurements at new temperatures until you reach a bath temperature of about 10 °C.

NOTE: At this low temperature the reaction may take a very long time.

Questions: Q5.   Plot a graph of $\log_{10}$ rate (vertical axis) versus $1/T$ (K^{-1}) (horizontal axis). The graph will be in the fourth quadrant. Draw the best straight line through the points. Then draw another line that goes reasonably well through the data points, but which has a somewhat steeper slope than what the best fit would have. Finally, draw a third line that has a reasonable fit, but would have a shallower slope than the best-fit line. In this way, you are doing a max/best estimate/min analysis of your data.

Q6.   Determine the slope of the line (with units!). Note: The slope is negative.

Q7.   Use the three slopes to calculate three energy of activation values (with units!) for the deblueing reaction. Calculate the uncertainty of E_a, where uncertainty is (maximum–minimum)/2. Report your best estimate E_a with the uncertainty and the correct number of significant figures.

$$\text{slope} = -\frac{E_a}{2.303 \times R}$$

where E_a = energy of activation (in joules/mole)

and R = the gas constant, 8.314 $JK^{-1}\,mol^{-1}$

The 2.303 factor comes from the conversion of natural logarithms to logarithms of base 10. (See the Background Chemistry section.)

To put your value for the activation energy into perspective, generally any process that has an activation energy greater than 21 kJ/mol involves bond breaking and is probably chemical in nature. There are some naturally occurring processes that surprisingly exhibit an exponential increase in rate with temperature. Two examples of such processes are the chirping of crickets and the flashing of fireflies, both of which have activation energies of around 51 kJ/mol. The chemical nature of these processes are not well understood.

Q8.   Draw a potential energy profile for this reaction (see Figure 13.1) using your experimentally determined E_a, and assuming that $\Delta E_{RXN} = -40$ kJ per mole of reaction.

14

Experiment 14

Acid–Base Equilibria

"How inappropriate to call this planet Earth, when clearly it is Ocean."

—Arthur C. Clarke

Introduction

Life on Earth flourishes in a water environment in which the acidity is maintained within a very narrow range by dynamic acid–base reactions. A variety of interrelated reactions bind and release hydrogen ions and, in the process, keep the pH not too far from seven. The pH of natural fluids is a useful index of the status of equilibrium reactions in which water participates. The reaction of dissolved carbon dioxide with water is one of the most important processes that release hydrogen ions:

$$CO_2(g) \rightleftarrows CO_2(aq)$$

$$CO_2(aq) + H_2O \rightleftarrows H_2CO_3$$

$$H_2CO_3 \rightleftarrows H^+ + HCO_3^-$$

$$HCO_3^- \rightleftarrows H^+ + CO_3^{2-}$$

Pure water in contact with air having an average CO_2 content has a pH that stays about 5.65. In man, the hydrogen ion concentration in blood is maintained very close to 4×10^{-8} M (pH 7.4), which is a requirement for the optimal performance of many enzyme systems. The ability of natural systems to maintain hydrogen ion concentrations at precise low levels is a direct consequence of the "feedback" properties of acid–base equilibria. These equilibria are dynamic, reversible, and fast. Any challenge to the natural system by abnormal or unusual changes is immediately detected and effectively neutralized.

The effect of an outside influence on a system at equilibrium may be predicted by means of *Le Châtelier's principle*, which states that if an equilibrium is upset, the system responds in a direction that will reestablish equilibrium. It is important to emphasize that the principle holds even in very complicated natural systems in which there are many connected chemical and biological equilibria. Equilibria are *connected* if a component of one reaction (either reactant or product) also takes part in another reaction. A good example is the carbon dioxide–water system introduced earlier. An increase in the atmospheric carbon dioxide concentration ($CO_2(g)$) will lead to an increase in dissolved carbon dioxide ($CO_2(aq)$), which will increase the carbonic acid (H_2CO_3) concentration and will eventually lead to increased acidity (H^+ concentration). Similarly, any reaction that results in the removal of carbonate (CO_3^{2-}) or bicarbonate (HCO_3^-) will have a ripple effect in the system and lead to increased acidity and an increased dissolution of gaseous carbon dioxide. Homeostasis (i.e., maintenance), which occurs as a result of Le Châtelier's principle, is often called *buffering action*. In chemistry, acid–base systems with these maintenance properties are called *buffer systems*.

Earth is the water planet. Water is the key to all maintenance of life. It is the liquid that mediates all terrestrial exchanges of hydrogen ions between acids and bases. Water, therefore, provides the reference point for all measures of acidity and alkalinity. In this series of laboratory experiments, you have the opportunity to investigate most of the important aspects of acid–base equilibria, including Le Châtelier's principle, strengths of acids and bases, and buffering action.

Background Chemistry

Many theories have been developed to interpret the nature of acids and bases. One of the simplest and most useful is the Brønsted-Lowry theory. In this theory, an acid is defined as a proton (H^+) donor and a base is defined as a proton acceptor. Let us consider the nature of water as a solvent. In liquid water, the water molecules collide billions of times per second, and a few of these collisions are powerful enough to break covalent bonds. A reaction occurs that may be written as

$$H_2O + H_2O \rightleftharpoons H_3O^+ + OH^-$$

in which the products are hydronium ions (H_3O^+) and hydroxide ions (OH^-). The double arrow $\rightleftharpoons$ is used to show that the reaction is dynamic and reversible. Water molecules are continuously breaking up, and hydronium ions and hydroxide ions are continuously combining to produce water molecules. The rate of the forward reaction

$$H_2O + H_2O \rightarrow H_3O^+ + OH^-$$

is equal to the rate of the reverse reaction

$$H_2O + H_2O \leftarrow H_3O^+ + OH^-$$

and, therefore, the concentration of the reactants and products does not change with time. The water system is said to be at *equilibrium*.

It is interesting to note that in the above equilibrium reaction, water is acting both as an acid (proton donor) and as a base (proton acceptor). In *pure* water, the self-dissociation produces (at 25 °C) equal concentrations of H_3O^+ and OH^-, which are 10^{-7} M. The law of mass action can be applied to any reaction at equilibrium, and when applied to the self-dissociation of water, gives

$$K_c = \frac{[H_3O^+][OH^-]}{[H_2O]^2}$$

where K_c is called the equilibrium constant for the reaction. Now the molar concentration of H_2O in water is 55.6 M and can be regarded as constant. We can simplify the above expression to

$$K_w = [H_3O^+][OH^-]$$

where K_w is called the *ion-product* constant of water. Since at 25 °C,

$$[H_3O^+] = [OH^-] = 10^{-7} M$$

Then

$$K_w = 10^{-7} \times 10^{-7} = 10^{-14}$$

Of course, all equilibrium constants are temperature dependent. The value for K_w at 25 °C, i.e., 1.00×10^{-14}, is used throughout this laboratory module. It is convenient to use logarithmic scales for the expression of $[H^+]$ and often for equilibrium constants:

$$pH = -\log_{10}[H^+]$$

$$pK = -\log_{10}K$$

and generally,

$$pX = -\log_{10}X$$

Thus, the pH of pure water at 25 °C is 7.00, and the pK_w for water at 25 °C is 14.00.

We can now consider what happens when an acid, e.g., acetic acid (CH_3COOH), is added to water. Since CH_3COOH is an acid, protons are donated by CH_3COOH and are accepted by the solvent water, which acts as a base:

$$CH_3COOH + H_2O \rightleftharpoons CH_3COO^- + H_3O^+$$

The equilibrium constant for this reaction is called an acid dissociation constant K_a, and applying the law of mass action,

$$K_a = \frac{[CH_3COO^-][H_3O^+]}{[CH_3COOH]}$$

The value of K_a is 1.75×10^{-5} at 25 °C. This very small value means that the equilibrium lies very much to the left. Very few molecules of CH_3COOH dissociate to give CH_3COO^- (acetate ion) and H_3O^+. Acids that have K_a values smaller than 10^{-2} are said to be *weak acids*. Acids with K_a values greater than 10^{-2} (usually $\gg 10^{-2}$) are said to be *strong acids*. Hydrochloric acid is an example of a strong acid in aqueous solution:

$$HCl + H_2O \rightleftharpoons Cl^- + H_3O^+$$

where the acid dissociation constant is so large ($\sim 10^{+4}$) that the equilibrium lies almost completely to the right, and the reaction is normally written as

$$HCl + H_2O \rightarrow Cl^- + H_3O^+$$

The addition of acids to water, whether weak or strong, will always result in an increase in $[H_3O^+]$ and, therefore, a *decrease* in pH (since pH = $-\log_{10}[H^+]$). The pH of acidic solutions is always less than 7.00.

Bases in aqueous solution can also be characterized as weak or strong depending on the value of the base dissociation constant K_b. The addition of the base ammonia (NH_3) to water results in

$$NH_3 + H_2O \rightleftharpoons NH_4^+ + OH^-$$

where the solvent water acts as an acid and

$$K_b = \frac{[NH_4^+][OH^-]}{[NH_3]} = 1.75 \times 10^{-5}\,(\text{at } 25\,^\circ\text{C})$$

Ammonia is a *weak* base and is not dissociated to any great extent in aqueous solution. Sodium hydroxide (NaOH) is an example of a strong base that is completely dissociated in aqueous solution. The pH of basic solutions is always greater than 7.00.

All the reactions discussed so far and all the reactions you will investigate in this module involve water as the solvent. All the equilibrium constants are, therefore, valid only for *aqueous* solutions and are dependent on the proton-donating and proton-accepting ability of the water molecule. It is very convenient to employ a simpler way of writing acid–base equilibria in aqueous solution than that used thus far. It may be assumed that all ions in an aqueous solution are hydrated, including the H_3O^+ ion. Thus, self-dissociation of water may be written as

$$H_2O \rightleftharpoons H^+ + OH^-$$

and the dissociation of a weak acid HA may be written as

$$HA \rightleftharpoons H^+ + A^-$$

Unfortunately, the dissociation of weak bases must still be written with H_2O as a reactant in order to maintain the species balance, e.g.,

$$NH_3 + H_2O \rightleftharpoons NH_4^+ + OH^-$$

All the acids discussed thus far have been capable of donating *one* proton and are called *monoprotic acids*. There are many acids that can donate two or more protons, e.g., H_3PO_4 is an example of a triprotic acid:

$$H_3PO_4 \rightleftharpoons H^+ + H_2PO_4^- \qquad K_1$$

$$H_2PO_4^- \rightleftharpoons H^+ + HPO_4^{2-} \qquad K_2$$

$$HPO_4^{2-} \rightleftharpoons H^+ + PO_4^{-3} \qquad K_3$$

These polyprotic acids donate protons in a stepwise manner. The first acid dissociation constant is usually larger than the second acid dissociation constant, and so on. In the H_3PO_4 dissociation shown above, K1 > K2 > K3.

Acid–base equilibria are often investigated by carrying out titration reactions. An acid–base titration is the process of incremental addition of a solution of acid (or base) to a solution of base (or acid) such that the extent of the neutralization reaction can be monitored. A titration is really a very simple way of obtaining a tremendous amount of useful information about an acid–base system.

One of the most important criteria for the use of titration methods in the study of equilibria is that equilibrium be achieved rapidly. Proton transfer reactions, especially in water, are usually very fast, with half-lives of less than milliseconds. The rapid rate of chemical reactions involving protons is in part due to the rapid rate at which protons travel through an aqueous solution. It has been proposed that H^+ moves through an aqueous solution by a "jump" or "proton-hopping" mechanism (see Figure 14.1).

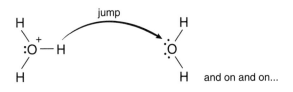

Figure 14.1 Proton-hopping mechanism in water.

Once the acid–base system has achieved equilibrium, then a wide variety of quantitative monitoring techniques can easily be used to probe the state of the system. The master variable in acid–base systems is [H^+] (or pH), and the most common method of analysis is to examine the change of concentration of other species (at equilibrium) as a function of changes in [H^+].

In this module you will experimentally investigate a wide variety of acid–base reactions and compare your results with computer simulations carried out on the main frame computer system at Colorado State University (a Cyber 205). Graphical presentation of the data in the form of titration curves reveals a rich source of useful information about acids and bases and their reactions.

Quiz Outline—Part 1

Your quiz will NOT cover all of the information below, but it will cover some subset of the information given below.

Be able to identify/define Brønsted-Lowry acids and bases.

Be able to identify an acid, base, conjugate acid, and conjugate base in an acid–base reaction.

Be able to explain the difference between weak/strong acids and weak/strong bases. This includes an understanding of K_a, K_b, pK_a, and pK_b.

Be able to write the dissociation reactions for mono or polyprotic acids or bases.

e.g., $H_2O + HCOOH \rightarrow HCOO^- + H_3O^+$

Be able to calculate K_a from pK_a and vice versa. Be able to calculate pH from $[H^+]$ and vice versa.

Be able to explain what it means to be a buffer solution and identify examples of buffer solutions.

Be able to locate the buffer region and the equivalence point on a titration curve.

Be able to derive the Henderson–Hasselbalch equation from the equilibrium expression,

$$K_a = \frac{[H^+][A^-]}{[HA]}, \text{ for the weak acid, HA.}$$

Sample Pre-Laboratory Quiz—Part 1

1. Give the Brønsted-Lowry definition of a base.

2. Write out a reaction equation for the reaction of hydrogen chloride with water. Indicate which substances are the acid, base, conjugate acid, and conjugate base in the reaction that you have written.

3. Explain the difference between a strong acid and a weak acid. Give an example of a K_a value that would represent a weak acid, and a second K_a value that would represent a strong acid.

4. Explain what is meant by K_b.

5. Calculate the pH of a 0.01 solution of hydrochloric acid.

Quiz Outline—Part 2

Your quiz will NOT cover all of the information below, but it will cover some subset of the information given below.

This particular quiz is a post-lab quiz—i.e., the questions are based on work you did in Part 1 of this experiment.

Many of the concepts below are covered by the questions that need to be handed in for your report on this experiment. Doing the questions in the report is an excellent way to prepare for this quiz.

Be able to sketch the titration curve for? M HCl being titrated with? M NaOH (like Section E, Part 1, of *Chemtrek*). Be able to label the axes correctly, identify the pH at the beginning of the titration (before NaOH added), the volume of NaOH added at the equivalence point, and the pH at the equivalence point.

Figure 14.4 shows titration curves of monoprotic strong acids titrated with 0.10 M NaOH. Be able to calculate the molarity of the acid, given that:

Curve A = 25.00 mL of unknown acid titrated with 0.10 M NaOH

Curve B = 5.00 mL of unknown acid titrated with 0.10 M NaOH

Curve C = 10.00 mL of unknown acid titrated with 0.10 M NaOH

Curve D = 25.00 mL of unknown acid titrated with 0.10 M NaOH

Given a list of indicators with their pH transition ranges, be able to select the appropriate indicator for a titration and explain your choice.

Be able to determine the K_a and pK_a of a weak acid from its titration curve with a strong base.

Be able to calculate the pH (using the Henderson-Hasselbalch equation) for a buffer solution (similar to calculations done in Section E, Part 4).

Sample Pre-Laboratory Quiz—Part 2

1. (a) Draw a sketch of the titration curve for 5 mL of 0.01 M HCl titrated with 0.01 M NaOH.

    (b) On the same axis overlay a sketch of the titration curve for 5 mL of 1×10^{-5} M HCl titrated with 1×10^{-5} M NaOH.

    (c) For both plots: (1) Indicate the pH at the beginning point (i.e., before any NaOH is added). (2) Indicate the volume of NaOH (added) at the equivalence point. (3) Indicate the pH at the equivalence point.

2. (a) From the titration curve given below, calculate the K_a and the pK_a of the weak acid being titrated. Show your work for full credit.

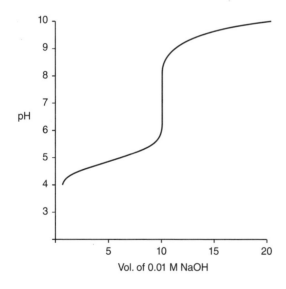

    (b) Suppose you were going to use an indicator for the above titration. What would be the ideal "transition range" for the indicator you would choose?

3. A particular weak acid (HA) with a K_a of 2.0×10^{-5} is 75% titrated with a strong base to produce a buffer solution. What is the pH of this final solution? Show your work for full credit.

Laboratory Experiments

Flowchart of the Experiments

Section A.	Conductimetry and the Strength of Acids and Bases

Section B.	Acid–Base Equilibria and Indicator Dyes

Section C.	Determination of the K_a Values of Weak Acid Indicators

Section D.	pH Measurement with Indicator Color Probes

Section E.	The Study of Acid–Base Equilibria by Graphical Interpretation of Titration Data

Part 1. Titration of a Strong Acid with a Strong Base
Part 2. Titration of a Weak Acid with a Strong Base
Part 3. The Measurement of the K_a of a Weak Acid
Part 4. The Henderson-Hasselbalch Equation
Part 5. Titration Curves and Buffer Solutions
Part 6. The Dilution of Buffers
Part 7. The Selection of Weak Acids to Make Buffer Solutions
Part 8. The Titration of Weak Bases with Strong Acids

Section F.	The Titration of Polyprotic Acids

CAUTION: Most acids and bases are corrosive. If you get any of these solutions on your skin, wash well with cold water and inform your instructor.

Requires two four-hour class periods to complete.

Throughout this module you will be investigating acid–base equilibria by analyzing the progress of acid–base reactions in volumetric titrations. The quality of the results from these experiments will depend on the care with which you carry out solution transfers, dilutions, and drop additions. Large-drop pipets are satisfactory for most of the titrations. Pipets may be calibrated (when necessary) by means of an analytical balance or volumetrically.

Section A.   Conductimetry and the Strength of Acids and Bases

Goals: *(1) To be able to interpret the conductivity experiments. (2) To be able to identify strong and weak acids and bases by means of K_a, K_b, pK_a, and pK_b values.*

Discussion: 1.   The ability of a solution to conduct electricity depends on the concentration of ions in the solution. A 0.1 M HCl solution is a good conductor because the HCl molecules are completely dissociated into ions:

$$HCl + H_2O \rightarrow H_3O^+ + Cl^-$$

which may be conveniently abbreviated

$$HCl \rightarrow H^+ + Cl^-$$

because the water is the solvent in aqueous solutions. The dissociation occurs extremely rapidly to instantaneously give a solution that is 0.1 M H^+ and 0.1 M Cl^-. Acids that dissociate completely are called *strong acids*, and the K_a value is very large (>10^4 for HCl).

2.   The 0.1 M CH_3COOH (acetic acid) solution is a poor conductor because the solution contains mostly undissociated molecules. Acetic acid dissociates rapidly, but only to an extent:

$$CH_3COOH + H_2O \rightleftarrows H_3O^+ + CH_3COO^-$$

This reaction may be abbreviated

$$CH_3COOH \rightleftarrows H^+ + CH_3COO^-$$

The K_a of CH_3COOH is small (1.8×10^{-5}); thus, the solution contains only small concentrations of H^+ and CH_3COO^- (acetate ion). Acids that do not appreciably dissociate in aqueous solution are called *weak acids*. Weak acids have K_a values that are smaller than about 10^{-2}.

Experimental Steps: 1.   A conductivity meter should be located at your arm's reach station. Touch both leads against a piece of metal (such as a key) and press the button on the side. All of the lights should light up, indicating excellent conductivity through the piece of metal.

2.   At your arm's reach station should be dropper bottles of 0.1 M NH_3/NH_4OH, 0.1 M acetic acid, 0.1 M HCl, and 0.1 M NaOH for conductivity testing. Put these solutions in separate wells of a *clean*, dry 24-well tray. Also add some tap water to one of the wells, and distilled water to another. Test the conductivity of each of these solutions. To avoid cross contamination, rinse the leads off with distilled water between testing each solution. Record your observations.

Questions: Q1.   Arrange the six solutions tested from the lowest to the highest conductivity. Explain the order observed—i.e., why do solutions of the same concentration have different conductivities? If you cannot differentiate between them, explain why not.

Q2.   The conductivity of an H_2SO_4 solution was followed as it was titrated with the strong base $Ba(OH)_2$. Predict the relative conductivities of:

(a) the starting solution

(b) the solution at the equivalence point

(c) the solution well past the equivalence point

HINT: First write a balanced reaction. Remember that $BaSO_4$ is insoluble.

Section B.   Acid–Base Equilibria and Indicator Dyes

Goal: *To investigate several aspects of acid–base equilibria by means of a colored dye called bromocresol green.*

Discussion: Bromocresol green is one of a class of organic compounds that can exist in different colored forms depending on whether the compound is *protonated* or *unprotonated*. (The terms protonated and unprotonated refer to the acid form and the conjugate base form of the indicator.) You have already done experiments on a naturally occurring dye (red cabbage extract) in an earlier module. The chemical structure of most of these organic indicators is rather complex; e.g., bromocresol green has the formula $C_{21}H_{14}O_5Br_4S$ (molar mass: 698 g mol^{-1}). However, these structures can be symbolized in a simple and convenient way by writing the protonated, acid form of the dye as HIn. The dissociation of the acid indicator can thus be written

$$HIn \rightleftarrows H^+ + In^-$$

for which

$$K_a = \frac{[H^+][In^-]}{[HIn]}$$

The protonated form HIn usually has a different color than the unprotonated form In$^-$.

Experimental Steps: 1.   Clean a 1×12 well strip.

2.   Locate a pipet of 0.03% bromocresol green indicator solution. Deliver 1 drop to each of 3 wells.

3.   Add 1 drop of 0.01 M HCl to the first well. Stir.

•   What observation would lead you to conclude that the time for mixing to occur is much longer than the time required for the acid–base reaction?

- You have just added a strong acid (HCl)—a solution of H^+ and Cl^- ions (each of which is 0.01 M concentration)—to the dye system that was originally at equilibrium. On the basis of Le Châtelier's principle, why did the color change?

4.   Add 1 drop of 0.01 M NaOH to the indicator in the third well.

- What happened? Can you explain the change according to Le Châtelier's principle?

    HINT: What did it look like *before* you stirred it?

5.   Save this 1×12 well strip for Section C, step 12.

Section C.   Determination of the K_a Values of Weak Acid Indicators

Goal: *To carry out a determination of the acid dissociation equilibrium constant of several colored, weak acid indicators.*

Discussion: One of the simplest ways to measure K_a values of weak acid indicators is to place the weak electrolyte in a series of solutions of exactly known pH values and allow any acid–base reactions to come to equilibrium. Once equilibrium is achieved— and of course, with acid–base reactions this happens rapidly—the appropriate color changes reveal the relative concentration of HIn and the In⁻ in the various solutions.

Experimental Steps: 1.   Clean a 96-well tray (preferably with flat-bottomed wells).

2.   Locate the 12 reagent bottles containing solutions of known pH 1.0 through 12.0. Deliver 2 drops of pH 1.0 to wells A1, B1, C1, and D1. Then deliver 2 drops of pH 2.0 to wells A2, B2, C2, and D2. Continue in a similar manner though pH 12. When you are done you will have 4 rows of 12 solutions going from pH 1.0 on the left to pH 12.0 on the right.

3.   Use a pipet to deliver 1 drop of methyl orange to each well of row A.

4.   Similarly, deliver 1 drop of bromocresol green to the wells of row B, 1 drop of bromothymol blue to the wells of row C, and 1 drop of phenophthalein to row D. Stir the solutions with a microstirrer.

- Record the solution colors in a table in your laboratory notebook.

5.   Let us now determine the K_a values of our weak acid indicators and consider why the colors of the indicators change as the pH changes. We can write an equilibrium expression for each weak acid indicator.

$$HIn \rightleftarrows H^+ + In^-$$

$$K_a = \frac{[H^+][In^-]}{[HIn]}$$

Taking $\log_{10}$ of the K_a expression

$$\log_{10}K_a = \log_{10}[H^+] + \log_{10}[In^-] - \log_{10}[HIn]$$

and changing the sign throughout results in

$$-\log_{10}K_a = -\log_{10}[H^+] - \log_{10}[In^-] + \log_{10}[HIn]$$

Since $pK_a = -\log_{10}K_a$ and $pH = -\log_{10}[H^+]$, after substitution and rearranging

$$pH = pK_a + \log_{10}\left(\frac{[In^-]}{[HIn]}\right)$$

This *Henderson-Hasselbalch equation* links the pH of a solution, which varies from 1 to 12 in our experiments, with the pK_a of the weak acid indicator.

6.   Consider what the addition of acid does to an indicator. To remove the excess H^+, by Le Châtelier's principle the equilibrium for the dissociation of the indicator shifts towards the HIn form of the indicator.

$$HIn \rightleftarrows H^+ + In^-$$

Consequently, you see the color of the HIn form of the indicator when acid is added. Look at your bromocresol green results. What is the color of the HIn form of the indicator?

7.   Consider what addition of base does to an indicator. The base reacts with the free H^+ in the indicator solution. To compensate, by Le Châtelier's principle the indicator must dissociate more, thereby shifting the dissociation of the indicator to form more H^+ and In^-

$$HIn \rightleftarrows H^+ + In^-$$

Consequently, you see the color of the In^- form of the indicator under more basic conditions. Look at your bromocresol green results. What is the color of the In^- form of the indicator?

8.   Now, what if $[In^-] \cong [HIn]$? This is the transition point between the different colors of HIn and In^- and so the *color of the solution will be intermediate between the color of HIn and the color of In^-*. Look at your bromocresol green results. What is the color when you have equal amounts of HIn and In^-? Does this make sense?

Substituting $[In^-] = [HIn]$ into the Henderson-Hasselbalch expression yields

$$pH = pK_a + \log_{10}(1), \text{ or } pH = pK_a$$

Consequently, you can determine the pK_a of a weak acid indicator by looking at the pH where the color of the indicator is intermediate between the HIn and In^- forms. At this pH, $pH = pK_a$. What is the pK_a of bromocresol green?

9. Now, what if $\dfrac{[\text{In}^-]}{[\text{HIn}]} = \dfrac{10}{1}$? By substituting into the Henderson-Hasselbalch equation:

$$\text{pH} = \text{pK}_a + 1$$

Or, at pH = pK$_a$ + 1 the "pure" color of In$^-$ will appear. Look at your bromocresol green solutions. Do you have the pure color of In$^-$ at pH = pK$_a$ + 1?

10. Now, what if $\dfrac{[\text{In}^-]}{[\text{HIn}]} = \dfrac{1}{10}$? By substituting into the Henderson-Hasselbalch equation:

$$\text{pH} = \text{pK}_a - 1$$

Or, at pH = pK$_a$ − 1 the "pure" color of HIn will appear. Look at your bromocresol green solutions. Do you have the pure color of HIn at pH = pK$_a$ − 1?

11. Thus, the pH transition range of an indicator from one "pure" color to another is

$$\text{pH transition range} = \text{pK}_a \pm 1.0$$

Table 14.1 lists some common acid–base indicators, along with pH transition ranges and colors in acidic and basic solutions. Notice that the pH transition range is roughly 2 pH units for many of these indicators.

12. Using the 1 × 12 well strip from Section B, add 3 drops of pH 4.0 buffer solution to wells 1, 2, and 3. Stir.

    • Record your observations.

    NOTE: The pH 4.0 solution is a buffer solution (you will be exploring buffers in a later section) that reacts with strong acids *and* strong bases to produce a final solution that has a pH of approximately 4, i.e., [H$^+$] = 10^{-4} M.

Questions: Q3. Based on your lab experiments, report (a) K$_a$, (b) pK$_a$, and (c) the pH transition range for each of the four acid–base indicators that you used. Also show the pH transition range for each indicator on Figure 14.3, in a similar manner to how it is shown for the indicator Orange IV.

                Q4. Explain why the solutions turned green, instead of blue or yellow in step 12. Approximately what are the relative concentrations of In$^-$ and HIn in the three wells?

Section D.   pH Measurement with Indicator Color Probes

Goal: *To use a solution of a combination of indicators (a universal indicator) as a color probe for sensing [H⁺] and, therefore, pH.*

Discussion: The author and Peter Markow have tested over 5000 combinations of acid–base indicators and have selected a universal indicator that may be used to obtain an easily seen color change, over small intervals, from pH 1.0 to pH 12.0. You will be preparing a set of solutions of different pH and color to use a *colorimetric pH meter* for measuring the pH of various sample solutions.

Experimental Steps: 1.   Clean a 1×12 well strip.

2.   Use a large–drop pipet to deliver 1 drop of the Thompson-Markow universal indicator solution to each well.

3.   Using a large–drop pipet add 3 drops of pH 1.0 solution to the first well, 3 drops of pH 2.0 solution to the second well, and so on. Use good wash and transfer techniques for each buffer solution. Stir.

   •   Describe the color of each pH value in your lab book.

   NOTE: You now have 12 solutions of known pH, each of which has a different color.

   This set of solutions can now be used to measure the pH of any unknown solution by a simple color comparison.

4.   Keep the pH meter strip for the next series of experiments. Evaporation of the solutions may be stopped by sealing the strip with a piece of transparent sticky tape.

Table 14.1 Some Common Acid–Base Indicators

Name	pH Transition Range	Acid Color	Basic Color
Malachite green	0–2.0	Yellow	Green
Cresol red	0.2–1.8	Red	Yellow
Metacresol purple	1.2–2.8	Red	Yellow
Thymol blue	1.2–2.8	Red	Yellow
Orange IV	1.3–3.2	Red	Yellow
Methyl yellow	2.9–4.0	Red	Yellow
Bromophenol blue	3.0–4.6	Yellow	Purple
Congo red	3.0–5.0	Blue	Red
Methyl orange		Red	Yellow
Bromocresol green		Yellow	Blue
Methyl red	4.4–6.2	Red	Yellow
Chlorophenol red	4.8–6.4	Yellow	Purple
Litmus	4.5–8.3	Red	Blue
Paranitro phenol	5.0–7.0	Colorless	Yellow
Bromocresol purple	5.2–6.8	Yellow	Purple
Bromothymol blue		Yellow	Blue
Neutral red	6.8–8.0	Bluish red	Yellow
Phenol red	6.4–8.2	Yellow	Red
Cresol red	7.0–8.8	Yellow	Purple
Metacresol purple	7.4–9.0	Yellow	Purple
Curcumin	7.8–9.2	Yellow	Brown
Thymol blue	8.0–9.6	Yellow	Blue
Phenolphthalein		Colorless	Pink
Thymolphthalein	9.3–10.5	Colorless	Blue
Alizarin yellow R	10.0–12.1	Yellow	Brown-red
Curcumin	10.2–11.8	Red	Orange
Malachite green	11.5–14.0	Blue	Colorless
Clayton yellow	12.2–13.2	Yellow	Amber
Red cabbage extract	2.5–4.0	Red	Pale violet
Red cabbage extract	6.0–8.5	Pale violet	Blue
Red cabbage extract	9.0–10.5	Blue	Green
Red cabbage extract	10.5–14.0	Green	Yellow

| **Section E.** | **The Study of Acid–Base Equilibria by Graphical Interpretation of Titration Data** |

Goal: *To investigate various quantitative aspects of acid–base chemistry by interpreting experimental titration curves and by comparing the data with computer-simulated titrations.*

Discussion: Titration curve data provide a simple, powerful basis for both experimental and theoretical analysis of reaction stoichiometry (the measurement of concentration of acid, base, and salt solutions); the determination of equilibrium constants of acids and bases; the determination of molar mass; the buffer concept; the nature of polyprotic acid systems; and the use of Henderson-Hasselbalch expressions.

Section E is subdivided into Parts 1 through 8. Each part is an investigation of a particular type of titration and the information that can be derived from graphical presentations of titration data. Recall from the Background Chemistry section of this chapter that an acid–base titration is the process of incremental addition of a solution of acid (or base) to a solution of base (or acid) such that the extent of the neutralization reaction can be monitored. Each point in the titration represents the state of the acid–base system after equilibrium has been reached. The reason is that acid–base reactions are very fast, and equilibrium is usually achieved in less than a millisecond—provided that the reaction mixture is stirred! The change in $[H^+]$ that occurs during the titration may be measured by color comparison with the colorimetric pH meter.

As you work through each of the experimental sections in this chapter, you will need to refer to Figures 14.2 through 14.11. All these figures are located in sequential order at the end of this chapter. You have additional copies of some of these figures, on which you can plot and include in your notebook in your student packet.

| **Section E.** | **Part 1. Titration of a Strong Acid with a Strong Base** |

Experimental Steps: 1.   Clean a 96-well tray (flat-bottomed wells).

2.   Deliver 1 drop of universal indicator to each well of row A.

   NOTE: Use a clean small-drop pipet for all titrations. First, use good transfer technique to rinse and half-fill the pipet with 0.05 M HCl.

3.   Quantitatively deliver (using standard technique) 1 drop of 0.05 M HCl to each well of row A.

4.   Wash, rinse, and half-fill the same pipet with 0.01 M NaOH.

5.   Carry out a *serial* titration of the 0.05 M HCl with 0.01 M NaOH, i.e., add 1 drop NaOH to the first well, 2 drops NaOH to the second well, and so on. Stir.

6. Use the pH meter strip (from the last section) to measure the pH values for the solution in each well by placing the pH meter strip and the second strip together and viewing against a white background. Slide the strips relative to each other and decide on a match.

    NOTE: If the color of the unknown lies between 2 wells of the pH meter strip, then try to interpolate the pH value. The accuracy of pH measurement by this method depends on your ability to discriminate color hue differences. If you have difficulty with color discrimination, consult your instructor.

    •   Record the pH values.

    •   In your notebook, plot a graph of pH versus drops of added 0.01 M NaOH using similar scaling to Figure 14.2. Draw a *smooth* curve through the data points using a sharp pencil. Label this graph "Figure 14.1."

    NOTE: Figure 14.2 is a computer-simulated titration curve for the titration that you have just carried out experimentally. This type of graph is called a *titration curve*. The simulated curve was computer generated by solving the exact mathematical equations for the acid–base equilibria involved in this titration. The pK_a of water was given a value of 14.00. The dilution of the solutions by the added indicator was taken into account in computing the pH values in the titration.

7. Since all drops from the same pipet are the same volume, the addition of 1 drop of 0.01 M NaOH to 1 drop of 0.05 M HCl will neutralize one-fifth of the HCl. This occurs because of the stoichiometry of the reaction. All the HCl will have been neutralized by the addition of 5 drops of base. This point in the titration is called the *equivalence point*. The computer data show that the equivalence point occurs at exactly pH 7.00 and 5.00 drops of 0.01 M NaOH.

    •   Look at your experimental titration curve.

    NOTE: The equivalence point is not easy to locate on experimental curves. One way is to draw a vertical line at the 5 drop point. You can see that the difficulty arises because of the very large pH rise (i.e., approximately 8 pH units, a change in $[H^+]$ of 100,000,000!) that occurs close to the equivalence point.

8. Look at Figure 14.3.

    Seven titration curves are shown for strong acid (HCl) with strong base (NaOH). For each curve the concentration of acid and base are the same, e.g., the curve labeled 1 M is the curve for the titration of 5 drops of 1 M HCl with 1 M NaOH. You will see that there is a rapid rise in pH around the equivalence point, but that the size of the rise decreases with decreasing acid/base strengths.

Questions: Q5.   What is the **net ionic** equation for the reaction between HCl and NaOH?

Q6.   Consider a titration in which 0.03 M NaOH is added to 1 drop of 0.12 M HCl. Sketch the pH curve. A sketch is a rough picture of the general shape of the curve with the requested points and axes correctly labeled.

On your curve, show:

(a) The volume of 0.03 M NaOH needed to reach the equivalence point.

(b) The pH at the equivalence point.

(c) The pH at the beginning of the titration before any 0.03 M NaOH has been added to the 0.12 M HCl.

(d) The pH when you are *well past* the equivalence point.

Q7.   Considering your data for methyl orange, bromocresol green, bromothymol blue, and phenolphthalein (Figure 14.3), which indicator would be the most suitable for a titration between 0.001 M HNO_3 with 0.001 M KOH solution? Explain your selection.

Section E.   Part 2. Titration of a Weak Acid with a Strong Base

Experimental Steps: 1.   Deliver 1 drop of universal indicator to each well in row B of the 96-well tray.

2.   Use good wash, rinse, and transfer technique to deliver 1 drop of 0.05 M CH_3COOH to each well of row B.

3.   Carry out a serial titration of the acetic acid with 0.01 M NaOH. Stir.

4.   Match colors with the pH meter strip and measure the solution pH values.

•   Plot the titration curve on the same graph paper as the previous titration—i.e., Figure 14.1. Draw a smooth titration curve. The computer-simulated curve is shown in Figure 14.5.

NOTE: Data selected from the computer simulation show that the equivalence point pH is 8.31 and that it occurs after the addition of exactly 5 drops of 0.01 M NaOH.

The solution at the equivalence point in the acetic acid titration is a sodium acetate solution. Sodium acetate (CH_3COONa) is a salt that is completely dissociated in aqueous solution into acetate ions CH_3COO^- and sodium ions Na^+:

$$CH_3COONa \rightarrow CH_3COO^- + Na^+$$

The acetate ion is a weak base (i.e., it can accept a proton):

$$CH_3COO^- + H_2O \rightleftarrows CH_3COOH + OH^-$$

Thus, the solution at the equivalence point is slightly basic (pH 8.31) because of the hydroxide ions (OH^-) produced in the last reaction.

Section E.	**Part 3. The Measurement of the K_a of a Weak Acid from the Titration Curve**

Goal: *You found in Section B that one way to determine the pK_a of a weak acid is to lock the indicator into an equilibrium position by setting the pH with different buffer solutions. The pH at which the solution changed color from the HIn to In⁻ forms was also the pK_a value. pK_a values for weak acids can also be determined from titration curves, as you will see in this section.*

Experimental Steps: 1.   Look at Figure 14.5. The part of the curve before the equivalence point gives the pH of partially neutralized acetic acid solutions.

In this region a complex system of equilibria exists, as shown in the following reactions. The solution contains unreacted acetic acid, which dissociates into acetate ions and H⁺. Additional acetate ions are present from the neutralization reaction. Also, water is autoionizing into H⁺ and OH⁻.

$$CH_3COOH + H_2O \quad \overset{K_a = 10^{-5}}{\rightleftarrows} \quad CH_3COO^- + H_3O^+$$

$$CH_3COOH + OH^- \quad \overset{K_a = large}{\rightarrow} \quad CH_3COO^- + H_2O$$

$$^-H_2O + H_2O \quad \overset{K_w = 10^{-14}}{\rightleftarrows} \quad H_3O^+ + OH^-$$

At a point in the titration halfway from the start to the equivalence point (at 2.5 drops NaOH), 1/2 of the CH_3COOH has been neutralized. If we ignore the $[CH_3COO^-]$ from the dissociation of CH_3COOH because its dissociation equilibrium constant is small, and furthermore has been suppressed by the acetate ions from the neutralization reaction, then

$$[CH_3COOH] \approx [CH_3COO^-]$$

at halfway from the start to the equivalence point. $[CH_3COO^-]$ has come primarily from the neutralization of half of the acetic acid.

Substituting this into the Henderson-Hasselbalch expression, we obtain

$$pH = pK_a + \log_{10}\left(\frac{[CH_3COO^-]}{[CH_3COOH]}\right)$$

$$pH = pK_a + \log_{10}(1)$$

$$pH = pK_a \text{ at the midpoint of the titration!}$$

So, for any weak acid/strong base titration you can determine the pK_a of the acid by looking at the pH on the titration curve when the titration is halfway to the equivalence point.

- To find the pK_a of CH_3COOH from Figure 14.5, draw a vertical line from 2.5 drops to intersect the curve. From the intersection draw a horizontal line to the pH axis, and $pH = pK_a$.

- What is the K_a of CH_3COOH?

This K_a value is typical of the K_a values for many organic carboxylic acids that have the structure

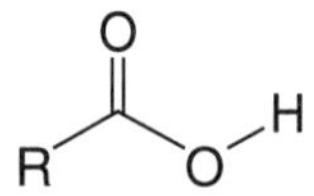

The hydrogen atom that dissociates is the H atom attached to the oxygen atom of the carboxylate group.

Section E.   Part 4. The Henderson-Hasselbalch Equation

Discussion:

You saw in Section E, Part 3 how to determine the pK_a of a weak acid from the pH at halfway to the equivalence point. When you are not at the midway point in the weak acid/strong base titration, you simply use the Henderson-Hasselbalch equation to determine the relationship between pH and pK_a.

$$pH = pK_a + \log_{10}\left(\frac{[CH_3COO^-]}{[CH_3COOH]}\right)$$

The last term in the above equation is simply the logarithm of the ratio of $[CH_3COO^-]$, formed in the neutralization, to the unreacted $[CH_3COOH]$.

Question: Q8.   By consulting Figure 14.5, complete the following table. Also, show a sample calculation for the pH determined using the Henderson-Hasselbalch equation.

Hint: This titration begins with 1 drop of 0.05 M CH_3COOH, to which 0.01 M NaOH is added one drop at a time. To obtain the CH_3COO^-/CH_3COOH ratio, think about:

(a) The amount of CH_3COOH that you begin with.

(b) How much CH_3COO^- is formed from CH_3COOH for each drop of NaOH added.

(c) How much CH_3COOH remains after each drop of NaOH is added.

NOTE: Use the pK_a value for CH_3COOH that you obtained in Part 3.

Drops of 0.01 M NaOH added	$\dfrac{[CH_3COO^-]}{[CH_3COOH]}$	pH from Curve	pH Calculated from the H-H Equation
1	1/4		
2			
3			
4			

Section E.   Part 5. Titration Curves and Buffer Solutions

Goal: *To prepare an acetic acid/sodium acetate buffer solution from acetic acid and sodium hydroxide.*

Discussion: Look at Figure 14.5, particularly the part of the curve before the equivalence point.

Note that the pH change that occurs upon the addition of strong base NaOH is quite small. Partially neutralized solutions of weak acids (or weak bases as you will see later) that resist change in pH upon the addition of small amounts of strong acid or strong base are called *buffer solutions*. The part of the titration curve where buffering occurs is called the *buffer region*. This buffering action occurs because the solutions contain relatively large concentrations of weak acid CH_3COOH and its salt, CH_3COONa (produced in the neutralization reaction). The addition of OH^- from a strong base to a buffer solution of this type results in

$$CH_3COOH + OH^- \rightarrow CH_3COO^- + H_2O$$

The pH of the solution will change, but not by very much. The addition of H^+ from a strong acid to a buffer solution of this type results in

$$CH_3COO^- + H^+ \rightarrow CH_3COOH$$

and produces the *weak* acid CH_3COOH. The pH of the solution will change, but not by very much. In general, acidic buffer solutions are prepared by titrating appropriate weak acids with strong bases until the desired pH is obtained. You will now prepare a buffer solution in approximately this manner.

Experimental Steps: 1.   Suppose that you are going to prepare a buffer solution that contains 15 drops of 0.05 M CH_3COOH. Determine how many drops of 0.01 M NaOH need to be added to the acetic acid so that

$$\frac{[CH_3COO^-]}{[CH_3COOH]} = \frac{3}{2}$$

NOTE: Consult Figure 14.5 and your table in Section E, Part 4.

2.   Using a large-drop pipet and good wash and transfer techniques, prepare this buffer solution in a 24-well tray.

3.   Measure the pH of this solution using the pH checker as follows:

(a) Remove the pH checker from the water that it is stored in.

(b) Gently shake the pH checker to dislodge any drops that cling to the electrode.

(c) Place the electrode in the 24-well tray and swirl gently. Turn the checker on and wait a minute or so for the reading to stabilize. Record the pH.

NOTE: The checker has an accuracy of ± 0.2 pH units.

(d) Leave checker on, rinse it with distilled water, then return it to its water bath.

Question: Q9.   Report how many drops of NaOH you used to prepare your buffer solution and report the pH measured for this buffer solution. Based on the titration curve in Figure 14.5 and your table from Q8, is this the pH that you expected? Explain.

Section E.   Part 6. The Dilution of Buffers

Goal: *To study the effect of dilution on the pH of a buffer.*

Discussion: In the previous section you prepared a buffer solution by adding a strong base to a weak acid. This is probably the most common way to prepare a buffer solution. However, there are other ways to prepare buffer solutions. In this section you are going to prepare buffer solutions by mixing a solution of weak acid with a solution of its conjugate base.

Experimental Steps: 1.   Using a large-drop pipet, make a total of 40 drops of buffer solution in a 24-well tray from 0.05 M CH_3COONa and 0.05 M CH_3COOH such that

$$\frac{[CH_3COO^-]}{[CH_3COOH]} = \frac{1}{1}$$

Save this solution (hereafter referred to as the "original buffer") for subsequent experiments in Section E, Part 7.

2.   Measure the pH of this buffer solution as follows: Using a large–drop pipet, put 3 drops of this solution into a well of a 1 × 12 strip and add 1 drop of universal indicator. Use the pH meter strip to measure the pH value by placing the pH meter strip and the second strip together and viewing against a white background. Slide the strips relative to each other and decide on a match.

NOTE: If the color lies between 2 wells of the pH meter strip, then try to interpolate the pH value.

• Is this the pH that you expect?

3.   Now prepare 40 drops of a diluted buffer solution that is 1/4 (i.e., 25%) as concentrated as the original buffer solution. Note: This solution is still

$$\frac{[CH_3COO^-]}{[CH_3COOH]} = \frac{1}{1}$$

but has only 1/4 as many moles of acetic acid and sodium acetate as it had in the original buffer. You may prepare this solution either by dilution of the original buffer, or from appropriate amounts of 0.05 M CH_3COONa, 0.05 M CH_3COOH, and distilled water. Save this solution for subsequent experiments in Section E, Part 7.

- Measure the pH of the diluted buffer solution as you did above, by comparison with the pH meter strip.

4. Look at Figure 14.6. The 5 titration curves are for *assorted dilutions of buffer solutions.*

(a) 1.0 M CH_3COOH with 1.0 M NaOH

(b) 0.1 M CH_3COOH with 0.1 M NaOH

(c) 0.01 M CH_3COOH with 0.01 M NaOH

(d) 0.001 M CH_3COOH with 0.001 M NaOH

(e) 0.0001 M CH_3COOH with 0.0001 M NaOH

- Draw a vertical line at 2 drops of added NaOH to intersect all 5 curves.

- What are the pH values of the 5 solutions?

Questions: Q10.   Explain how you made both the "original" and the 25% as concentrated buffer solutions (give amounts). Report the pH values obtained for your original and 25% dilution buffer solutions. Considering these experimental results, what is the effect of dilution on the pH of buffer solutions?

Q11.   Consider Figure 14.6. For each curve the concentration of acid and base are the same, e.g., the curve labeled 1 M is for the titration of 5 drops of 1 M weak acid with 1 M NaOH.

Why are the titration curves for the different reagent concentrations so similar in the buffer region? Are these solutions all buffers? Explain.

Section E.   Part 7. The Selection of Weak Acids to Make Buffer Solutions of Desired pH

Experimental Steps: 1.   Look at Figure 14.7 which shows titration curves for a series of weak acids with different K_a values.

NOTE: All the curves are for 0.1 M acid solutions titrated with 0.1 M strong base. The K_a values range from very large (strong acid) to 10^{-10} (very weak acid) as shown in the figure. The buffer regions with good buffer capacity are in the pH range of $pK_a \pm 1$.

The slope of the titration curves in Figure 14.7 is a quantitative measure of the buffering ability, or *buffer capacity*, of the solution. Titration curves with small values of slope—i.e., "flat" regions—mean that those solutions have good buffer capacity. The steep part of the titration curve—i.e., close to the equivalence point— means that these solutions have small or no buffer capacity. One way to test the buffer capacity of a solution is to add strong acid or base to it and measure the pH change.

NOTE: One interesting feature of the titration curves in Figure 14.7 is that all the curves give a small-slope, good buffer region *after* the equivalence point. All the solutions contain the salt of the weak acid and excess of strong base NaOH. Solutions that contain strong bases (or strong acids, e.g., see titration curves on Figure 14.3) are also regarded as buffers. The buffering action arises as a consequence of the high concentration of water in aqueous solutions ≈ 55.6 M H_2O) and the nature of the pH scale. These buffers are called *pseudobuffers*.

Testing the buffer capacity of buffer solutions:

2. Using a large-drop pipet, place 10 drops of your original buffer in each of two wells of a 24-well-tray. To one of the wells, add 10 drops 0.01 M HCl. To the other well, add 10 drops of 0.01 M NaOH. Stir the contents of each well. Remove 3-drop samples from each well, add 1 drop of universal indicator to each sample in a 1 × 12 strip, and determine the pH by comparison with the pH color strip.

    •   Record the pH.

3. Using a large-drop pipet, place 10 drops of your 25% diluted buffer in each of two wells of a 24-well-tray. To one of the wells, add 10 drops 0.01 M HCl. To the other well, add 10 drops of 0.01 M NaOH. Stir the contents of each well. Remove 3-drop samples from each well, add 1 drop of universal indicator to each sample in a 1 × 12 strip, and determine the pH by comparison with the pH color strip.

    •   Record the pH.

Questions: Q12.   Considering Figure 14.7 (the number 10^{-2} through 10^{-10} are the K_a values of the acids), what is the pH region of good buffer capacity for the titration with the acid having a $K_a = 1 \times 10^{-6}$?

Q13.   Report the pH values for your tests of the buffer capacity of the original and the 25% diluted buffer solutions. Which solution has the greater buffer capacity? Explain. How does dilution affect buffer capacity?

NOTE: The buffer capacity corresponds to a buffer's ability to resist changes in pH upon addition of strong acids or bases. The smaller the change in pH, for a given amount of added strong acid or base, the better the buffer capacity. Buffer capacity is extremely important in biological systems. If our blood did not have large enough of a buffer capacity, drinking a can of soda could kill!

Section E.   Part 8. The Titration of Weak Bases with Strong Acids

Experimental Steps: 1.   Deliver 1 drop of universal indicator into each well of row C of the 96-well tray.

2. Carry out a serial titration of the weak base 0.05 M NH_3 with 0.01 M HCl. Stir.

3. Measure the pH values of the solutions.

    •   Plot the titration curve on the same graph with your strong acid/strong base and weak acid/strong base titration curves.

    •   Compare with the computer-simulated curve (Figure 14.8).

    NOTE: Data from the computer calculation give an equivalence point pH of 5.70 at 5.0 drops of added 0.01 M HCl.

Questions: **Q14.** Considering Figure 14.8, what are the K_b and pK_b of ammonia and the K_a and pK_a of the ammonium ion? Explain how you determined these values. Show calculations where relevant.

Hint: Even though this is a titration of a weak base with a strong acid, pH still equals pK_a at halfway to the equivalence point. But in this titration, what is the acid in the buffer system? When you obtain the pK_a, you will be determining it for this acid.

Q15. Why is the equivalence point acidic for the titration between ammonia and HCl?

Hint: Think about what species are present at the equivalence point.

Q16. Suppose you want to make a buffer solution of pH 8.2 for a clinical physiological experiment. Using Figure 14.10, describe how you would do this. Include the K_b of the base used as well as the amount of added HCl.

NOTE: Figure 14.10 shows the effect of K_b of the weak base on titration curves. All the titration curves are for 0.1 M base with 0.1 M monoprotic strong acid.

Q17. You should have curves drawn for the strong acid/strong base, weak acid/strong base, and strong acid/weak base titrations—be sure to distinguish between the curves and have axes appropriately labeled. Please reference the page in your notebook where this graph is located.

Section F.   The Titration of Polyprotic Acids

Goal: *To apply the principles of graphical interpretation of titration data to investigate polyprotic acid equilibria.*

Experimental Steps: 1.   Deliver 1 drop of universal indicator to each well of row D of the 96-well tray.

2.   Use a small-drop pipet to deliver 1 drop of 0.04 M H_3PO_4 (phosphoric acid) to each well in row D.

3.   Carry out a serial titration of the phosphoric acid with 0.01 M NaOH. Stir.

   •   Determine the solution pH values and plot the titration curve on the same graph as the computer-simulated titration curve (Figure 14.11 provided in packet).

4.   Look at Figure 14.11.

There appear to be only 2 equivalence points, even though phosphoric acid H_3PO_4 is a *triprotic acid*! The pH at the 2 equivalence points can be found from the computer data. The first equivalence point pH is 4.83 and occurs after 4.0 drops of NaOH have been added. The second equivalence point pH is 9.36 after a total of 8.0 added drops of NaOH.

5.   On the computer-simulated titration curve in Figure 14.11, label the start of the titration as point A, the first equivalence point B, and the second equivalence point C.

At point A, no NaOH has been added, and the solution contains phosphoric acid (H_3PO_4) and dihydrogen phosphate ions ($H_2PO_4^-$) from

$$H_3PO_4 \rightleftharpoons H^+ + H_2PO_4^-$$

The first dissociation constant K_1 of H_3PO_4 has a value of 7.02×10^{-3}:

$$K_1 = \frac{[H^+][H_2PO_4^-]}{[H_3PO_4]} = 7.02 \times 10^{-3}$$

which shows that H_3PO_4 is a borderline weak/strong acid. Thus, the first dissociation is significant, and the pH of the solution is quite low (≈ 2). Now as NaOH is added in the titration, some of the H_3PO_4 is neutralized according to

$$H_3PO_4 + NaOH \rightarrow NaH_2PO_4 + H_2O$$

- Which ionic species are present in solution at any point between A and B (excluding indicator ions)?

At point B, all the H_3PO_4 has been titrated, and the solution contains only NaH_2PO_4 (completely dissociated, of course, because it is a salt).

As the titration proceeds beyond B, the weak acid $H_2PO_4^-$ is neutralized:

$$NaH_2PO_4 + NaOH \rightarrow Na_2HPO_4 + H_2O$$

and NaOH is the limiting reagent.

At the second equivalence point C, the predominant species is HPO_4^{2-} (and the spectator ion Na^+), which is the very weak acid.

After point C further titration produces *no* third equivalence point. The reason is that the neutralization of HPO_4^{2-} by NaOH, i.e.,

$$Na_2HPO_4 + NaOH \rightarrow Na_3PO_4 + H_2O$$

produces the phosphate ion PO_4^{3-}, which is as strong a base as NaOH. Another way of looking at it is that HPO_4^{2-} is such a weak acid ($K_a = 4.68 \times 10^{-13}$!) that it cannot be titrated in aqueous solution.

Questions: Q18.   Which two salts form the buffer system in the buffer region between points B and C?

                     Q19.   Include the plot of your titration for H_3PO_4 and NaOH (Figure 14.11).

Computer-Simulated Titration Curve

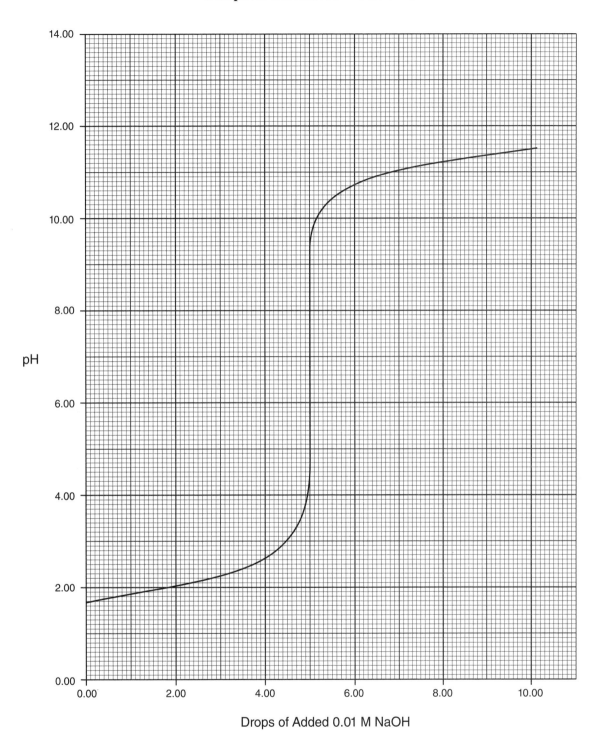

Figure 14.2 1 Drop of 0.05 M HCl titrated with 0.01 NaOH.

Computer-Simulated Titration Curves For 5 Drops of Strong Acid With Strong Base

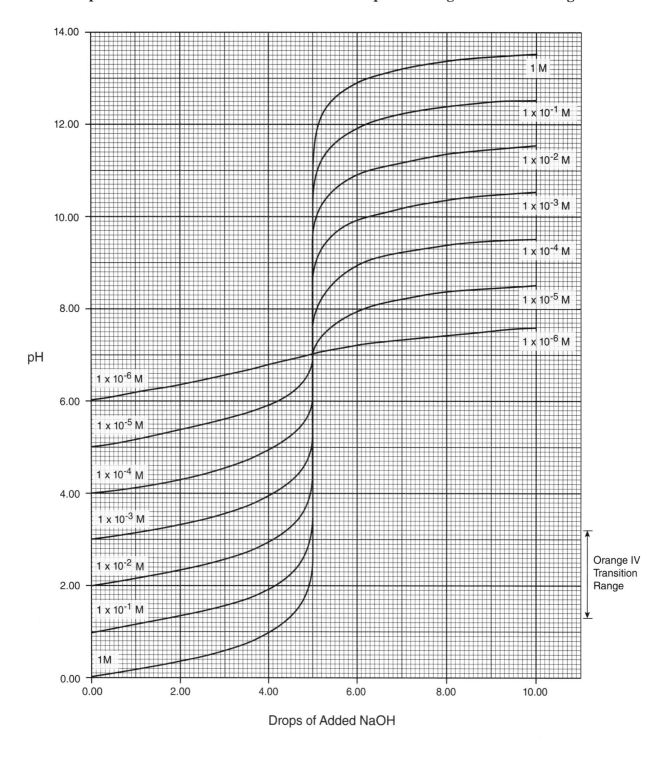

Figure 14.3 Effect of concentration of reactants.

Computer-Simulated Titration Curves

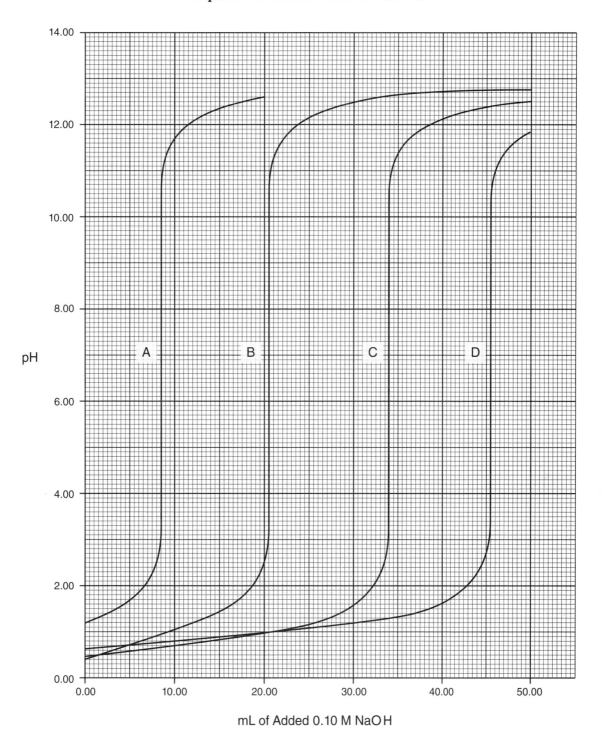

Figure 14.4 Strong acids titrated with strong base.

Computer-Simulated Titration Curve

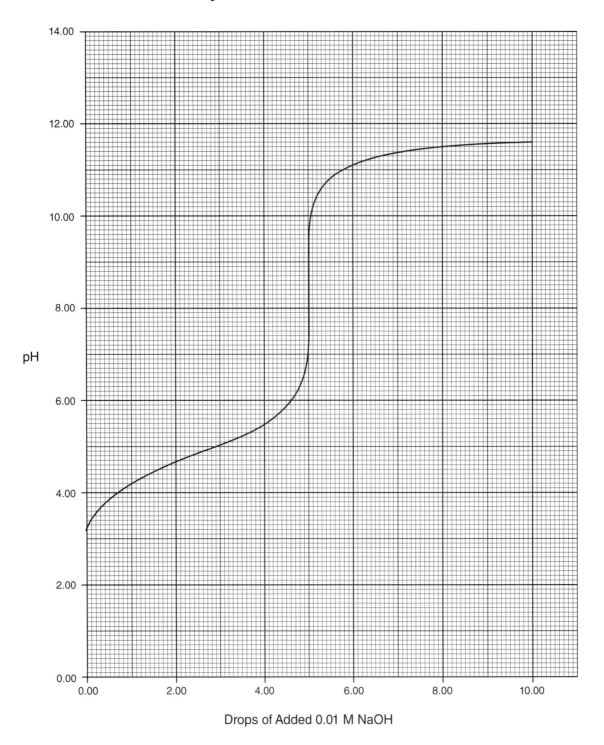

Figure 14.5 1 drop of 0.05 M CH$_3$COOH with 0.01 M NaOH.

Computer-Simulated Titration Curves for 5 Drops of Weak Acids with Strong Base

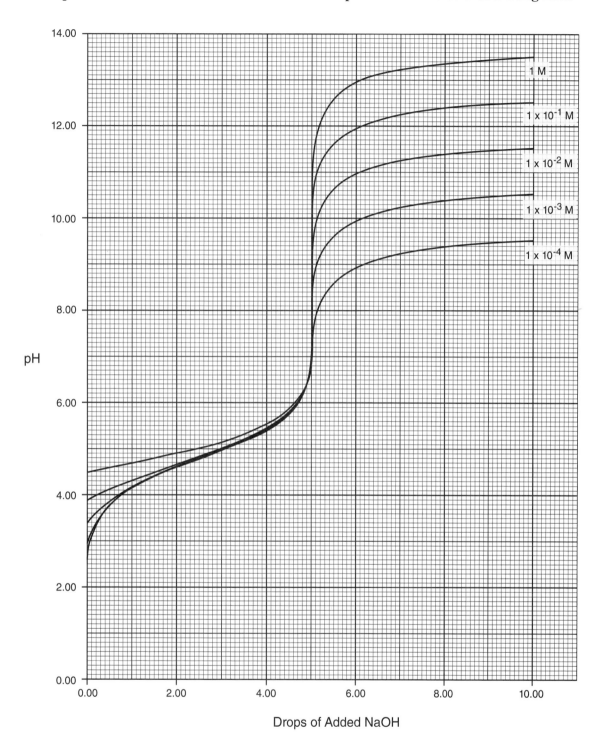

Figure 14.6 Effect of the concentration of reagents.

Computer-Simulated Titration Curves for
5 Drops of Various 0.10 M Weak Acids with Strong Base

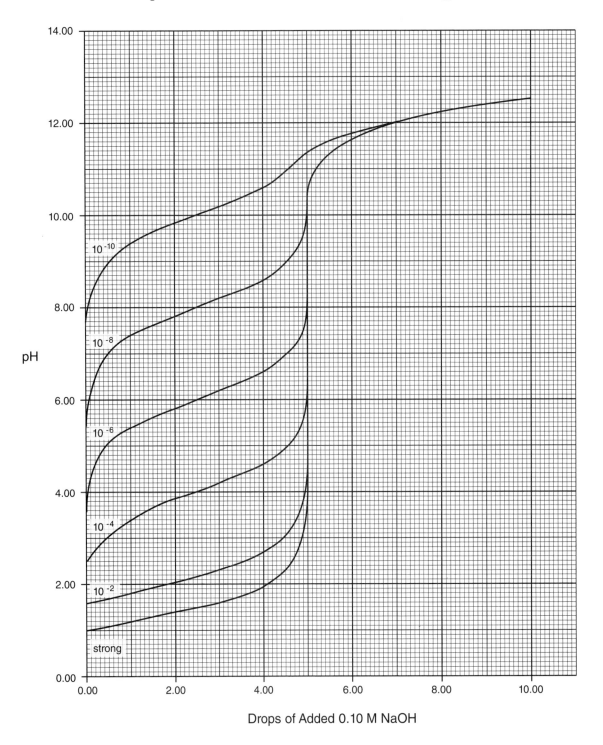

Figure 14.7 Effect of K_a.

Computer-Simulated Titration Curve

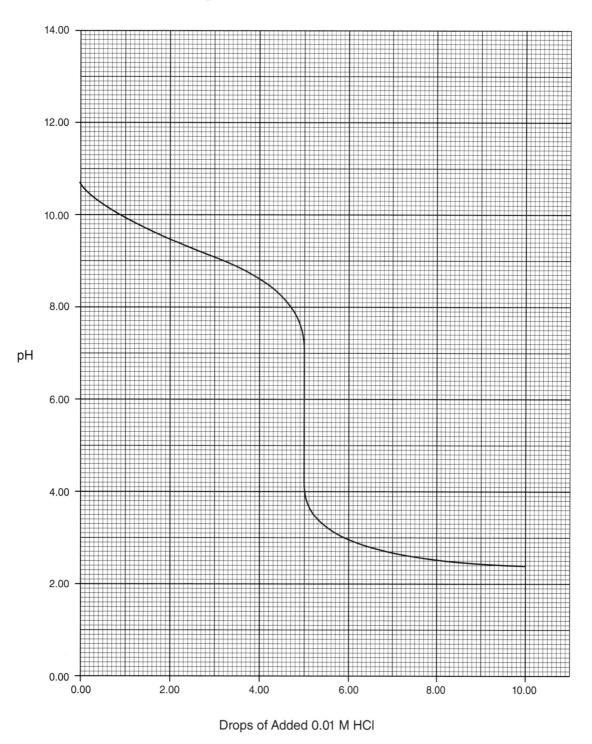

pH

Drops of Added 0.01 M HCl

Figure 14.8 1 drop of 0.05 M NH$_3$ titrated with 0.01 M HCl.

Computer-Simulated Titration Curves for 5 Drops of NH_3 with Strong Acid (HCl)

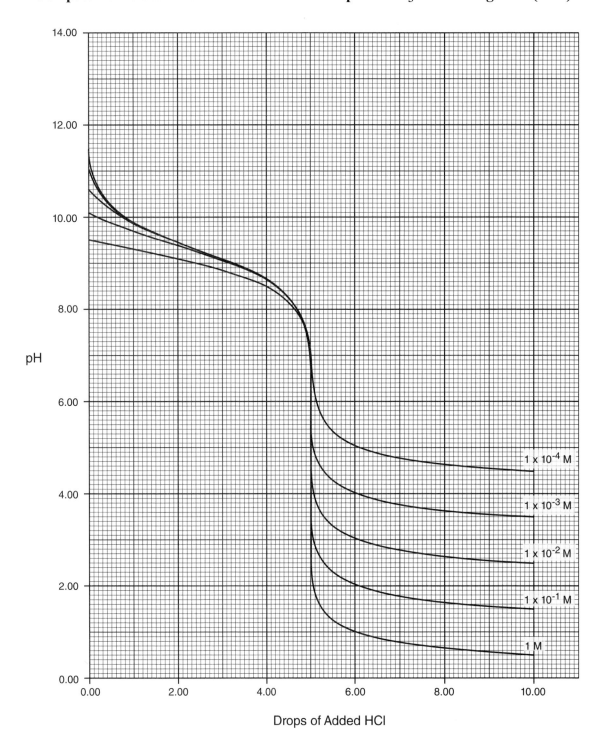

Figure 14.9 Effect of the concentration of reagents.

**Computer-Simulated Titration Curves for
5 Drops of Various 0.10 M Weak Bases with Strong Acid**

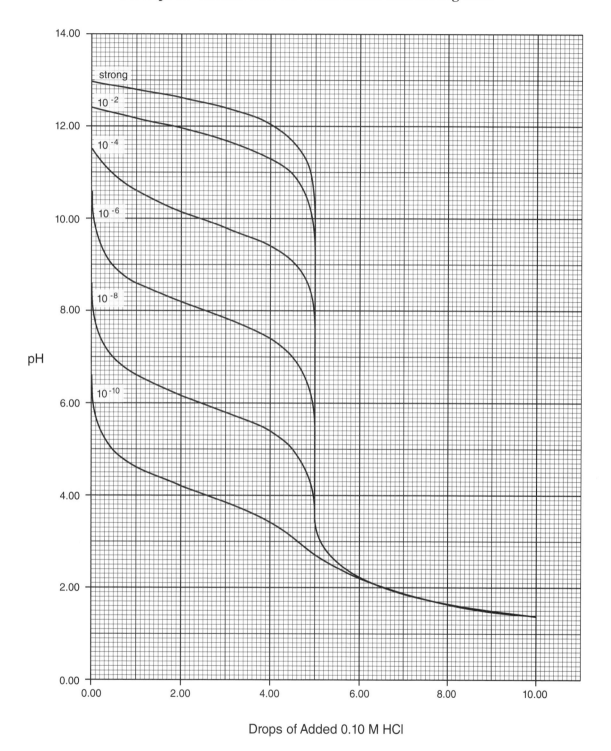

Drops of Added 0.10 M HCl

Figure 14.10 Effect of K_b.

Computer-Simulated Titration Curve

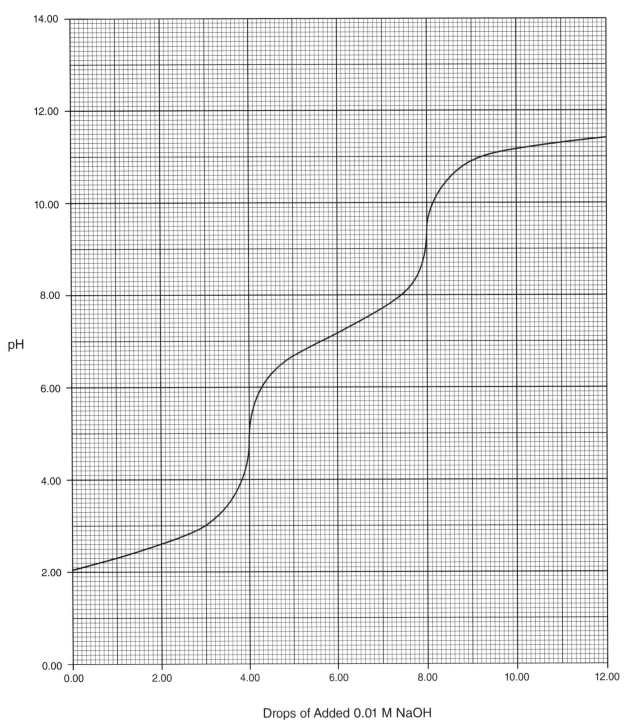

Figure 14.11 1 drop of 0.04 M H$_3$PO$_4$ with 0.01 M NaOH.

Experiment 15

Redox Equilibria
and Electrochemistry

"It is better to wear out than to rust out."

—Bishop Richard Cumberland,
1631–1718

Introduction

Life on this planet derives from the photosynthetic process by which plant cells trap and use solar energy. The deceptively simple photosynthetic equation

$$H_2O + CO_2 \xrightarrow{\text{light}} Carbohydrates + O_2$$

occurs via a complex cascade of biochemical reactions. The critical events are a light-activated transfer of an electron to an acceptor in the chloroplast, a flow of electrons from water through an electron transport chain, and the resulting formation of carbohydrates from carbon dioxide. The key reactions that involve electron transfer are called redox reactions. In evolutionary terms the change from anaerobic life to aerobic (oxygen-using) life was an important step because it allowed a rich energy source to be used. The redox reactions of oxygen with glucose, mediated by the transport proteins myoglobin and hemoglobin, provide an efficient way of generating the energy for life processes.

Most of the energy used by our industrial society comes from the combustion of fossil fuels, such as gas, coal, and oil. Fossil fuels are the end products of millions of years of sun-trapping reaction by plants. The burning of fossil fuels is a redox process by which electrons are transferred from dioxygen to water and carbon dioxide. As you can see, the common thread in the production of useful energy by plant and animal life involves reactions that involve the gain and loss of electrons.

The study of electron transfer processes in natural and synthetic systems has became an extremely important subfield of chemistry and is called electrochemistry. The field of electrochemistry is broadening rapidly as research reveals the incredibly varied part played by redox reactions in such diverse disciplines as neurophysiology, meteorology, and geochemistry. Indeed, it is worth quoting an axiom of electrochemists—"There are only two kinds of reactions: redox and the rest!" In this series of experiments, you have the opportunity to explore the fundamentals of solution electrochemistry. The experiments have been designed such that the basic principles of redox equilibria can be investigated. You may then apply the principles to your own field of endeavor.

Background Chemistry

Chemical reactions that involve the movement of electrons between chemical species are called *redox reactions* (an abbreviation of reduction–oxidation reaction). Redox reactions can be identified, and the movement of electrons can be followed, by using a sort of formal "bookkeeping" of the number of electrons associated with atoms. This accounting of electrons involves assigning arbitrary *oxidation numbers* to individual atoms within a chemical species. Redox reactions are reactions in which there are changes in oxidation numbers. Every redox reaction can be divided into two *half-reactions:* one that involves a gain of electrons and one that involves a loss of electrons. The gain of electrons is called *reduction* and the loss of electrons is called *oxidation*.

Consider the following interesting chemical reaction in which a copper coin is dropped into a dilute solution of silver nitrate ($AgNO_3$). Beautiful, shining needles of metallic silver crystals grow slowly from the copper surface, especially if the solution is not disturbed. The solution also slowly changes from colorless to a pale blue color, indicating that Cu^{2+} ions are being produced. The overall chemical equation is

$$Cu(s) + 2AgNO_3 \rightleftarrows Cu(NO_3)_2 + 2Ag(s)$$

for which the net ionic equation is

$$Cu(s) + 2Ag^+ \rightleftarrows Cu^{2+} + 2Ag(s)$$

This reaction is a redox reaction because the oxidation number of copper is changing from 0 to +2 ($Cu(s)$ to Cu^{2+}) and that of silver is changing from +1 to 0 (Ag^+ to $Ag(s)$). The NO_3^- ion remains unchanged during the reaction and is called a *spectator ion*. The reaction can be divided into two half-reactions:

Reduction: $2Ag^+ + 2e^- \rightleftarrows 2Ag(s)$

Oxidation: $Cu(s) \rightleftarrows Cu^{2+} + 2e^-$

which add together to give the redox reaction. Redox reactions in which the reactants are observed to react and produce products—i.e., proceed from left to right—are called *spontaneous* reactions. The reverse reaction,

$$Cu^{2+} + 2Ag(s) \rightleftarrows Cu(s) + 2Ag^+$$

will not occur and is said to be a nonspontaneous reaction. The energy given out in the spontaneous reaction in which the copper coin reduced Ag^+ to

silver crystals is lost as heat to the solution. The redox reaction will eventually come to equilibrium, and no more heat will be given out.

Redox reactions in which electrons are completely lost by one species and completely accepted by another are very useful because the two half-reactions can often be physically separated. The electrons that are transferred may then be allowed to flow through external wires in a circuit and be made to do useful work. *Electrochemistry* is the study of redox reactions that either produce or utilize electrical energy (moving electrons and/or ions) in devices called electrochemical cells.

In the redox reaction

$$Cu(s) + 2Ag^+ \rightleftarrows Cu^{2+} + 2Ag(s)$$

the two half-reactions can actually be separated by placing the reactants in different compartments, partitioned by some type of porous medium that prevents mixing, but not ion flow. The compartments, called *half-cells*, each contain a metal electrode in contact with its own metal ion, as shown in Figure 15.1.

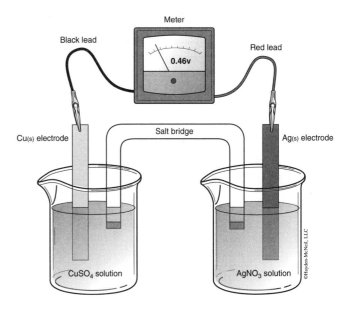

Figure 15.1 An electrochemical cell made up of two half-cells.

An external connection between the two electrodes completes the circuit, and electrons will flow from the copper electrode through the external wire and meter and into the silver electrode. The copper electrode will dissolve, forming Cu^{2+} ions in solution, and Ag^+ ions will pick up electrons at the surface of the silver electrode and be deposited as silver atoms. The electrode at which oxidation takes place (the copper electrode) is called the *anode*, and the electrode at which reduction takes place (the silver electrode) is called the *cathode*. The combination of the two half-cells is called an *electrochemical cell*.

In the electrochemical cell under discussion, it is a fact that oxidation,

$$Cu(s) \rightleftarrows Cu^{2+} + 2e^-$$

occurs at the copper electrode (anode) and that reduction,

$$2Ag^+ + 2e^- \rightleftarrows 2Ag(s)$$

occurs at the silver electrode (cathode). The relative tendency of a particular species to give up or accept electrons is manifested as a measurable electrical force, or voltage (*potential*), between the two electrodes. This force may be considered as being the sum of two potentials called *half-cell potentials* or *single-electrode potentials*.

The tendency of a species to give up or accept electrons can only be compared relative to another species. In order to obtain consistent electrochemical data, it is necessary to compare all single electrodes to a standard reference electrode. The universal reference electrode, chosen by international agreement, is the *standard hydrogen electrode* (SHE), which is shown in the diagram in Figure 15.2.

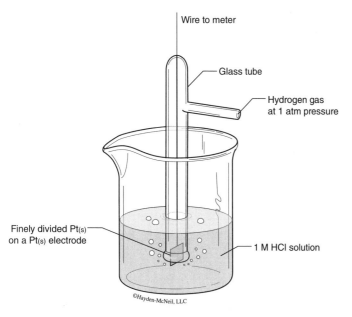

Figure 15.2 A standard hydrogen electrode.

The half-reaction at the SHE,

$$2H^+ + 2e^- \rightleftarrows H_2(g)$$

is arbitrarily written, for the moment, as a reduction.

An arbitrary assignment of *zero* electrode potential (0.00 V) is given to the SHE, and all other electrode potentials are referred to it. It is now customary to report *single* electrode potentials in tables, and it must be remembered that these single half-cell potentials are really measured in combination with a SHE at 0.00 V.

The single-electrode potential value is dependent on the concentration of the ion surrounding the electrode and on the temperature. Standard conditions of 1 M concentration and 298 K (25 °C) have been chosen, and by international agreement all standard electrode potentials are reported as *standard reduction potentials* (E°). Some examples follow.

$Al^{3+} + 3e^- \rightleftarrows Al(s)$	$E° = -1.66$ V
$Cu^{2+} + 2e^- \rightleftarrows Cu(s)$	$E° = 0.34$ V
$2H^+ + 2e^- \rightleftarrows H_2(g)$	$E° = 0.00$ V
$Ag^+ + e^- \rightleftarrows Ag(s)$	$E° = 0.80$ V

A useful way of thinking about these E° values is to remember that the more *positive* the E° value, the more that reaction goes to the right. The E° value for oxidation reactions is obtained simply by changing the *sign* of the appropriate reduction reaction, e.g.,

$$Cu(s) \rightleftarrows Cu^{2+} + 2e^- \qquad E° = -0.34 \text{ V}$$

One very important practical consideration in the measurement of cell potentials is that the cell reaction must be carried out under standard conditions. A simple wire connection between the two electrodes would allow the electrons to flow and the redox reaction to go to completion. In the process, the concentrations of ions in each half-cell would change dramatically, and the cell voltage would drop to zero, its equilibrium value. Cell potential measurements are, therefore, usually made with instruments that have very high resistance in order to minimize the flow of electrons during the measurement.

Another important consideration is the electrical connection that must be made between the two half-cell solutions before the cell voltage measurement can be made. The connection is called a *salt bridge*. The salt bridge allows electrical neutrality to be maintained in each half-cell. In the voltage measurement, a few electrons must flow from the anode, through the meter, and into the cathode. Cations are generated in the anode half-cell solution, and to maintain a charge balance, anions flow from the salt bridge. Cations are consumed in the cathode half-cell, and to maintain charge balance, cations flow from the salt bridge. The net result is simply a flow of inert electrolyte from the salt bridge into the cell.

Standard reduction potential values refer, of course, to voltages measured under standard conditions. In the case of nonstandard conditions, the reduction potential value will be different from those reported at 1 M and 25 °C. The quantitative relationship between cell potential and concentration (and temperature) is called the *Nernst law*:

$$E = E° - \frac{RT}{nF} \ln Q$$

where $E°$ is the standard potential, Q is the reaction quotient, F is the Faraday constant, n is the number of moles of electrons transferred in the cell reaction, R is the gas constant, and T is the absolute temperature. Q, the reaction quotient, is calculated in the same way that the equilibrium constant (K) is calculated. For example, for a reaction $aA + bB \rightleftarrows cC + dD$, $Q = [C]^c[D]^d / [A]^a[B]^b$. The difference is that Q is the value of this quotient at whatever the concentrations of the reactants and products happen to be at—i.e., not necessarily at equilibrium. If the value of Q is smaller than K, then it means that the reaction must move forward to reach equilibrium. If Q is larger than K, then the reaction must move backwards to reach equilibrium. If $Q = K$, then the system is at equilibrium. The Nernst law may be rewritten, after substituting for all constants and putting $T = 298$ K, as

$$E = E° - \frac{0.0592}{n} \log_{10} Q$$

The Nernst law is valid both for the potentials of half-reactions and for overall redox reactions. For a reaction that has come to equilibrium, the cell voltage must be *zero*, i.e.,

$$E = 0 \text{ and } Q = K$$

where K is the equilibrium constant for the reaction. At equilibrium the Nernst law becomes

$$E = 0 = E° - \frac{0.0592}{n} \log_{10} K$$

and, rearranging,

$$\log_{10} K = \frac{nE°}{0.0592}$$

The value of the equilibrium constant for a redox reaction (at 25 °C) can be calculated using the above relationship.

An electrochemical cell in which a spontaneous redox reaction can occur is called a *voltaic cell*, or battery. Voltaic cells are useful energy storage devices in which a suitable redox system is packed into an appropriate container. The voltage produced by a voltaic cell is, of course, dependent upon the particular redox reaction used, the concentration of materials, and the design of the package. A battery in use is a device in which chemical energy is converted into flowing electrons in a redox reaction that eventually winds down to an equilibrium state. At equilibrium, the battery is dead and the cell voltage is zero.

An electrochemical cell in which a nonspontaneous redox reaction is made to occur by means of an external power source is called an *electrolysis cell*. Automobile batteries that are being recharged are examples of electrolysis cells. When a run-down, lead-acid automobile battery is recharged, an outside voltage source pushes the nonspontaneous reaction to completion. Electrolysis cells are used extensively in the industrial production of a wide variety of useful chemicals such as chlorine, sodium hydroxide, aluminum, and in metal finishing and plating.

Unfortunately, spontaneous electrochemistry is not always a useful process. The corrosion of iron and steel is estimated to cost over 80 billion dollars a year in the United States. We see the results in automobiles and other consumer products, as well as in bridges, buildings, and in storage tanks. Many of the typical results of corrosion are best explained in terms of electrochemical mechanisms. Iron, which shows evidence of corrosion, is often found to have anodic areas at which

$$Fe(s) \rightleftarrows Fe^{2+} + 2e^-$$

and cathodic areas at which atmospheric dioxygen is reduced to OH^- ions:

$$O_2(g) + 2H_2O + 4e^- \rightleftarrows 4OH^-$$

Iron (II) hydroxide ($Fe(OH)_2$) precipitates as an insoluble solid and is subsequently oxidized to a loose, flaky deposit of hydrated iron oxide called rust. The rusting process is spontaneous under a wide variety of conditions. The major factors appear to be the presence of dioxygen, water, microimpurities, and dissimilar metals in contact with each other.

Quiz Outline

Your quiz will NOT cover all of the information below, but it will cover some subset of the information given below.

Be able to explain the difference between voltaic and electrolytic cells.

Be able to identify for BOTH the voltaic and electrolytic cells the (a) sign of the anode, (b) sign of the cathode, (c) location of reduction half reaction (cathode or anode?), and (d) location of the oxidation half–reaction (cathode or anode?).

Be able to balance a redox equation.

Be able to identify oxidation and reduction half–reactions as well as the oxidizing and reducing agents.

Understand the relationship between the equilibrium constant and the spontaneity of a reaction.

Be able to explain the purpose of the salt bridge.

Be able to use the Nernst equation for calculations.

Read the article in your packet on "Metals in groundwater...." Be able to answer questions from it such as (a) what is the difference between "pump and treat" and "in-situ" methods of treating metals in groundwater, and (b) what are the main advantages of the "in-situ" approach?

Note: Please bring your chemistry textbook AND a penny with you to lab.

Sample Pre-Laboratory Quiz

1. Explain the difference between a "voltaic" and an "electrolytic" cell.

2. The following figure is given in the Introduction to this experiment:

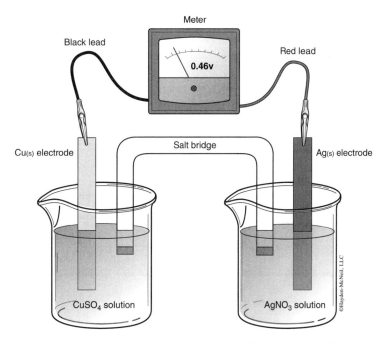

Meter

Black lead

Red lead

0.46v

Cu(s) electrode

Salt bridge

Ag(s) electrode

CuSO$_4$ solution

AgNO$_3$ solution

©Hayden-McNeil, LLC

   Answer the following questions regarding the above figure: (a) Given that this is a voltaic cell, and the Cu(s) is the anode, write the half-cell reactions and the overall reaction. (b) What is the sign of the anode in the above cell? (c) What is the purpose of the salt bridge in the above cell?

3. The observed voltage (+0.46 V) occurred when the temperature was 25 °C, and the concentrations of the Ag$^+$ ion and the Cu^{2+} ion were both 1 Molar. Set up an equation which could be solved to determine what the voltage would be if the silver ion concentration was 0.01 M, and the copper ion concentration was 2.0 M, and the temperature was 30 °C. (It is not necessary to solve the equation, just set it up.)

4. Suppose the K$_{eq}$ for the reaction shown in #2 was exactly equal to 1. Would it be a spontaneous reaction under the standard conditions? Explain your answer.

Laboratory Experiments

Flowchart of the Experiments

Section A.	Redox Reaction Investigations

Section B.	A Small-Scale Electrochemical Cell

Section C.	An Electrochemical Series from Cell Data

Section D.	Electrographic Analysis of Metals

Section E.	Lead-Acid Automobile Battery

Requires one four-hour class period to complete.

The overall goal in this series of experiments in electrochemistry is to be able to identify, write, balance, and apply common reduction–oxidation (electron transfer) reactions. You should also be able to construct a variety of electrochemical cells, both voltaic and electrolytic, and be able to use standard electrochemical instrumentation and conventions to measure and calculate standard reduction potentials.

CAUTION: Solutions of many transition metal ions, e.g., Pb^{2+}, Cu^{2+}, and Sn^{2+}, are toxic. Even though you will be using only very small amounts of these solutions, it is important to exercise caution when using these chemicals. It is also important to observe the hazardous waste regulations in this experiment. All transition metal ion solutions and waste will be collected and disposed of by the instructors and technical staff. Acids and bases, e.g., H_2SO_4 and NH_3, are also corrosive and toxic. Please use these solutions with caution. If you get any of these chemicals on your hands, wash well with cold water and report to your instructor.

Section A. Redox Reaction Investigations

Goals: *(1) To study a redox reaction involving copper and zinc species. (2) To describe and characterize some of the electrochemical properties of the reaction.*

Experimental Steps: 1. Clean your plastic reaction surface.

2. Use tweezers to transfer a piece of Zn foil and Cu foil to the surface.

3. Drop 2 drops of 1 M $CuSO_4$ solution onto the *top* of a piece of Zn(s).

4. Drop 2 drops of 1 M $ZnSO_4$ solution onto the *top* of a piece of Cu(s).

5. Study each of the solution-metal interfaces with your hand lens.

   • Describe and record what you see.

   • Describe the surface of each metal under the drop. A good way to do this is to remove the drop with a cotton swab. Why is one of the metals discolored under the drop?

Section B. A Small-Scale Electrochemical Cell

Goals: *(1) To construct a small-scale electrochemical cell using the redox system investigated in Section A. (2) To learn how to use a multimeter to measure electrochemical cell potentials and be able to use the appropriate sign conventions to calculate standard reduction potentials from cell potentials.*

Experimental Steps: 1. Obtain a multimeter from your instructor. Set up the meter to measure DC voltage. Use the two needle probes (red and black).

   NOTE: If you don't know how to do this, check with your instructor.

2. Place a small rectangular piece of filter paper (already cut for you) onto the plastic surface.

3. Place a piece of Cu(s) and a piece of Zn(s) onto the paper about 3 cm apart. The diagram illustrates the locations of the solutions delivered in steps 4–6.

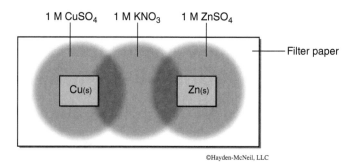

1 M CuSO$_4$ 1 M KNO$_3$ 1 M ZnSO$_4$

©Hayden-McNeil, LLC

4. Deliver 1–2 drops of 1 M CuSO$_4$ to the paper just at the edge of the copper metal so that the solution soaks under the metal piece.

5. Deliver 1–2 drops of 1 M ZnSO$_4$ to the paper so that it soaks under the zinc metal piece.

6. Deliver 2 drops 1 M KNO$_3$ to the dry paper in between the wet circles.

    NOTE: The KNO$_3$ solution will spread out and run into the part of the paper wet with CuSO$_4$ and ZnSO$_4$.

7. Switch the multimeter on and touch the red probe to the piece of copper metal and the black probe to the piece of zinc metal.

    • Read and record the voltage. Don't forget the sign!

    • Estimate the fluctuation in your measurement by moving the probe around on the surface of the metals and taking a few more voltage readings.

8. Reverse the probes.

    • Record what happens to the sign and switch the meter off.

    You have just made a micro battery that is capable of delivering almost as much voltage as a flashlight battery (although not as much current). This battery is made up of two half-cells joined electrically by wires (the probes) and the salt bridge solution (KNO$_3$).

    The sign conventions in electrochemistry are confusing. In a voltaic cell (a battery, like the one you just made) reduction occurs at the cathode which is positive. (One mnemonic device that might help you to remember this is "Vern the Roman Catholic Priest.") The multimeter has two probes, one red (which is the positive terminal), and one black (which is the negative terminal). If you get a positive reading when your red (+) probe is on the zinc strip, then zinc is acting as the cathode of the battery. If you get a negative reading, then your battery is running in the opposite direction, i.e., zinc is acting as the anode.

Questions: Q1.   (a) What is the net redox equation for the spontaneous reaction that you observed occurring in Parts A and B?

          (b) What are the oxidation and reduction half-reactions?

          (c) What are the oxidizing and reducing agents for the spontaneous redox reaction?

          (d) Identify which half-reaction occurs at the anode and which occurs at the cathode.

Q2.   The definition of "standard conditions" includes a "standard concentration" for ions in solution.

(a) What is the value of this "standard concentration"?

(b) Are your experimental conditions in Section B standard in concentration?

Q3.   The standard reduction potential, $E°_{red}$, for

$$Cu^{2+}(aq) + 2e^- \rightleftarrows Cu(s)$$

is 0.34 V (measured against a standard hydrogen electrode).

Using $E°_{cell} = E°_{ox} + E°_{red}$ and the value for the standard reduction potential for copper, and your experimentally determined $E°_{cell}$, calculate $E°_{ox}$, the standard oxidation potential for

$$Zn(s) \rightleftarrows 2e^- + Zn^{2+}(aq)$$

Then, reverse the sign to obtain the standard reduction potential, $E°_{red}$, for

$$Zn^{2+}(aq) + 2e^- \rightleftarrows Zn(s)$$

Q4.   Calculate the equilibrium constant for the redox reaction

$$Cu^{2+}(aq) + Zn(s) \rightleftarrows Cu(s) + Zn^{2+}(aq)$$

By using the relationship

$$\log_{10} K = \frac{nE°_{cell}}{0.0592 V \cdot mol}(\text{at } 25° C)$$

where K is the equilibrium constant, n is the number of moles of electrons transferred in the redox reaction, and $E°_{cell}$ is the standard cell potential.

Q5.   Does the value of K that you calculate represent the equilibrium constant for a spontaneous or nonspontaneous reaction, under standard conditions? Explain.

NOTE: Equilibrium constants for redox reactions cannot be found in the usual reference literature (as can equilibrium constants for acid–base reactions, etc.). Redox reaction equilibrium constants are generally calculated from standard reduction potential data.

Section C.   An Electrochemical Series from Cell Data

Goals: *(1) To construct a series of electrochemical cells. (2) To obtain cell potentials for the calculation of standard reduction potentials.*

Discussion: The standard potential data obtained in this section may then be used to interpret corrosion phenomena, design voltaic and electrolytic cells, and arrange reduction reactions into an electrochemical series.

Experimental Steps: 1.   Obtain a round 9 cm diameter filter paper and make a cell template similar to the template shown in the diagram below.

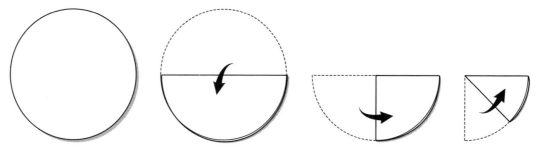

Fold filter paper three times (i.e., into 8 sections)

Cut out the shaded section

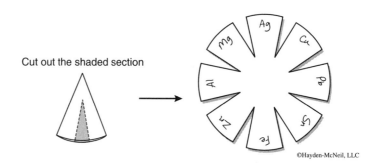

©Hayden-McNeil, LLC

2.   Write on each sector the atomic symbols of the metals, as shown.

3.   Place the cutout paper into the lid of a clean, dry plastic Petri dish.

4.   Use your tweezers to transfer the appropriate metal pieces (e.g., Ag(s) wire, Cu(s) squares, etc.) to each sector. Note: Copper squares work better than copper wire.

NOTE: Make sure they are arranged in the order shown.

5.   Drop 2 drops of the appropriate metal ion solutions onto the paper at the edge of each metal piece so that each metal is contacting the solution (as in Section B).

6.   Drop 1 M KNO_3 salt bridge solution into the middle so that it soaks outwards and contacts all the other wet areas. Try not to use too much!

7.   Make a table in your notebook of the cells, with room to record the cell voltages.

8.   Switch the multimeter to measure DC voltage and start making measurements with the red probe on Cu(s), moving the black probe around the other metals in the circle in a clockwise manner. Don't forget the sign! When you have finished, shut the meter off.

NOTE: The measurements made on Mg(s) and Al(s) may be unstable. Just try to obtain an approximate voltage.

9.   Clean up by placing the filter paper and metal pieces in the appropriate waste containers.

Question: Q6.   Use the principles that you learned in Section B to calculate the standard reduction potential for one of the half-cells, given that the $E°_{red}$ for

$$Cu^{2+} + 2e^- \rightleftarrows Cu(s)$$

is 0.34 V. Show your calculation.

Note that $E°_{red}$ for a half-reaction is not dependent on the coefficients, provided, of course, that the reaction is balanced, i.e., $E°_{red}$ for

$$Ag^+ + e^- \rightleftarrows Ag(s)$$

is the same as $E°_{red}$ for

$$2Ag^+ + 2e^- \rightleftarrows 2Ag(s)$$

This is because $E°_{red}$ depends on *what* the species is (an intensive property), not on *how much* of the species you have (an extensive property).

NOTE: You will be completing the calculation of the standard reduction potentials for the rest of the half-cells as additional questions at the end of lab.

Section D.   Electrographic Analysis of Metals

Goal: To carry out a chemical analysis of a metal sample by making the sample the anode of an electrolytic cell.

Discussion: An electrolytic cell is one in which an external power supply is used to force a nonspontaneous reaction to occur. In an e̲lectrolytic cell, r̲eduction occurs at the c̲athode which is n̲egative. A mnemonic device that may help you to remember this is "E̲ve the R̲oman C̲atholic N̲un."

Experimental Steps: 1.   Obtain from Reagent Central the following items: a piece of aluminum foil (approx. 5 cm × 5 cm), a piece of 3MM chromatography paper (approx. 2 cm × 4 cm), a penny, a 9 V battery, and leads with clips.

                     2.   Check the battery voltage to make sure it is at least 8 volts.

                     3.   Place the foil into a Petri dish.

                     4.   Fold the chromatography paper in half and place it onto the foil. Add 4 or 5 drops of 1 M KNO_3 to the paper.

                     5.   Place a clean penny onto the paper.

                     6.   Clip an electrical lead to the foil and clip the other end of it to the negative terminal of the battery.

                     7.   Clip the other lead to the positive terminal of the battery. Then, using the other end, *press hard* in the center of the penny for around 5 seconds.

                     8.   Remove the coin, lift up and unfold the paper, and place it on a small piece of microtowel. Add a few drops of phenolpthalein to both the upper half (which was in contact with the penny), and the lower half of the piece of filter paper. Observe and record your results.

9. **Attach the paper to your notebook.**

Questions: Q7.   What image did you observe on the chromatography paper?

                    Q8.   Which metal is the cathode and which is the anode in this experiment?

                    Q9.   (a) What half-reaction is occurring at the coin?

                          (b) Speculate on the species involved in the other half-reaction. To do this, list all the substances that are contacting the aluminum foil. Using the table of standard reduction potentials in your textbook, decide which of these are the *most likely to receive electrons under your reaction conditions.* An additional aid is the color of the chromatography paper after treatment with phenolphthalein. Note: Phenolphthalein is an acid/base indicator which is not redox active.

                    Q10. Write out the overall electrochemical reaction that you observed.

Section E.   Lead-Acid Automobile Battery

Goals: *(1) To build a single-cell, lead-acid battery. (2) To charge it to produce the electrode surface conditions necessary for the system to act as a battery.*

Experimental Steps: 1. Half-fill a well of a 24-well tray with 1 M H_2SO_4 solution.

                    2. Place two small strips of lead into the solution in the well so that they *do not touch.*

                    3. Switch the multimeter to measure DC voltage and clip the leads to the two lead strips in such a manner that each clip holds the lead against the side of the well. Measure $E°_{cell}$.

                    4. Remove the multimeter and "charge" the Pb-acid battery by clipping electrical leads to the 9 V battery from each strip of Pb metal. Allow to charge ~30 seconds to 1 minute.

                        NOTE: There will be an immediate vigorous reaction as the H_2SO_4 is electrolyzed. *Do not allow the lead strips to touch!*

                    5. Unclip the battery and examine the strips of lead.

                        NOTE: One of the strips is a clean Pb(s) surface; however, the other has a brownish colored layer of PbO_2(s) on the surface. The initial charging reaction involves the electrolysis of dilute sulfuric acid,

$$2H_2O(l) \rightleftarrows 2H_2(g) + O_2(g)$$

                        and the dioxygen oxidizes the Pb(s) surface to PbO_2(s). Once the electrode surfaces are established, the equation for the *spontaneous* discharge of a lead acid battery is:

$$Pb(s) + PbO_2(s) + 2H_2SO_4 \rightleftarrows 2PbSO_4(s) + 2H_2O(l)$$

                    6. Remove the battery from the circuit and place the two Pb leads back into solution. Switch the multimeter to measure DC voltage and clip the leads to the two Pb strips. Measure $E°_{cell}$ for the spontaneous discharge of the battery.

Questions: Q11.   Do the voltages determined in steps 3 and 6 make sense, i.e., did you get what you expected? Explain.

Q12.   How would you construct the usual 12 V car battery from lead-acid cells?

Q13.   For the *spontaneous* discharge of a lead-acid automobile battery, which electrode would be the anode and which the cathode? Explain your answer.

Homework: HW1.   (a) Complete the calculation of the standard reduction potentials for each half-cell in Section C. Then, arrange the standard reduction potentials and corresponding half-reactions in order, starting with the most negative at the top of the table and ending with the most positive at the bottom. By doing this you are making a table of reduction potentials to compare with your textbook.

NOTE: All solutions are 1.0 M, except for Ag^{1+}, which is 0.1 M. You should use the Nernst equation,

$$E_{cell} = E^{\circ}_{cell} - \frac{0.0592V \cdot mol}{n} \log_{10} Q \, (at \, 25\,^{\circ}C)$$

to determine E°_{cell} for the cell involving Ag^{1+}.

Include literature values (your textbook would be useful) for the standard reduction potentials in your table. Reference your source!

(b) Which is the strongest oxidizing agent in the table? Which is the strongest reducing agent in the table?

(c) Why is it important that the precious metals Au, Ag, and Pt are poor reducing agents? What would happen to them if they weren't?

(d) Write a balanced redox equation for the *spontaneous reaction* between the Cu/Ag half-cells.

HW2.   Consider the Zn/Cu battery that you made in Section B.

(a) Using standard reduction potentials (literature values), calculate the standard cell potential, E°_{cell}, i.e., the voltage when $[Zn^{2+}] = 1.00$ M and $[Cu^{2+}] = 1.00$ M.

(b) Using the Nernst equation, calculate the value of E_{cell} when $[Zn^{2+}] = 2.00$ M and $[Cu^{2+}] = 1.00$ M $\times 10^{-4}$ M.

(c) What is happening to the observed cell potential, E_{cell}, as $[Zn^{2+}]$ increases and $[Cu^{2+}]$ decreases?

(d) What is happening to the standard cell potential, E°_{cell}, as $[Zn^{2+}]$ increases and $[Cu^{2+}]$ decreases?

(e) What will be the value of E_{cell} when the Cu/Zn battery has "run down," i.e., reached equilibrium?

(f) What will be the value of E°_{cell} when the Cu/Zn battery has "run down," i.e., reached equilibrium?

(g) Will the concentrations of $Zn^{2+}(aq)$ and $Cu^{2+}(aq)$ be large or small when the battery has "run down"? Does this make sense?

HW3.   An electrochemical cell was constructed from Sn/Sn^{2+} and Pb/Pb^{2+} with KNO$_3$ as the salt bridge. The concentrations were [Sn^{2+}] = 1.0 M and [Pb^{2+}] = 0.1 M.

$$Sn^{2+}(aq) + Pb(s) \rightleftarrows Sn(s) + Pb^{2+}(aq)$$

Is the above reaction spontaneous under the conditions given? Explain how you arrived at your conclusions.

HW4.   Reconsider your data from Section B to obtain an estimate of the uncertainty in your calculation of the equilibrium constant, K, for the reaction:

$$Cu^{2+}(aq) + Zn(s) \rightleftarrows Cu(s) + Zn^{2+}(aq)$$

(a) Use your average reading for your best estimate of E°$_{cell}$ for this reaction. Now, calculate the maximum and minimum values for a 0.1% fluctuation in your E°$_{cell}$. e.g., if E°$_{cell}$ = 1.000V, then the maximum value is 1.001 V and the minimum is 0.999 V.

(b) Calculate the equilibrium constant, K, using the maximum and minimum values:

$$\log_{10} K = \frac{nE°_{cell}}{0.0592V \cdot mol}(at\ 25\ °C)$$

Calculate the uncertainty in K, where uncertainty = (maximum − minimum)/2. Report your best estimate of K (from Q4) with the uncertainty using the correct number of significant digits.

(c) Consider the multiple measurements (to observe fluctuations in values) that you made for E°$_{cell}$ in Section B, step 7. Were your fluctuations smaller or larger than 0.1%?

(d) How much does a 0.1% increase in E°$_{cell}$ change your value of K? Are you surprised?

Standard Reduction Potentials at 25 °C

Half-Reaction	$E°$(V)	Half-Reaction	$E°$(V)
$Ag^+(aq) + e^- \rightarrow Ag(s)$	+0.799	$2 H_2O(l) + 2 e^- \rightarrow H_2(g) + 2 OH^-(aq)$	–0.83
$AgBr(s) + e^- \rightarrow Ag(s) + Br^-(aq)$	+0.095	$HO_2^-(aq) + H_2O(l) + 2 e^- \rightarrow 3 OH^-(aq)$	+0.88
$AgCl(s) + e^- \rightarrow Ag(s) + Cl^-(aq)$	+0.222	$H_2O_2(aq) + 2 H^+(aq) + 2 e^- \rightarrow 2 H_2O(l)$	+1.776
$Ag(CN)_2^-(aq) + e^- \rightarrow Ag(s) + 2CN^-(aq)$	–0.31	$Hg_2^{2+}(aq) + 2 e^- \rightarrow 2Hg(l)$	+0.789
$Ag_2CrO_4(s) + 2 e^- \rightarrow 2 Ag(s) + CrO_4^{2-}(aq)$	+0.446	$2 Hg^{2+}(aq) + 2 e^- \rightarrow Hg_2^{2+}(aq)$	+0.920
$AgI(s) + e^- \rightarrow Ag(s) + I^-(aq)$	–0.151	$Hg^{2+}(aq) + 2 e^- \rightarrow Hg(l)$	+0.854
$Ag(S_2O_3)_2^{3-}(aq) + e^- \rightarrow Ag(s) + 2 S_2O_3^{2-}(aq)$	+0.01	$I_2(s) + 2 e^- \rightarrow 2 I^-(aq)$	+0.536
$Al^{3+}(aq) + 3e^- \rightarrow Al(s)$	–1.66	$2 IO_3^-(aq) + 12 H^+(aq) + 10 e^- \rightarrow$	
$H_3AsO_4(aq) + 2 H^+(aq) + 2 e^- \rightarrow$		$\quad I_2(s) + 6H_2O(l)$	+1.195
$\quad H_3AsO_3(aq) + H_2O(l)$	+0.559	$K^+(aq) + e^- \rightarrow K(s)$	–2.925
$Ba^{2+}(aq) + 2 e^- \rightarrow Ba(s)$	–2.90	$Li^+(aq) + e^- \rightarrow Li(s)$	–3.05
$BiO^+(aq) + 2 H^+(aq) + 3 e^- \rightarrow Bi(s) + H_2O(l)$	+0.32	$Mg^{2+}(aq) + 2 e^- \rightarrow Mg(s)$	–2.37
$Br_2(l) + 2 e^- \rightarrow 2 Br^-(aq)$	+1.065	$Mn^{2+}(aq) + 2 e^- \rightarrow Mn(s)$	–1.18
$2BrO_3^-(aq) + 12 H^+(aq) + 10 e^- \rightarrow$		$MnO_2(s) + 4 H^+(aq) + 2e^- \rightarrow$	
$\quad Br_2(l) + 6 H_2O(l)$	+1.52	$\quad Mn^{2+}(aq) + 2 H_2O(l)$	+1.23
$2 CO_2(g) + 2 H^+(aq) + 2 e^- \rightarrow H_2C_2O_4(aq)$	–0.49	$MnO_4^-(aq) + 8 H^+(aq) + 5 e^- \rightarrow$	
$Ca^{2+}(aq) + 2 e^- \rightarrow Ca(s)$	–2.87	$\quad Mn^{2+}(aq) + 4 H_2O(l)$	+1.51
$Cd^{2+}(aq) + 2 e^- \rightarrow Cd(s)$	–0.403	$MnO_4^-(aq) + 2 H_2O(l) + 3 e^- \rightarrow$	
$Ce^{4+}(aq) + e^- \rightarrow Ce^{3+}(aq)$	+1.61	$\quad MnO_2(s) + 4 OH^-(aq)$	+0.59
$Cl_2(g) + 2e^- \rightarrow 2 Cl^-(aq)$	+1.359	$HnO_2(aq) + H^+(aq) + e^- \rightarrow NO(g) + H_2O(l)$	+1.00
$2 HClO(aq) + 2 H^+(aq) + 2 e^- \rightarrow$		$N_2(g) + 4 H_2O(l) + 4 e^- \rightarrow 4 OH^-(aq) + N_2H_4(aq)$	–1.16
$\quad Cl_2(g) + 2 H_2O(l)$	+1.63	$N_2(g) + 5 H^+(aq) + 4 e^- \rightarrow N_2H_5^+(aq)$	–0.23
$ClO^-(aq) + H_2O(l) + 2 e^- \rightarrow Cl^-(aq) + 2 OH^-(aq)$	+0.89	$NO_3^-(aq) + 4 H^+(aq) + 3 e^- \rightarrow NO(g) + 2 H_2O(l)$	+0.96
$2 ClO_3^-(aq) + 12 H^+(aq) + 10 e^- \rightarrow$		$Na^+(aq) + e^- \rightarrow Na(s)$	–2.71
$\quad Cl_2(g) + 6 H_2O(l)$	+1.47	$Ni^{2+}(aq) + 2 e^- \rightarrow Ni(s)$	–0.28
$Co^{2+}(aq) + 2 e^- \rightarrow Co(s)$	–0.277	$O_2(g) + 4 H^+(aq) + 4 e^- \rightarrow 2 H_2O(l)$	+1.23
$Co^{3+}(aq) + e^- \rightarrow Co^{2+}(aq)$	+1.842	$O_2(g) + 2 H_2O(l) + 4 e^- \rightarrow 4 OH^-(aq)$	+0.40
$Cr^{3+}(aq) + 3 e^- \rightarrow Cr(s)$	–0.74	$O_2(g) + 2 H^+(aq) + 2 e^- \rightarrow H_2O_2(aq)$	+0.68
$Cr^{3+}(aq) + e^- \rightarrow Cr^{2+}(aq)$	–0.41	$O_3(g) + 2 H^+(aq) + 2 e^- \rightarrow O_2(g) + H_2O(l)$	+2.07
$CrO_7^{2-}(aq) + 14 H^+(aq) + 6 e^- \rightarrow$		$Pb^{2+}(aq) + 2 e^- \rightarrow Pb(s)$	–0.126
$\quad 2 Cr^{3+}(aq) + 7 H_2O(l)$	+1.33	$PbO_2(s) + HSO_4^-(aq) + 3 H^+(aq) + 2 e^- \rightarrow$	
$CrO_4^{2-}(aq) + 4 H_2O(l) + 3 e^- \rightarrow$		$\quad PbSO_4(s) + 4 H_2O(l)$	+1.685
$\quad Cr(OH)_3(s) + 5 OH^-(aq)$	–0.13	$PbSO_4(s) + H^+(aq) + 2 e^- \rightarrow Pb(s) + HSO_4^-(aq)$	–0.356
$Cu^{2+}(aq) + 2 e^- \rightarrow Cu(s)$	+0.337	$PtCl_4^{2-}(aq) + 2 e^- \rightarrow Pt(s) + 4 Cl^-(aq)$	+0.73
$Cu^{2+}(aq) + e^- \rightarrow Cu^+(aq)$	+0.153	$S(s) + 2 H^+(aq) + 2 e^- \rightarrow H_2S(g)$	+0.141
$Cu^+(aq) + e^- \rightarrow Cu(s)$	+0.521	$H_2SO_3(aq) + 4 H^+(aq) + 4 e^- \rightarrow S(s) + 3 H_2O(l)$	+0.45
$CuI(s) + e^- \rightarrow Cu(s) + I^-(aq)$	–0.185	$HSO_4^-(aq) + 3 H^+(aq) + 2 e^- \rightarrow$	
$F_2(g) + 2 e^- \rightarrow 2 F^-(aq)$	+2.87	$\quad H_2SO_3(aq) + H_2O(l)$	+0.17
$Fe^{2+}(aq) + 2 e^- \rightarrow Fe(s)$	–0.440	$Sn^{2+}(aq) + 2 e^- \rightarrow Sn(s)$	–0.136
$Fe^{3+}(aq) + e^- \rightarrow Fe^{2+}(aq)$	+0.771	$Sn^{4+}(aq) + 2 e^- \rightarrow Sn^{2+}(aq)$	+0.154
$Fe(CN)_6^{3-}(aq) + e^- \rightarrow Fe(CN)_6^{4-}(aq)$	+0.36	$VO_2^+(aq) + 2 H^+(aq) + e^- \rightarrow VO^{2+}(aq) + H_2O(l)$	+1.00
$2 H^+(aq) + 2 e^- \rightarrow H_2(g)$	+0.000	$Zn^{2+}(aq) + 2 e^- \rightarrow Zn(s)$	–0.763

16

Experiment 16

The Case of the Failed
Carbon Dioxide Scrubber

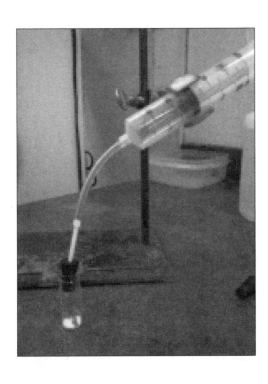

Adapted by Angela M. Jovanovic from J. Chem. Educ. 2011, 88(2), 189–191.[5]

Introduction

Carbon dioxide has several natural and anthropogenic (man-made) sources. Natural sources of carbon dioxide include aerobic respiration by humans and other animals, decomposition of organic matter, release from the oceans, and volcanic eruptions (a very minor source). In addition to natural sources of carbon dioxide, there are also natural sinks which remove the CO_2 from the air and sequester it in another form. Plants absorb CO_2 along with water and sunlight to produce sugars during photosynthesis and the Calvin Cycle. The oceans also absorb carbon dioxide from the atmosphere where it can react with calcium and other cations to form insoluble carbonate minerals such as limestone, chalk, and marble.

Anthropogenic sources of carbon dioxide include the combustion of fossil fuels, such as coal and oil. The amount of carbon dioxide has increased approximately 31% since the Industrial Revolution,[1] and continues to increase as more fossil fuels are burned. This increase in atmospheric carbon dioxide can have a variety of environmental impacts including the acidification of rain and many bodies of water and overall global climate change (commonly known as global warming).[1] Carbon dioxide is referred to as a greenhouse gas, which is a gas that traps outgoing infrared radiation from Earth to space leading to an increase in temperature. Carbon dioxide has a very long atmospheric lifetime, which means that it breaks down more slowly than it is produced.

Currently, there are efforts being made to remove the carbon dioxide from the effluent gases of coal-fired power plants using amine absorbers and cryogenic coolers.[2] Current carbon dioxide capture technologies are not cost effective enough to be used at at a commercial scale. The U.S. Department of Energy estimates that if current carbon capture technologies were implemented, it would cost the consumer an extra 2.5–4 cents per kilowatt-hour.[2] In 2009, the average household in Pennsylvania used 842 kWh of electricity per month at an average rate of 11.65 cents/kWh.[3] With the estimated increase of implementing current carbon sequestration methods, it would cost the average Pennsylvanian an extra $21–$34 per month (or $253–$404 per year). In order to develop more cost effective strategies for CO_2 capture the U.S. Department of Energy and private donors have invested over 1 billion dollars in research that aims to capture carbon dioxide from industrial sources and repurpose it for other uses.[4] While these projects may have the same up-front costs for carbon capture, repurposing the CO_2 may provide a way to reduce the direct cost to consumers.

Carbon dioxide is also a major concern in submarines and spacecraft, where missions can last for an extended period without fresh air supplies. The main source of CO_2 in these situations is respiration by the people who occupy the submarine or spacecraft (the average human exhales 0.90 kg of carbon dioxide per day).[5] In these cases, the air must be recycled continuously and the carbon dioxide removed for safety reasons. At concentrations of 10%, CO_2 can cause loss of consciousness after a few minutes or death.[6] Because of this, submarines and spacecraft must be equipped with enough of the appropriate CO_2 absorber for the entire mission to ensure the safety of the people who occupy these spaces. Older methods for the removal of CO_2 in spacecraft and submarines included the use of lithium hydroxide canisters, which were only able to be used once.[5] Newer methods for removing carbon dioxide from the air in these cases utilize absorbers that can be regenerated and used multiple times.[5]

Background Chemistry

The reaction of lithium hydroxide with carbon dioxide occurs via a two-step process, shown in (1) and (2). The overall reaction for this process is given in (3).

$$2\ LiOH_{(s)} = 2H_2O_{(g)} \rightarrow 2\ LiOH \cdot H_2O_{(s)} \qquad (1)$$

$$2\ LiOH \cdot H_2O_{(s)} + CO_{2(g)} \rightarrow Li_2CO_{3(s)} + 3\ H_2O_{(g)} \qquad (2)$$

Overall:
$$2\ LiOH_{(s)} + CO_{2(g)} \rightarrow Li_2CO_{3(s)} + H_2O_{(g)} \qquad (3)$$

One common test for solid carbonates is the addition of strong acid, which forms carbon dioxide as a product, as shown in (4).

$$Li_2CO_{3(s)} + 2\ HCl_{(aq)} \rightarrow 2\ LiCl_{(aq)} + CO_{2(g)} + H_2O_{(l)} \quad (4)$$

Activated carbon can also be used to remove carbon dioxide from the air. Activated carbon or activated charcoal is a porous material with an extremely high surface area (around 500 m^2/g–or one tenth the size of a football field).[7] The high surface area allows gases, such as carbon dioxide, to adsorb to the surface. Activated carbon can be regenerated by blowing a stream of air over the bed of carbon, which releases the CO_2 from the pores of the material.[8]

The amount of carbon dioxide that is absorbed can be calculated using the Ideal Gas Law (5), where P is the pressure, V is the volume of gas, n is the moles of gas, R is the ideal gas constant $\left(R = 0.08206 \frac{L*atm}{mol*K} \right)$, and T is the temperature in Kelvin.

$$PV = nRT \qquad (5)$$

One way that the efficiency of carbon dioxide absorbers is described is the absorption capacity, which is defined in equation (6).

$$Absorption\ capacity = \frac{mass\ of\ CO_2\ absorbed}{mass\ of\ absorber} \qquad (6)$$

In this experiment you will experimentally determine the absorption capacity of lithium hydroxide, activated carbon, and regenerated activated carbon. You will use this information in order to solve a problem presented as a case study.

References

1. Karl TR, Trenberth KE. Modern global climate change. *Science (New York, N.Y.).* 2003;302(5651):1719-23. Available at: http://www.ncbi.nlm.nih.gov/pubmed/14657489. Accessed June 15, 2011.

2. US D. U.S. Department of Energy Carbon Capture Research. 2011. Available at: http://www.fossil.energy.gov/programs/sequestration/capture/index.html. Accessed January 11, 2011.

3. US E. U.S. Energy Information Administration Frequently Asked Questions. 2011. Available at: http://205.254.135.24/tools/faqs/faq.cfm?id=97&t=3. Accessed January 11, 2011.

4. US D. U.S. Department of Energy Carbon Capture and Storage from Industrial Sources. 2011. Available at: http://www.fossil.energy.gov/programs/sequestration/industrial/industrial_ccs.html. Accessed January 11, 2011.

5. Ticich TM. Carbon Dioxide Absorbers: An Engaging Experiment for the General Chemistry Laboratory. *Journal of Chemical Education.* 2011;88(2):189-191.

6. US N. Tox Town Carbon Dioxide. 2011. Available at: http://toxtown.nlm.nih.gov/text_version/chemicals.php?id=6. Accessed July 11, 2011.

7. Anon. Activated Carbon. *Wikipedia.* 2012. Available at: http://en.wikipedia.org/wiki/Activated_carbon. Accessed January 30, 2012.

8. Anon. Carbon dioxide scrubber. *Wikipedia.* 2012. Available at: http://en.wikipedia.org/wiki/Carbon_dioxide_scrubber#Activated_carbon. Accessed January 30, 2012.

Quiz Outline

Be able to answer prelab quiz questions similar to those asked in the sample quiz for this experiment.

Also know:

- What is meant by absorption capacity

- The overall reaction that occurs between lithium hydroxide and carbon dioxide

- The reaction that occurs between Li_2CO_3 and a strong acid, such as HCl

- How to use the Ideal Gas Law

- Natural carbon dioxide sinks

- Sources of carbon dioxide (natural and anthropogenic sources)

- The information given in the PowerPoint presentation

- Pros and cons of lithium hydroxide and activated carbon as CO_2 absorbers

Sample Pre-Laboratory Quiz

1. Calculate the volume of CO_2 that reacts with 1 gram of LiOH according to the following equation. Assume the reaction goes to completion at a pressure of 1 atm and temperature of 300 K. MW Li = 6.941 g/mol; MW O = 16 g/mol; MW H = 1 g/mol; MW C = 12.01 g/mol; R = 0.08206 (L*atm)/(mol*K).

$$2LiOH_{(s)} + CO_{2(g)} \rightarrow Li_2CO_{3(s)} + H_2O_{(g)}$$

2. What is absorption capacity?

3. Calculate the absorption capacity of LiOH if 0.102 moles of CO_2 react with 5 grams of LiOH.

4. Name two sources of atmospheric carbon dioxide.

5. Name two situations where removal of CO_2 from the air is important.

Laboratory Experiments

Flowchart of the Experiment

Section A.	**Case Study — The Problem**

Section B.	**Stoichiometry and Theoretical Calculations**

Section C.	**Determination of the Absorption Capacity of Lithium Hydroxide**

Section D.	**Determination of the Absorption Capacity of Activated Carbon**

Section E.	**Case Study—Why Did the Astronauts Die?**

Requires one four-hour laboratory to complete.

Section A.   Case Study — The Problem

Goal: *To obtain an understanding of why carbon dioxide absorbers are important.*

Ten astronauts boarded a space shuttle for a routine sixty-day mission. 590 kg of lithium hydroxide was loaded aboard to remove the carbon dioxide exhaled by the astronauts from the air. By the end of the mission, all of the astronauts had tragically and mysteriously died. It is your mission to figure out why this tragedy occurred and how it could have been prevented during the course of this laboratory.

Section B.   Stoichiometry and Theoretical Calculations

Goal: *To predict the amount of CO_2 absorbed by LiOH using stoichiometric calculations.*

1.   Weigh approximately 0.05 g LiOH into your 8 mL vial and seal tightly with a cap, record the mass.

Questions: Q1.   Predict the mass of carbon dioxide absorbed by your sample of LiOH, assuming that the reaction goes all the way to completion.

Use the following reaction:

$$2LiOH_{(s)} + CO_{2(g)} \rightarrow Li_2Co_{3(s)} + H_2O_{(g)}$$

Q2.   Predict the volume of carbon dioxide absorbed by your sample of LiOH, assume that the reaction goes all the way to completion, using P = 1.00 atm and T = 298K.

Use the Ideal Gas Law: PV = nRT

Q3.   Assuming the reaction goes to completion, what is the absorption capacity of LiOH?

$$\text{Absorption capacity} = \frac{\text{g } CO_2 \text{ absorbed}}{\text{g absorber}}$$

Section C.   Determination of the Absorption Capacity of Lithium Hydroxide

---

Goal: *To determine the experimental absorption capacity of LiOH.*

1.   Use the LiOH that you weighed out in Section B.

2.   Obtain a pre-assembled syringe attachment and a 60 mL syringe from the front of the room.

3.   Put a pea-sized piece of dry ice (approximately 0.2 g) into the 60 mL syringe by removing the plunger.

In steps 4–7 you will be allowing the $CO_{2(s)}$ to sublime and flush the air out of the syringe. This will allow you to capture a known volume of $CO_{2(g)}$ at a known temperature and pressure.

4.   Push the plunger all the way in (there should be a small amount of room in the tip of the syringe for the dry ice).

5.   Cover the end of the plastic straw with your finger. The plunger should move freely enough so that it moves as the dry ice sublimes.

6.   Once the volume has reached approximately 25 mL, remove your finger, and depress the plunger to expel all of the gas from the syringe.

7.   Cover the straw with your finger again until the volume reaches approximately 50 mL.

8.   There should still be a small amount of dry ice left at this point. Remove your finger until the rest of it sublimes. Once it has all sublimed, cover the end of the straw with your finger again.

9.   Quickly remove the solid stopper from your vial and place the straw attached to the syringe inside the vial. ***Do not seal the vial.***

10. Depress the plunger to approximately 40 mL (record the actual volume to the nearest 0.5 mL—*this is the initial volume*) **then quickly seal the vial completely.**

   •   What observations can you make that tell you a reaction is occurring? (Hint: Feel the bottom of the vial, do you see any liquid forming?)

11. Once the plunger stops moving, wait another minute to be sure the reaction is finished, then record the final volume to the nearest 0.5 mL.

   •   How does the solid compare to what was originally present?

Questions: Q4.   Calculate the mass of carbon dioxide absorbed. How does this compare to your predicted value?

              Q5.   Calculate the actual absorption capacity of LiOH based on your data.

              12.   Add a few drops of 2 M HCl to the vial and record your observations.

Question: Q6.   Write a reaction that explains your observations from step 12.

              13.   Add 2 M HCl until no further reaction occurs. The remaining liquid can be washed down the drain with water.

              14.   Obtain the data from your neighbors for their trials (you should have a total of four trials now)—make sure to properly reference them. Include the information for all four trials in a table.

Question: Q7.   Calculate average absorption capacity of LiOH and the standard deviation. Record this information in your table.

Section D.   Determination of the Absorption Capacity of Activated Carbon

---

Goal: *To determine the experimental absorption capacity of activated carbon.*

1.   Weigh out approximately 0.5 g of activated carbon into a clean, dry 8 mL vial. Do not discard the activated carbon from this trial when you are done.

2.   Put a pea-sized piece of dry ice (approximately 0.2 g) into the 60 mL syringe by removing the plunger.

3.   Push the plunger all the way in (there should be a small amount of room in the tip of the syringe for the dry ice).

4.   Cover the end of the plastic straw with your finger. The plunger should move freely enough so that it moves as the dry ice sublimes.

5.   Once the volume has reached approximately 25 mL, remove your finger, and depress the plunger to expel all of the gas from the syringe.

6.   Cover the straw with your finger again until the volume reaches approximately 50 mL.

7.   There should still be a small amount of dry ice left at this point. Remove your finger until the rest of it sublimes. Once it has all sublimed, cover the end of the straw with your finger again.

8.   Quickly remove the solid stopper from your vial and place the straw attached to the syringe in the vial. ***Do not seal the vial.***

9.   Depress the plunger to approximately 40 mL (record the actual volume to the nearest 0.5 mL—*this is the initial volume*) **then quickly seal the vial completely.**

10. Gently depress the plunger of the syringe 1 mL at a time, removing your hand from the plunger after each time.

11. Once the plunger rebounds after you depress it (i.e., when you observe that the plunger rebounds slowly to the previous volume), record the volume it stops at to the nearest 0.5 mL—*this is the final volume.*

     •   For example, if you depress the plunger to 45 mL but once you remove your thumb, the plunger returns to 46 mL, this is your stopping point. You would record the final volume as 46 mL in this case.

     •   Did you observe any changes?

Questions: Q8.   Calculate the mass of carbon dioxide absorbed using your data.

                     Q9.   Calculate the absorption capacity of activated carbon using your data.

                           •   Obtain data from your neighbors so that you have the data for four trials. Record this information in a table.

                     Q10. Calculate the average absorption capacity of activated carbon and the standard deviation. Record this information in the table from the previous step.

Question:		Q11.	How does this compare to the average absorption capacity of LiOH?

		12.	Try blowing a light stream of air over the used activated carbon for 1 minute. This should regenerate the activated carbon by liberating the absorbed CO_2.

		13.	Now perform another trial using the regenerated activated carbon.

		14.	When you are finished, you can dispose of the activated carbon in the trash.

Questions:		Q12.	How does the absorption capacity compare to the previous trial? Does this surprise you?

		Q13.	How many times would 1 kg of activated carbon have to be regenerated to remove the same amount of CO_2 as 1 kg of LiOH?

## Section E.		Case Study—Why Did the Astronauts Die?

Goals:		*To determine the reason the astronauts died in the case study.*

Questions:		Q14.	Based on your knowledge, why did the tragic death of the 10 astronauts occur? Explain your answer thoroughly. Hint: Calculate the absorption capacity of the LiOH on board using the mass of CO_2 exhaled by the astronauts.

		Q15.	Using the average absorption capacity you determined, how many days would it have taken for all of the LiOH on board to be used up?

		Q16.	What could have prevented the death of the astronauts? Show your calculations.

		Q17.	Which absorber would you pick for use in a space shuttle? An industrial power plant? Explain why based on the knowledge you gained during this lab.

Experiment 17

Paper, Thin Layer, and Liquid Chromatography

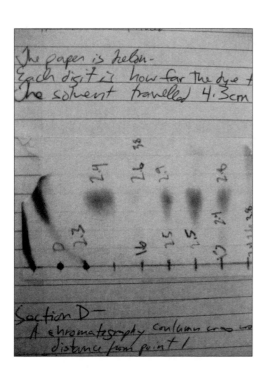

Note: Ch. 18, Paper and Liquid Chromatography, in *Chemtrek* by Stephen Thompson was expanded and edited by Guy Anderson, August 2009, and is presented here as Experiment 17.

Introduction

It is perhaps true that great progress in science occurs after new inventions in technique occur. In the history of science, the battery and the vacuum pump are examples of such inventions. In modern science, the invention and application of two techniques, spectroscopy and chromatography, have revolutionized chemistry and biology. Chromatography is probably the most widely used and most powerful of all the techniques of chemical analysis. Chromatography was invented in the late nineteenth century by the Russian botanist Mikhail Tswett, who used it to separate naturally occurring chlorophylls. He extracted green plant material with organic solvents and allowed the extract to percolate through glass tubes full of powdered solids (e.g., sugar and calcium carbonate). A slightly more polar solvent was then used to wash the extract through the powder. Broad bands of color separated down the length of the column of powder. Tswett claimed that the different bands were different types of chlorophyll and other pigments and that chromatography was indeed the best way to investigate the chemistry of complex natural mixtures. As with many other inventions of true genius in the history of science, Mikhail Tswett's claims were dismissed as nonsense by the scientific establishment of the time, and the new technique was neglected for almost three decades. Chromatography was rediscovered, albeit in a different form called partition chromatography, by the English chemists Martin and Synge in the late 1930s. Martin's research group at the Wool Industries Research Association then developed the first microanalytical chromatography method, called paper chromatography, as a means to analyzing the structure of proteins. Martin and Synge received the Nobel Prize in chemistry in 1952 for the invention of partition chromatography.

The power of chromatography as a scientific tool lies in the fact that it is a simple, gentle, inexpensive, and general way of unmixing (separating) and analyzing complex mixtures of substances. Of course, once a mixture has been separated into pure components, it becomes a relatively straightforward matter to investigate the properties of each component. An interesting historical example, briefly mentioned earlier, is the application of partition chromatography to the study of proteins. The properties and behavior of fibers (e.g., wool) are very much determined by the particular chemical structure of the fiber. Martin et al. were trying to elucidate the structure of wool by breaking down the fiber with hot acid. Unfortunately, the resulting mixture of products from the destruction of fiber was so complicated that there was little progress. The problem was resolved by the invention of the partition chromatographic method. This method enabled the horrendous reaction mixtures to be easily separated into the individual amino acid and peptide products and eventually led to a complete structure of wool protein. It is interesting to note that partition chromatographic methods are now being applied extensively to solve gene sequencing problems in molecular biology.

Chromatography is now one of the major methods for chemical analysis and purification. Advances in technology, particularly in the miniaturization of columns and detectors, have resulted in the development of extraordinarily sensitive and quantitative chromatographic instruments (chromatographs). Micro gas chromatographs have been used in outer space probes, and micro liquid chromatographs have recently been explored as *in vivo* implantable analytical monitors. The objective in this series of chromatography experiments is to construct several small-scale chromatographic instruments and to investigate the nature of chromatographic processes in several useful applications.

Background Chemistry

Chromatography is a method of separation in which the components to be separated are distributed between two phases, one of these being a porous substance or stationary phase, the other being a fluid that flows through the porous stationary phase. A small volume of the original sample containing the components to be separated is placed at the start of the porous stationary phase. It is important in most types of separation to try to place the sample in as small a volume of the stationary phase as possible or the separation becomes more difficult. The fluid, called the *mobile phase*, is allowed to flow through the porous bed, and as it does, the sample components begin to migrate through the bed. Each component will have a different affinity for the stationary phase and for the mobile phase. Components that have a higher affinity for the stationary phase will be slowed down relative to the other components. Components that tend to stay in the mobile phase will move farther along the stationary phase than the other components. The greater the fraction of time a component spends in the mobile phase, the farther it will move from the start. A component that remains only on the stationary phase will not move at all!

On the molecular scale, component molecules (or ions, atoms, etc.) do not simply move directly along the stationary phase in straight lines. Even though the component molecules are being pushed along in the general direction of the mobile phase, there is a tremendous amount of molecular jostling and bumping. Component molecules, therefore, diffuse in all directions as they migrate in the general direction in which the mobile phase is going. Thus, the chromatographic process is the sum of the billions and billions of molecular events involving diffusion to and from the surface of the stationary phase, random molecular bumping, and migration along the stationary phase in the general direction of the mobile phase. Chromatography may be described graphically in terms of the concentration profiles of the various components as they move along the stationary phase. A computer modeling of the chromatographic process for the separation of four components from a sample is shown in the computer graphic sequence in Figure 17.1.

The chromatographic sequence illustrated in Figure 17.1 represents the behavior of sample components in *elution chromatography*. Elution chromatography, by far the most commonly used type of chromatography, is also one of the three major types of chromatography. The elution technique involves the chromatography of very small amounts of sample and results in concentration profile shapes similar to those shown in Figure 17.1.

The objective of chromatography is to obtain a complete separation of the individual components of a sample mixture. In chromatographic instruments, separation is obtained by trying to

* Maximize the component migration *differences* of all components

* Minimize the component *spreading* that occurs during the chromatographic process

If you look at the computer model pictures, you can see that as the chromatography proceeds, the center (or peak) of the concentration profile of each component gets farther and farther apart, leading to a complete separation of the four components (as in the last picture of Figure 17.1). At the same time, all components spread out and occupy more and more of the space in the system. You can see that if the sample contained a large number of components, then overlapping might occur and a good separation might not be obtained.

In modern chromatography, component migration differences are maximized by choosing the correct stationary phase and mobile phase based on an understanding of the chemical interactions involved. Sample components can interact with the stationary phase in a variety of ways—e.g., by partition, by adsorption, by ion exchange, by size, or by exclusion. A careful choice of the type of chemistry used in the system generally results in good separations. It must be emphasized that chromatography is now carried out on almost every conceivable type of chemical component, including proteins, gases, food dyes, etc., and on extraordinarily complex mixtures, such as oils, gasoline, urine, etc. Often, different stationary phases and different mobile phases are required in order to separate different groups of components from the same sample!

Much effort has been spent over the last 20 years to find ways of minimizing component spreading during chromatography. Narrow component bands are particularly important if complex mixtures are to be resolved, i.e., well separated. The magnitude of the spreading process depends on several factors— e.g., the particle size of a solid stationary phase— and is usually measured in terms of the *efficiency* of the chromatographic system. The efficiency of a particular system is quantitatively expressed by the number of *theoretical plates* (N). N may be calculated from

$$N = 16\left(\frac{V_R}{W_b}\right)^2$$

where V_R, the *retention volume*, is defined as the volume of mobile phase required to carry a component through the chromatographic system. W_b is the width of the base of the component concentration profile (often called the *band width*). A better way of expressing the efficiency is to use the *height equivalent to a theoretical plate* (H), where

$$H = \frac{L}{N}$$

and where the *column* is the porous stationary phase and L is its length. Modern high-performance chromatography instruments can provide many thousands of plates per meter of column (i.e., H < 0.1 mm); consequently, the component bands are extraordinarily narrow. These high efficiencies have been achieved by technological developments in the manufacture of solid stationary phases and the tubes (columns) in which the phases are contained. In *high-performance liquid chromatography* (HPLC), the particles of stationary phase are often spherical, very small (diameters less than 5×10^{-6} m), and packed into the tube in a highly uniform manner. One unfortunate aspect of all this efficiency is that it has become very difficult to force the mobile phase through the very small particles packed into a tube. Most modern HPLC instruments contain very high pressure pumps to force the mobile phase through the column at reasonable flow rates.

Frame 1

A sample consisting of four components is injected into the chromatographic system. The mobile phase is allowed to flow and the various component molecules (represented by the different symbols in the figure) begin to move along the column. The concentration profile of each component is shown directly below the picture of the column.

Frames 2–7

The components migrate along the column in the direction of the mobile phase. The components' migration differences increase until a complete separation (almost) of all four components is obtained (Frame 7). Notice that the molecular spreading increases as the components move farther along the column.

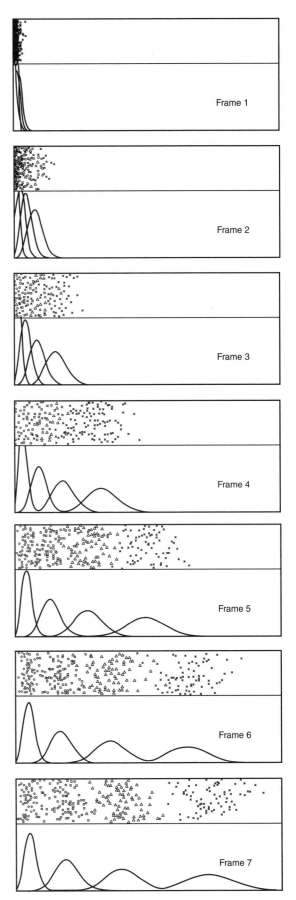

Figure 17.1 A computer model of the chromatographic process.

Table 17.1 Types of Phases and Distribution Processes in Chromatography

Nature of the Distribution Process	Mobile Phase	Stationary Phase	Type of Chromatography and Acronym
Partition	Liquid	Liquid	Paper and thin layer on cellulose (PC, TLC); reverse phase liquid (HPRPLC); gas liquid (GLC)
Partition	Gas	Liquid	
Adsorption	Liquid	Solid	Normal phase liquid, thin layer, and ion exchange (LC, TLC, IC); gas solid (GSC)
Adsorption	Gas	Solid	
Size sorting	Liquid	Gel	Gel permeation (GPC)

There are literally thousands of different chromatographic methods in use in the vast array of applications. The acronyms are legion—e.g., PC, IC, LC, GC, HPLC, HPTLRPC, GC/MS, GPC/ED, etc.,—and the techniques are used in all areas of science and technology. The ubiquity of chromatography makes it difficult to organize a simple classification of chromatographic systems. However, it is useful to classify systems on the basis of the types of phases and on the major distribution processes, shown in Table 17.1.

In this laboratory you will have the opportunity of constructing and investigating three major types of chromatographic systems: paper chromatography (PC), liquid chromatography (LC), and thin layer chromatography (TLC). The sections that follow provide you with some background chemistry that is pertinent to paper and liquid chromatography. Gas chromatography is discussed in Experiment 19, although you should note that the introduction given earlier pertains to all elution chromatography, including GC.

Paper Chromatography

Paper chromatography (PC) is a technique developed in England in the 1940s by Martin, Synge, and Consden that uses paper for separating the complex mixtures of amino acids obtained from the breakdown of wool. The separation and subsequent identification of individual amino acids and peptides led to the elucidation of the structure of wool protein. Paper chromatography is the name that is used to describe chromatography carried out on a stationary phase consisting of specially prepared, porous paper. The sample, usually dissolved in a solvent, is directly applied to one end of a sheet of paper. The sheet is

then placed in a large glass or plastic chromatography tank and the mobile phase is allowed to contact the paper. The mobile phase is "pulled through" the paper by capillary action. PC has a somewhat limited use and is not used extensively now, although it is interesting to note that there have been several recent applications to the separation of complex enzyme mixtures with modified celluloses. Paper is cellulose and the structure is shown in Figure 17.2.

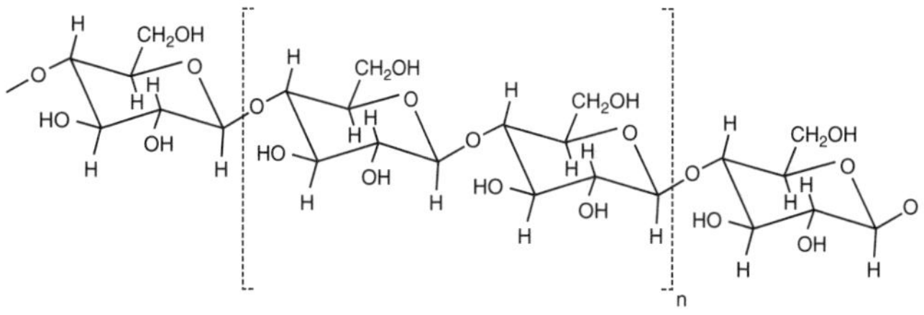

Figure 17.2 The cellobiose repeating unit in cellulose.

The hydroxyl groups (−OH) in the cellulose are responsible for the hydrogen bonding of water, which makes up about 6% of the weight of the paper. It is this water layer, along with more water that is sometimes adsorbed during the chromatographic process, that forms the stationary phase in PC. Chromatography paper is unsized and is carefully manufactured to produce a highly porous paper with relatively uniform fiber structure. If the edge of a sheet of chromatography paper is placed in a liquid, the liquid will be pulled through the paper by capillary action. The liquid moving through the pores in the paper constitutes a mobile phase, and chromatography can occur. The mobile phase may be pulled along, up, or down, depending on where the liquid is initially applied.

Let us now look at the factors that control the way in which components move in a paper chromatographic separation. Consider a single nonelectrolyte component applied to the paper at the start (see Figure 17.3).

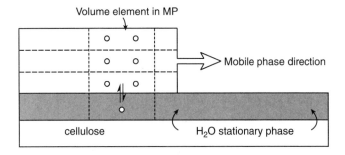

Volume element in MP

Mobile phase direction

cellulose H_2O stationary phase

Figure 17.3 Distribution of a single nonelectrolyte component in PC.

The component molecules are distributed by *partition* between the aqueous stationary phase and the nonpolar mobile phase. The partition coefficient k is defined as the ratio of the concentration of the component in the mobile phase to that in the stationary phase. In the above diagram, k = 2 because 1 volume of the mobile phase contains 2 molecules, and an equal volume of stationary phase contains 1 molecule. In practice, however, the volumes of the two liquid phases are not equal. For many chromatography papers the mobile phase volume is 3 times the stationary phase volume, and the phase ratio r is

$$r = \frac{\text{volume of mobile phase}}{\text{volume of stationary phase}} = \frac{3}{1}$$

The *distribution ratio* is defined as kr—i.e., the number of molecules in the mobile phase per solute molecule in the stationary phase. In our example, kr = 6. In PC the measure of retention is called the *retention factor*, and is given the symbol R_f. R_f is defined as the fraction of time spent by an "average" molecule in the mobile phase and is equal to the fraction of molecules present in the mobile phase. Since, in general, the total number of molecules is kr + 1 (kr molecules in the mobile phase and 1 in the stationary phase) then,

$$R_f = \frac{kr}{kr + 1}$$

Rearranging,

$$kr = \frac{R_f}{1 - R_f}$$

In an actual PC separation, the R_f value is defined experimentally by

$$R_f = \frac{\text{distance moved by the component}}{\text{distance moved by the mobile phase front}}$$

As you can see, the relative migration distance R_f depends on the partition coefficient k, the value of which depends on the chemical nature of the component and mobile phase. In a chromatographic experiment in which a sample mixture containing several components is applied to the paper at the start, the R_f value of each component will depend on the partition coefficient for each component in the system employed.

The discussion thus far has been restricted to the chromatography of a single *nonelectrolyte* component. Paper chromatography was really introduced to separate polar substances, such as amino acids, sugars, drugs, metabolites, etc. Most of these compounds are weak acids or bases.

Thin Layer Chromatography

In thin layer chromatography (TLC) the stationary phase is a thin layer of material on a glass or plastic support. Small samples are applied as in paper chromatography to prevent overlapping when the components move up the plate. The plate is then placed in a developing chamber with the mobile phase. The developing chamber is covered to prevent loss of the mobile phase. As the mobile phase moves up the plate it separates or develops the chromatogram. Again, it is important to keep the mobile phase below the level of the spots when the plate is placed in the developing chamber to prevent the spots from being washed off the plate.

In thin layer chromatography, as in paper chromatography, R_f values are calculated for each species. The R_f value for a sample depends upon the material used for the stationary phase and the solvent mixture used for the mobile phase. To eliminate variables, unknown samples and standards are often run together on the same plate.

The samples being studied are often clear and colorless and thus cannot be seen with the unaided eye. The spots may be visualized by examining the plate under ultraviolet light (UV) or by spraying the plate with a visualizer to make the spots appear. A TLC chromatogram can tell the researcher if a sample is pure, and if not, how many components are in the sample. The components may be identified by comparing the R_f values with those of known standards run under the same conditions.

Liquid Chromatography

Liquid chromatography (LC) is the name that is now universally used to describe chromatographic separations carried out in small tubular columns packed with small particles of stationary phase. A wide variety of different polarity may be used to pack the column. As the name implies, the mobile phase is liquid and may be a pure solvent or a variable composition mixture of solvents. The LC apparatus may be a simple plastic tube with gravity flow of liquid or a very complex instrument with stainless steel tubes, high-pressure mobile phase pumps, and sophisticated, sensitive analytical detectors. Much of the chemical analysis that is done in clinical, industrial, and research laboratories is carried out on commercial high-performance liquid chromatography (HPLC) instruments costing thousands of dollars. A quantitative analysis is obtained by injecting a known volume of sample into the instrument and by quantitatively measuring the concentration of each separated component with a detector placed at the end of the column. HPLC is often performed in the reverse phase mode (HPRPLC). A chromatographic process in which the liquid mobile phase is more *polar* than the stationary phase is referred to as a *reverse phase process*. One of the most common HPRPLC stationary phases consists of 5 μ particles of silica gel that has been *derivatized* (chemically reacted) with octadecyl hydrocarbon groups, as shown in Figure 17.4.

The mobile phase is often an aqueous buffer or a water/alcohol mixture. HPLC columns are extremely efficient, producing very narrow component bands. The biologist, biochemist, or chemist wishing to separate a mixture must select stationary and mobile phases that provide differences in attraction between the two phases. The composition and polarity of this mobile phase also plays an important role and provides the investigator with additional means to successfully separate a mixture. In some cases, a variety of solvents may be required to completely separate the mixture. The efficiency is mostly due to the extremely small uniform particle size of the stationary phase and homogeneous packing in the column.

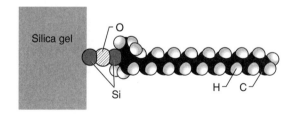

Figure 17.4 Octadecyl-derivatized silica gel.

Quiz Outline

Your quiz will NOT cover all of the information below, but it will cover some subset of this information.

Be able to define the following terms listed in your green packet under the heading "Terms that you should know from high school chemistry": equilibrium, hydrogen bond, mixture, polar molecule, solution, accuracy, and precision.

Be able to solve max/min/best estimate types of problems like the ones given in your pink packet.

Define "chromatography."

In order to obtain good separations in chromatography, what factor must be maximized and what factor must be minimized?

Surprisingly, the stationary phase in paper chromatography is considered to be water, not the paper. Explain why.

Certain chromatographic systems are referred to as "reversed phase." What is meant by this?

Be able to calculate the R_f value for compounds on a developed chromatogram.

Diffusion is a significant problem in chromatography. Explain why.

In high-performance liquid chromatography (HPLC), high pressures are involved. Explain why.

A safety question from your TA.

Sample Pre-Laboratory Quiz

1. Define "hydrogen bond."

2. Define "chromatography"

3. Explain why water is considered to be the stationary phase in paper chromatography, and not the paper.

4. Determine the R_f values for the two compounds contained in sample #4 (show below).

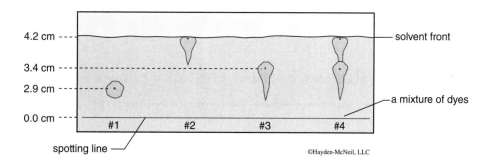

5. Using the max/min/best estimate method, determine the value of the expression below. Show all your work.

$$(215 \pm 3 - 47 \pm 1) \times (0.005 \pm 0.001) = ?$$

Laboratory Experiments

Flowchart of the Experiments

Section A.	Paper Chromatography of Dyes, Including Kool-Aid Dye Mixture

Section B.	Column Chromatography of Kool-Aid

Section C.	Verification of the Composition of Kool-Aid Dyes—Visible Spectroscopy

Section D.	Thin Layer Chromatography of Analgesics

Requires one four-hour class period to complete Sections A–D.

Section E.	Development of an Experiment to Identify Unknown Inks

Section F.	Development of an Experiment to Identify Unknown Dyes

Requires one four-hour class period to complete either Section E or Section F (as assigned by your TA).

Section A.   Paper Chromatography of Dyes, Including Kool-Aid Dye Mixture

Goal:

To carry out a series of ascending paper chromatographic separations of inks and food dyes in a small-scale tank system.

Discussion:

You will also characterize the relative attraction of individual compounds for the stationary vs. the mobile phase using R_f (retention factor) measurements.

NOTE: In paper chromatography, the stationary phase actually is not the paper, but water which is bound to the paper by hydrogen bonding.

Before You Begin:

Paper chromatography is a microanalytical technique. Extraordinarily small sample volumes are used (microliters), and the separation often yields very small amounts (often less than nanomoles) of product. It is particularly important to maintain good technique and to try to avoid contamination of the chromatography paper. Work on a clean piece of paper or paper towel when you are drawing lines and spotting samples.

Experimental Steps:

1.   Obtain 1 piece of chromatography paper from Reagent Central. Draw in the lines and points with a *pencil*, as shown below. A total of 17 samples will be analyzed.

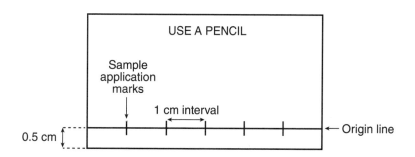

2.   Make a plastic capillary tube by first stretching the tip of a thin-stem pipet until it collapses to its small diameter size. Continue stretching until 2 or 3 inches of the thin stem has attained a small diameter. Then cut off both ends, leaving a 2–3 inch long plastic capillary tube. This tube can be used as an applicator to transfer small amounts of dye from your 24-well tray to your paper chromatogram. Note: Keep the applicator vertical. Cut off the tip of the capillary after applying each dye.

3.   Spot all of the food dye samples, cutting off the tip of the applicator after you spot each dye to avoid contamination. You will be spotting FD&C food dyes as standards and foods containing mixtures of dyes (e.g., Grape Kool-Aid).

   •   Record where each dye is spotted.

4.   Using small amounts of your FD&C food dyes, prepare your own mixture (the components are of your own choosing) of black dye (or at least as dark as you can get it) for spotting on the chromatogram. Spot the black dye.

   •   Record the components of your dye mixture.

5.   Obtain two pens of each color (black, blue, and red) from the front of the room and place a spot of ink in the designated places. Try to apply equal amounts of each color of ink.

•   Record where each pen (brand name/label) is spotted.

6.   Roll the paper into a cylinder and hold it while you staple it as shown below. *Do not overlap* the two edges of the cylinder. Your chromatogram should fit inside a plastic chromatography tank (a clear plastic cup, turned upside down) without touching the walls. If you need to, cut the chromatography paper shorter and restaple the cylinder to make it fit.

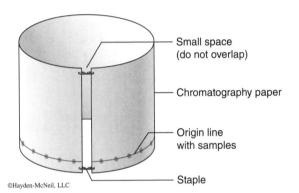

Small space
(do not overlap)

Chromatography paper

Origin line
with samples

©Hayden-McNeil, LLC   Staple

7.   Deliver three pipets of the mobile phase solvent, 2:1 1-propanol/water, to a solvent tray (half of a Petri dish). Place the paper cylinder into the solvent as evenly and centrally as possible.

8.   Place the tank over the cylinder. Try to keep the paper cylinder from flattening against the inside wall of the tank.

9.   Watch the mobile phase for a few moments so that you can see the mobile phase front as it climbs up the paper by capillary action.

The chromatography will take about 20–25 minutes. From time to time check the progress of the front. You will want to stop the chromatography when the solvent front reaches ~0.5 cm from the top of the paper.

While the paper chromatography is occurring, begin preparing the thin layer chromatography plate (Section B).

10. When the front reaches ~ 0.5 cm from the top of the paper, lift the tank and quickly remove the cylinder. Place it onto a clean paper towel. Using a pencil, mark the solvent front line. Replace the tank.

11. Pull the cylinder apart and hang it up to dry. The drying time is about 20 minutes.

12. While the paper is drying, continue with Section B if needed, then move on to Sections C and D. Interweave your analysis of the paper chromatogram and answering of questions with experimental sections.

13.   When the paper is dry (or when you are ready), place it flat on a towel on the table and locate the component zones or spots. The following figure shows how to draw the circles around the spots and determine the distance migrated. The measuring point is drawn considering, "Where would the spot have been if an incredibly tiny amount of dye had been spotted?"

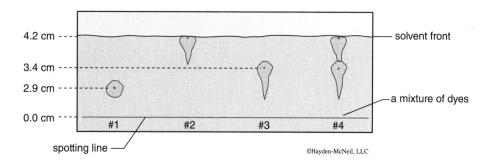

In sample #1, the dye migrated evenly, but diffused, so the location that an incredibly tiny amount of dye would migrate to would be the center of the spot. In sample #2, much of the dye migrated at the same rate as the mobile phase, but it didn't migrate evenly and left a trailing edge. If a much smaller amount had been used, most of it would have been at the solvent front. In sample #3, we see both a circular diffusion pattern and a trailing edge. In this case, the measurement should be made from the middle of the most concentrated area of the dye. Sample #4 illustrates a mixture of samples #2 and #3.

Questions:

Q1.   Measure and record the distance that each component migrated from the original sample application mark. Attach the chromatogram to your notebook.

Q2.   Create a table that includes the names of the samples, the distance each spot moved, and the R_f value for each spot. Calculate the R_f value for each component, where

$$R_f = \frac{\text{component migration distance}}{\text{mobile phase migration distance}} = \frac{\text{distance spot traveled}}{\text{distance solvent travels from spotting line}}$$

Q3.   Use R_f values and color to identify the FD&C dyes in the mixtures of dyes used in food samples (e.g., Grape Kool-Aid), and your mixture. If the compounds aren't present in similar amounts, then this should be noted. Record this information in the table.

Q4.   From comparison with the black dye that you prepared from FD&C dyes, do you think that any of the commercial pens contain FD&C dyes? If so, then list the FD&C dyes present in each pen.

Q5.   (a) Which FD&C dye standards migrated the greatest and least distance on your chromatogram?

(b) Look at the diagrams of the structures of Red #3, Blue #1, and Yellow #5. How many polar side groups are found on each of these dyes? Circle these side groups. Remember that $-OH$, SO_3^-, and $-COOH$ side groups contain polar bonds.

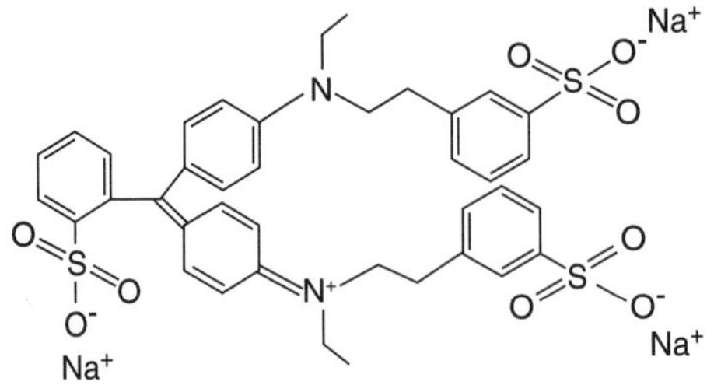

FD&C Blue #1 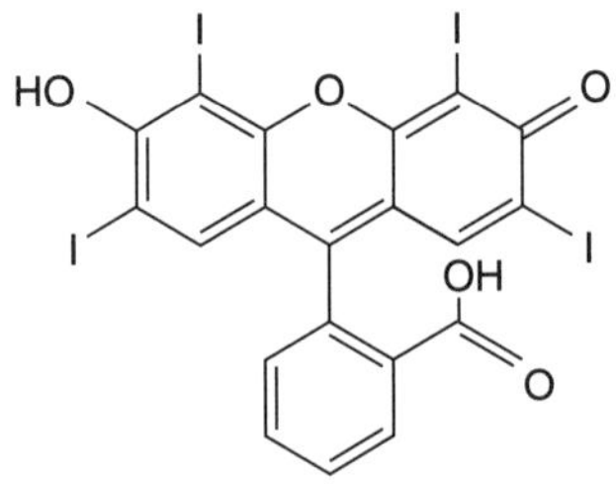   FD&C Red #3

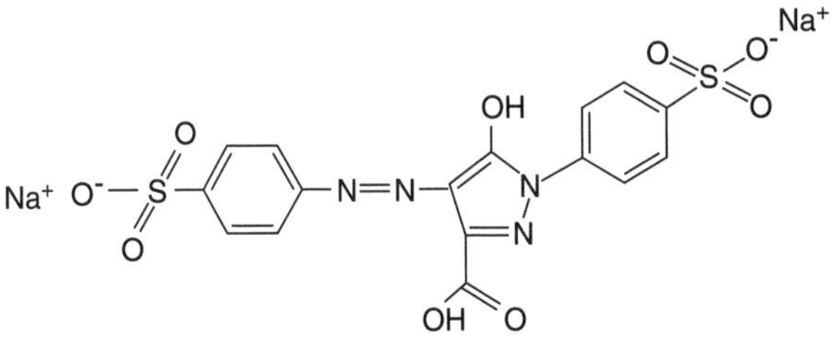

FD&C Yellow #5

*The above diagrams are from *Why There's Antifreeze in Your Toothpaste—The Chemistry of Household Ingredients,* Field, S. Q., Chicago Review Press, 2008, Ch. 10.

(c) Use your results of Q5b to explain the migration of the dyes in Q5a.

Q6.   With the mobile and stationary phases used, can you differentiate between all of the ink pen samples? What could you do differently to try to get the pen dyes to separate if they didn't separate in your experiment?

Q7.   How would the chromatogram appear if a more polar solvent mixture were used for the mobile phase?

Q8.   What do your results for the cheddar cheese and orange Kool-Aid tell you about the dyes used to make orange-colored products?

Section B. Column Chromatography of Kool-Aid

Goal: *To chromatographically separate a synthetic dye mixture into individual components using a C-18 derivatized silica gel column packing.*

Discussion: You should work in pairs for Sections B and C.

Experimental Steps: 1. Using a ring stand and clamp, support the C-18 column. Attach a 10 mL syringe to the column with a piece of clear tubing. The syringe can be attached and removed from the tubing by twisting the syringe. Practice removing and attaching the syringe before you begin.

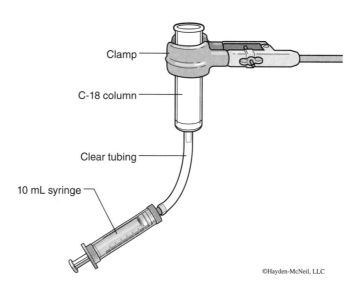

Clamp

C-18 column

Clear tubing

10 mL syringe

©Hayden-McNeil, LLC

NOTE: The packing material which makes up the stationary phase in the column is held in place by two discs or frits. These can be displaced and the column is ruined if the plunger of the syringe is pushed in while attached to the column. **Never push the plunger of the syringe in while the syringe is attached to the column.**

2. The column must be conditioned before it is used. Measure out 5 mL of 100% isopropyl alcohol (IPA). Pour it into the column and note the position of the liquid on the column. In future steps the liquid should reach this same level each time. It is not necessary to measure precise volumes.

3. Draw the isopropyl alcohol through the column by **slowly** pulling out the plunger on the syringe. Draw the alcohol level down to the top of the packing material in the column. When all of the liquid has passed through the column, twist the syringe to remove it from the tubing. Expel the liquid into your waste cup. Push the plunger in before attaching it to the tubing.

4. Repeat step 3 with 5 mL of distilled water. Draw the water level down to the top of the packing material in the column.

5.   Line up five 8 mL vials. Select a sample—grape or lemon lime Kool-Aid—to separate. The separation of the sample will occur in five steps. 5 mL of liquid will be used for each step and all of the samples drawn into the syringe will be saved and placed in one of the vials.

6.   Repeat step 3 with the following liquids. Record your observations of the column and the solutions placed in the vial for each step. Remember, you only need to fill to the mark made on the column in step 2.

(a) 5 mL of the Kool-Aid sample

(b) 5 mL of distilled water

(c) 5 mL of 5% isopropyl alcohol

(d) another 5 mL of 5% isopropyl alcohol

(e) 5 mL of 20% isopropyl alcohol

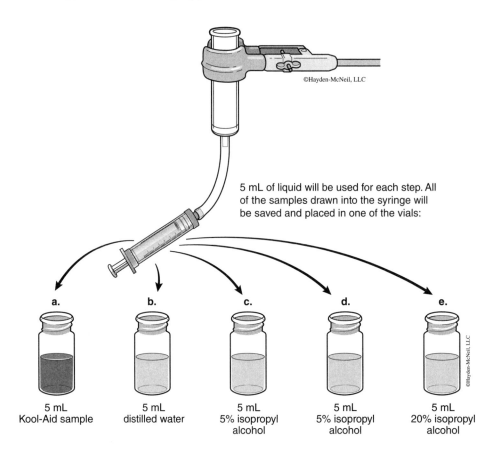

©Hayden-McNeil, LLC

5 mL of liquid will be used for each step. All of the samples drawn into the syringe will be saved and placed in one of the vials:

a.	b.	c.	d.	e.
5 mL Kool-Aid sample	5 mL distilled water	5 mL 5% isopropyl alcohol	5 mL 5% isopropyl alcohol	5 mL 20% isopropyl alcohol

7.   Add a final 5 mL sample of 100% isopropyl alcohol to remove any last traces of the synthetic dyes. This sample may be discarded. The column is now ready to be used again.

Questions: Q9.   Which sample did you separate? How many dyes were in the sample that you separated?

Q10.   Compare your group's results with groups using different samples. Which component of the mixture was removed first from the column? Which component came off the column last? Rank the FD&C dyes in order with the ease that they came off the column. What does this tell you about the affinity of the dyes to the column?

Q11.   What is happening to the polarity of the mobile phase in step 6?

Section C.   Verification of the Composition of Kool-Aid Dyes—Visible Spectroscopy

Goals: *(1) To determine the wavelength of maximum absorbance for samples of synthetic dyes. (2) To identify the dyes from these wavelengths (λ max).*

Discussion: Visible spectrometers are commonly used to find the concentration of a solution or to find the wavelength of light that a solution absorbs most strongly. The solutions to be studied must have a color or must produce a color when another reagent is added.

Experimental Steps: 1.   Plug in the instrument and let it warm up for 5–10 minutes. There are three knobs on the instrument. The left front knob also serves as the on-off switch. Turn the knob to the right until the red power light comes on.

2.   The top knob is used to select the wavelength of light that passes through your sample. Set the wavelength to 400 nm.

3.   Fill a test tube with distilled water and tap to dislodge any bubbles. This will serve as a blank sample.

4.   Select the best sample(s) that have the most distinct color from Part B. Check with your TA if you are not sure which samples to analyze. Transfer these samples to test tubes also.

5.   With nothing in the instrument, turn the left knob until a reading of 0 % T is obtained on the upper %T scale.

6.   Place the blank in the instrument. Make sure that the sample cover is closed. Turn the right knob until a reading of 100% T is obtained.

7.   Remove the blank and place your samples in test tubes in the instrument one at a time. Record the absorbance reading for each sample. If it is difficult to read the absorbance value because of the scale, a %T value may be converted to absorbance by the equation:

$$A = 2 - \log (\%T)$$

8.   Remove your sample and change the wavelength to 425 nm. Repeat steps 5–7 and record the values.

9.   Continue making measurement in 25 nm increments until a wavelength of 700 nm is reached.

Questions: Q12.   Construct a graph of absorbance vs. wavelength for the dyes in your Kool-Aid sample that you isolated in Section B. Determine the wavelength of maximum absorbance for each dye. Using the following list,* identify the dyes that were in your Kool-Aid sample.

Blue #1	630 nm	Red #40	502 nm
Blue #2	610 nm	Yellow #5	428 nm
Red #3	527 nm	Yellow #6	484 nm

*This is a partial list of wavelengths of maximum absorbance from *Handbook of U.S. Colorants, Foods, Drugs, Cosmetics, and Medical Devices*, 3rd Ed., Marmion, D. M., J. Wiley and Sons, New York, 1991, p. 249.

Q13.   (a) Which Kool-Aid sample was used?

(b) What dyes were identified in this section?

(c) How does this compare with the dyes identified in Section A for this sample?

Q14.   Compare the migration of the dyes you identified in your Kool-Aid sample in the paper chromatography and the column chromatography sections.

(a) Which dye in Kool-Aid moved the most and the least in paper chromatography?

(b) Which dye in Kool-Aid came off the column first and last in column chromatography?

(c) How can we explain the differences?

Section D.   Thin Layer Chromatography of Analgesics

Goals: *(1) To spot and develop a thin layer chromatography plate. (2) To identify the components of an analgesic.*

Experimental Steps: 1.   When handling the TLC plate, hold it by the edges as much as possible. Fingerprints on the surface of the plate may interfere with the development of the chromatogram.

2.   Using pencil, draw a line on the fuzzy side of the TLC plate, about 0.5 to 1 cm from the bottom of the plate and make four equally spaced marks on the line about 0.5 cm apart. Note: On the thin layer plate the spots will be barely visible.

3.   Obtain small samples of the standard samples (aspirin, acetaminophen, caffeine and the unknown) in the small vials.

4.   Using the same technique as in Section A, draw out a thin-stem pipet to make an applicator for the samples. Apply a small spot of one of the samples, let it dry, and reapply another spot. Better results are obtained if several spots are applied. Trim the end of the applicator to prevent contamination and repeat for the other samples.

5.   Spot the unknown on the TLC plate the same way that the known samples were applied.

6.   Place 2 or 3 droppers of the ethyl acetate–acetic acid mobile phase in the bottom of the chromatography jar. It is important that the level of the liquid in the jar is below the level of the samples on the TLC plate.

7.   Carefully place the TLC plate in the chromatography jar and place the lid on the jar. Let the jar sit undisturbed until the solvent front is 0.5–1 cm. from the top of the plate.

8.   Remove the TLC plate, mark the solvent front, and allow the plate to dry.

Q15.   (a) What do you observe on the TLC plate?

        (b) What do you observe when you place the dry TLC plate under a UV lamp?

9.   As in the paper chromatography section, draw a line around all of the spots on the TLC plate.

10.   Repeat this procedure using a different solvent for the mobile phase. Groups in your area will use different solvents. Share your results with the neighboring groups. Which solvent system worked best? Explain the results in terms of the polarities of the solvents.

Q16.   Draw a sketch of the TLC plate showing the original positions of the samples, the final positions of the spots, and the solvent front.

Q17. Construct a table listing the samples tested, the distances for each spot, and the R_f values. What components were found in the unknown?

Q18. Why is it good practice to run the standards and the unknown on the same thin layer plate?

Section E.   Development of an Experiment to Identify Unknown Inks

Goal:

Develop a procedure that will allow all colors of ink (red, blue, and black) to be better separated in order to identify them.

Discussion:

This section is designed to be more open-ended and will give you more control over the experiment. Keep "controls and variables" in mind for this section. If several variables are changed at the same time, you may not know which one had the desired effect on the results.

Experimental Steps:

Run samples of five pens of each ink color using last week's paper chromatography system. Make a key for easy identification of the samples.

To improve separation:

Form hypothesis.

Run samples with paper of greater height or change the mobile phase. Refer to the Snyder Index. You will be provided with a small sampling of solvents and their relative polarities. A more complete listing may be found at the site listed on the handout.

When you have a method developed:

Develop a set of unknowns and identify the brands of ink used.

Each member of the group will need a copy of all the chromatograms. These will be needed for your lab notebook as well as the formal report. Make copies in the format that is best for you—scan and print, photograph and print, or make color photocopies.

Section F.   Development of an Experiment to Identify Unknown Dyes

---

Goal: *Develop a procedure that will permit you to determine if a "grape beverage" contains natural pigments or artificial (FD&C) dyes.*

Discussion: This section is designed to be more open-ended and will give you more control over the experiment. Keep "controls and variables" in mind for this section. If several variables are changed at the same time, you may not know which one had the desired effect on the results.

Experimental Steps: Where to Start?

Use two samples as "standards."

- Natural—Grape Juice

- Artificial—Grape Kool-Aid

Grape Juice—Run an absorbance curve using a Spec 20. The sample should be diluted using distilled water.

Grape Kool-Aid—Separate the dyes with the C-18 column and determine the λ max value for each dye. DO NOT run the grape juice through the C-18 column.

Plot the data for the grape juice and the Kool-Aid in your lab notebook. These will be graphed using Excel for the formal report.

What is the basic difference that you observe for the two samples? What criteria would you use to determine if a beverage contains natural pigments or is artificially colored?

Other samples:

Try to run two samples with the scanning UV-Vis instrument. Samples may need to be diluted. This instrument is more sensitive than the Spec 20. If a curve runs "off scale," dilute with distilled water and run again.

Record the λ max value for each sample. Make a printout of one natural and one artificial sample. Photocopy so that each member of your group has a set of these spectra. They will be included in your formal report.

If your group cannot use the scanning instrument, scan using the Spec 20. Remember that darker samples will need to be diluted. Measure the absorbance values of several samples at the same wavelengths used in Section D. Make sure everyone has the data. Use Excel to plot a graph of a natural and an artificially colored sample.

Summarize your findings in a table.

Experiment 18

Paper Chromatography and Liquid Chromatography

Introduction

The introductory and background information needed for this experiment is the same as what is given in Experiment 17. Please review that information before conducting this experiment.

Quiz Outline

Your quiz will NOT cover all of the information below, but it will cover some subset of this information.

Be able to define the following terms listed in your green packet under the heading "Terms that you should know from high school chemistry": equilibrium, hydrogen bond, mixture, polar molecule, solution, accuracy, and precision.

Be able to solve max/min/best estimate types of problems like the ones given in your pink packet.

Define "chromatography."

In order to obtain good separations in chromatography, what factor must be maximized and what factor must be minimized?

Surprisingly, the stationary phase in paper chromatography is considered to be water, not the paper. Explain why.

Certain chromatographic systems are referred to as "reversed phase." What is meant by this?

Be able to calculate the R_f value for compounds on a developed chromatogram.

Diffusion is a significant problem in chromatography. Explain why.

In high-performance liquid chromatography (HPLC), high pressures are involved. Explain why.

A safety question from your TA.

Sample Pre-Laboratory Quiz

1. Define "hydrogen bond."

2. Define "chromatography"

3. Explain why water is considered to be the stationary phase in paper chromatography, and not the paper.

4. Determine the R_f values for the two compounds contained in sample #4 (show below).

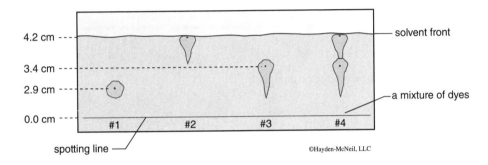

5. Using the max/min/best estimate method, determine the value of the expression below. Show all your work.

$$(215 \pm 3 - 47 \pm 1) \times (0.005 \pm 0.001) = ?$$

Laboratory Experiments

Flowchart of the Experiments

Section A.	**Paper Chromatography of Dyes**

Section B.	**Preparation of a Liquid Chromatography Column**

Section C.	**Derivatization of the Silica Gel Stationary Phase**

Section D.	**Chromatography of Selected Synthetic Dyes on a Derivatized Column**

Requires one four-hour class period to complete.

Section A.   Paper Chromatography of Dyes

Goal: *To carry out a series of ascending paper chromatographic separations of inks and food dyes in a small-scale tank system.*

Discussion: You will also characterize the relative attraction of individual compounds for the stationary vs. the mobile phase using R_f (retention factor) measurements.

NOTE: In paper chromatography, the stationary phase actually is not the paper, but water which is bound to the paper by hydrogen bonding.

Before You Begin: Paper chromatography is a microanalytical technique. Extraordinarily small sample volumes are used (microliters), and the separation often yields very small amounts (often less than nanomoles) of product. It is particularly important to maintain good technique and to try to avoid contamination of the chromatography paper. Work on a clean piece of paper or paper towel when you are drawing lines and spotting samples.

Experimental Steps: 1.   Obtain one piece of chromatography paper from Reagent Central. Draw in the lines and points with a *pencil*, as shown below.

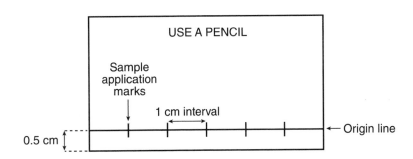

2.   Make a plastic capillary tube by first stretching the tip of a thin-stem pipet until it collapses to its small diameter size. Continue stretching until 2 or 3 inches of the thin stem has attained a small diameter. Then cut off both ends, leaving a 2–3 inch long plastic capillary tube. This tube can be used as an applicator to transfer small amounts of dye from your 24-well tray to your paper chromatogram. NOTE: Keep the applicator vertical. Cut off the tip of the capillary after applying each dye.

3.   Spot all of the food dye samples, cutting off the tip of the applicator after you spot each dye to avoid contamination. You will be spotting FD&C food dyes as standards, mixtures of dyes used in foods (e.g., grape), and dye mixture B.

•   Record where each dye is spotted.

4.   Using small amounts of your FD&C food dyes, prepare your own mixture (the components are of your own choosing) of black dye (or at least as dark as you can get it) for spotting on the chromatogram. Spot the black dye.

•   Record the components of your black dye.

5. Obtain 3 or 4 markers from the front of the room and touch each marker tip to an unused sample application mark (one marker per application mark).

    NOTE: Keep the pen vertical and try to make the spots small by touching and removing the tip quickly.

    •   Record where each pen (brand name/label) is spotted.

6. Roll the paper into a cylinder and hold it while you staple it as shown below. *Do not overlap* the two edges of the cylinder. Your chromatogram should fit inside a plastic chromatography tank (a clear plastic cup, turned upside down) without touching the walls. If you need to, cut the chromatography paper shorter and restaple the cylinder to make it fit.

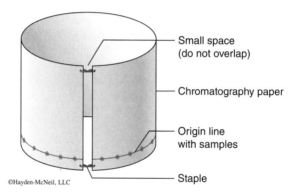

Small space (do not overlap)

Chromatography paper

Origin line with samples

Staple

©Hayden-McNeil, LLC

7. Deliver three pipets of the mobile phase solvent, 2:1 1-propanol/water, to a solvent tray (half of a Petri dish). Place the paper cylinder into the solvent as evenly and centrally as possible.

8. Place the tank over the cylinder. Try to keep the paper cylinder from flattening against the inside wall of the tank.

9. Watch the mobile phase for a few moments so that you can see the mobile phase front as it climbs up the paper by capillary action.

    The chromatography will take about 20–25 minutes. From time to time check the progress of the front. You will want to stop the chromatography when the solvent front reaches ~0.5 cm from the top of the paper.

    While the paper chromatography is occurring, begin preparing the liquid chromatography column (Section B).

10. When the front reaches ~ 0.5 cm from the top of the paper, lift the tank and quickly remove the cylinder. Place it onto a clean paper towel. Using a pencil, mark the solvent front line. Replace the tank.

11. Pull the cylinder apart and hang it up to dry. The drying time is about 20 minutes.

12.   While the paper is drying, continue with Section B if needed, then move on to Sections C and D. Interweave your analysis of the paper chromatogram and answering of questions with experimental sections.

13.   When the paper is dry (or when you are ready), place it flat on a towel on the table and locate the component zones or spots. The following figure shows how to draw the circles around the spots and determine the distance migrated. The measuring point is drawn considering, "Where would the spot have been if an incredibly tiny amount of dye had been spotted?"

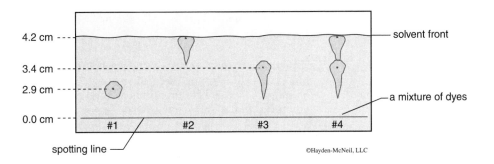

In sample #1, the dye migrated evenly, but diffused, so the location that an incredibly tiny amount of dye would migrate to would be the center of the spot. In sample #2, much of the dye migrated at the same rate as the mobile phase, but it didn't migrate evenly and left a trailing edge. If a much smaller amount had been used, most of it would have been at the solvent front. In sample #3, we see both a circular diffusion pattern and a trailing edge. In this case, the measurement should be made from the middle of the most concentrated area of the dye. Sample #4 illustrates a mixture of samples #2 and #3.

Questions:

Q1.   Measure and record the distance that each component migrated from the original sample application mark. Attach the chromatogram to your notebook.

Q2.   Calculate the R_f value for each component, where

$$R_f = \frac{\text{component migration distance}}{\text{mobile phase migration distance}} = \frac{\text{distance spot traveled}}{\text{distance solvent travels from spotting line}}$$

Q3.   Use R_f values and color to identify the FD&C dyes in the mixtures of dyes used in food (e.g., grape), and dye mixture B. If the compounds aren't present in similar amounts, then this should be noted.

Q4.   From comparison with the black dye that you prepared from FD&C dyes, do you think that any of the commercial pens contain FD&C dyes? If so, then list the FD&C dyes present in each pen.

Q5.   Which components are migrating the greatest distance on your chromatogram, the polar or nonpolar ones? Explain.

Q6.   Why did some of the pen dyes separate into distinct bands of color but others didn't? What could you do differently to try to get the pen dyes to separate if they didn't separate in your experiment?

Section B.   Preparation of a Liquid Chromatography Column

Goals: (1) To construct a liquid chromatography system from straws. (2) To prepare a silica gel chromatography column that can be used to test chromatographic processes and separations.

NOTE: Please do not discard the various plastic materials used in making the chromatography apparatus. We will recycle them wherever possible.

Experimental Steps: 1.   Construct a straw clamp and stand system as instructed in Section A of Experiment 4, "The Use and Abuse of Aluminum." This will be used to hold your liquid chromatography column.

2.   Obtain a third straw. This will be your chromatography column. Do not shorten this straw. You will need the full length. Place a small wad of polyester fiber into the end of it. Push a column tip (small red plastic piece with a narrow hole) firmly into the bottom of this straw so that the polyester fiber rests on it.

NOTE: Do not pack it too tightly or it will impede the flow of the mobile phase.

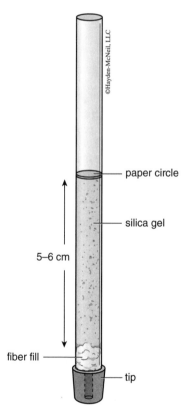

3.   Clamp your chromatography column into the stand you constructed in step 1.

4.   Place a small cup under the column straw and squirt a stream of water into the straw to wash the walls and wet the polyester.

5.   Use the plastic scoop (provided for you) to put one scoop of 100–200 mesh silica gel into a small cup. This should be enough to pack a column 5–6 cm long.

6. Add about 15 mL of water to the cup and stir thoroughly with a pipet to form a slurry. Suck up some slurry. Transfer the slurry to the column quickly!

    NOTE: The idea is to do this quickly to avoid settling of the large particles. If you get an air block in the column, insert a slim straw (available in the front of the room) and the block will disappear.

7. Transfer more slurry while the first batch is settling. Use the slim straw to work the packing in the column. Try to make a column silica gel slurry packing about 5–6 cm long.

    NOTE: You may need to add more water to the slurry in the cup to transfer it into the column.

8. Add water to the column until it is full (to the top).

9. Obtain a pump syringe and pull the plunger almost to the end, to push air, not pull air!

10. Push the plastic tubing into the top of the column and hold it there firmly. Gently push the syringe plunger in and push water through the column.

    CAUTION: *Do not push the liquid level below the top of the packed column or* **you will have to repack the column because severe channeling and cracking will occur.**

    The liquid level should not go below the top of the packing if you don't push it. The pressure you used helps to pack the silica gel tightly, and reduces the void volume considerably.

11. Tap the straw at the top of the packing and rotate the straw until the top of the silica gel is level.

12. Add 2–3 cm of water to the column and tap to flatten.

13. Place a punched circle of no. 3 paper (obtain from Reagent Central) into the top of the column. Push the circle down the column with a slim straw.

    NOTE: As it enters the water, the air bubble will disappear.

14. Push the paper until it is *flat* against the silica gel packing. Gently smooth with the slim straw while rotating the column.

15. Fill the column with water from your wash bottle and push water through with the syringe pump as in step 10. *Do not push water below the paper circle.*

16. Allow the column to drain naturally, and the liquid level should stay at the level of the paper. If you notice that it has dropped below the level of the paper, then add a little more water.

    You have just carried out a sophisticated slurry-packing procedure for the preparation of a liquid chromatography (LC) column of good efficiency. Note that the procedure appears to be a little difficult the first time, but once you are familiar with the technique, it takes about 2 minutes to pack a column. If you do make a mistake while making or running any of the columns, it's OK. Simply pump the mobile phase and any sample off the column, pull off the tip, wash the silica gel out, and repack the column.

Question: Q7.   In the above procedure you used pressure to pack the silica gel tightly, to reduce the void volume (empty spaces in the column). Why is it important to reduce the void volume, i.e., what would happen to samples that are run through a column with a large void volume?

Section C.   Derivatization of the Silica Gel Stationary Phase

Goal: *To carry out a derivatization (changing of the polarity) of the silica gel in which the pH of the surface of the gel is changed from 6.8 to 4.5. The derivatization is done in preparation of the separation of a dye mixture in Section D.*

Discussion: The derivatization is achieved by allowing a dilute solution of acetic acid to flow through the column. The surface of the silica gel contains SiO^- and $SiOH$ groups that react with acetic acid to make the surface less polar. Then the excess unreacted acetic acid is flushed from the column. Experimentation has shown that if the polarity of the column is not changed, then the dye mixture will not separate well.

Experimental Steps: 1.   Use your column from Section B.

                         2.   Transfer the 0.1 M CH_3COOH to the column with a thin-stem pipet until you have at least 5 cm of CH_3COOH in the column.

                         3.   Allow the CH_3COOH to flow under gravity until all the solution has gone through, but not further than the top of the packed column.

                         4.   Pump two column lengths of water through the column to remove excess CH_3COOH. *Do not* pump the water level below the paper circle. The surface of the silica gel has now been protonated, and the surface pH is about 4.5.

Section D.   Chromatography of Selected Synthetic Dyes on a Derivatized Column

Goal: *To chromatographically separate a synthetic dye mixture (called "dye mixture B") into individual components using a derivatized silica gel column packing.*

Discussion: You will be measuring the amount of mobile phase needed to remove each component of the dye mixture from the column. This is called the retention volume, V_R. Each component will have a different retention volume. Retention volume is to liquid chromatography what R_f is to paper chromatography, in the sense that it gives you a quantitative measure of how well a given substance sticks to the stationary phase. The larger the retention volume, the better a given substance sticks to the stationary phase.

                           This section is tricky, and so please read all of the experimental steps before starting.

Experimental Steps: 1.   Using your derivatized column from Section C, mark a point (with a fine point permanent marker) close to the top of the straw. Call this point 1.

                         2.   If your thin-stem pipet is not long enough to reach the paper circle in the straw, lengthen the stem a little by pulling.

3.   With a thin-stem pipet, suck up a small volume of dye mixture B, following the techniques shown below. Very carefully, keeping the pipet vertical, lower the tip of the pipet until it just touches the paper circle in the middle.

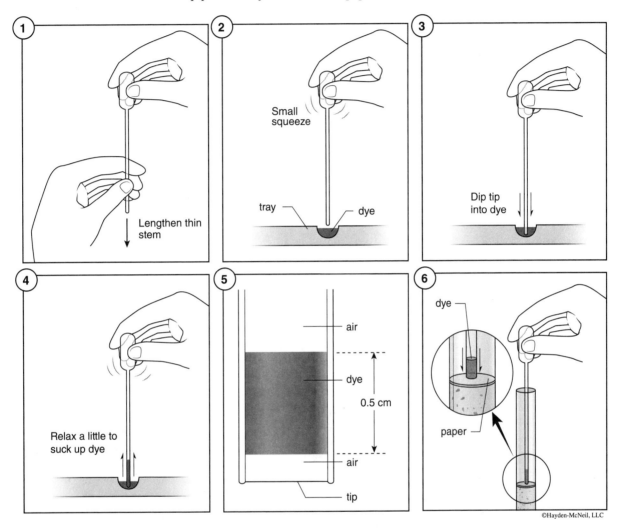

©Hayden-McNeil, LLC

4.   Very, very gently squeeze the pipet bulb until the dye is just soaked into the paper and *not* on the packing. Do not overload the column! Remove the pipet.

5.   Clean the thin-stem pipet and use it to add a 30% v/v ethanol/water solution (the mobile phase) to the column up to the mark you made in step 1. The chromatography will proceed.

6.   Watch the chromatographic process.

    •   Draw a picture of the separation.

7.   You want to determine the amount of mobile phase needed to wash a particular compound off the column. This determination begins by noting the level of the mobile phase when the first compound is halfway off the column (see following figure). The distance between the initial level of the mobile phase, and the level when the first compound is halfway off the column is d_1. Repeat this type of measurement (d_2, d_3, etc.) for each color that comes off the column.

NOTE: As you watch the chromatography proceed, try to determine the uncertainty in your estimates for when half of the band has come off the column for each component. Do you think that you've estimated that half of the band of color is off with an uncertainty of ± 0.1 cm or ± 0.2 cm or whatever it may be in distance on the straw column?

The chromatographic progress of an unretained component through the column is shown in the following:

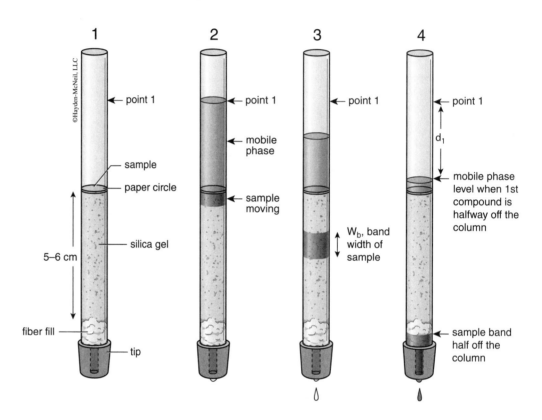

Questions: Q8.   Measure and record the distance "d" in cm—i.e., the distance between point 1 and the point at which a given component is halfway off the column. Include with each distance the estimate of uncertainty in distance on the straw for each component (e.g., ± 0.1 cm, or whatever you may have determined in step 7).

Q9.   Using the max/best estimate/min method for uncertainty analysis, calculate the retention volume V_R (with units!) for each of the dye components. Report the retention volume for each component with the correct number of significant figures and with the uncertainty.

The retention volume can be calculated by assuming that the straw column is a cylinder of constant radius 0.30 cm and therefore

$$V_R = d \times \pi \times (0.30)^2$$

Q10.   If a larger retention volume is used to remove one component from a chromatography column than another, what does that mean about the ability of the larger V_R component to stick to the column, compared to the smaller V_R component?

Q11.   How does the order of separation compare for the separation of dye mixture B using paper chromatography vs. liquid chromatography? For example, which component migrated the fastest in the paper chromatography experiment, compared to the liquid chromatography experiment?

Q12.   Explain your answer to Q11 in terms of the polarities of the stationary and mobile phases used.

Experiment 19

Gas Chromatography

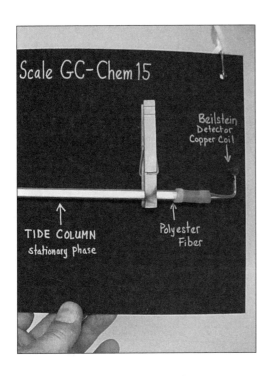

"The second proposal, to look for halocarbons, was rejected as frivolous because it was 'obvious' that no apparatus existed sensitive enough to measure the few parts per trillion of chlorofluorocarbons I was proposing to seek."

—James Lovelock, *The Ages of Gaia*

Introduction

Gas chromatography (GC) is one of the most powerful and widely used methods for the qualitative and quantitative analysis of volatile components in sample mixtures. Although a relatively new method—the first paper describing the use of a gaseous mobile phase was published by Martin and James in 1952—GC is now used in all areas of science, medicine, and industry. Some typical analytical applications are trace hydrocarbons and other pollutants in air; petroleum refinery products; barbituates and other drugs in blood, breath, saliva, and urine samples; flavoring agents in foods; trace contaminants in beer, wine, and spirits; and pheromone sex attractants in insects.

Gas chromatography is a technique for the separation of volatile substances by percolating a sample mixture (in vapor form) in a gaseous mobile phase through a porous stationary phase contained in a long tube. The technique can be divided into two fundamental types: gas-solid chromatography (GSC) and gas-liquid chromatography (GLC). In GSC the separation is accomplished by passing the sample, in a carrier gas, over a solid stationary phase. The different components in the sample have different adsorption affinities for the stationary phase, and some are slowed down with respect to others. In GLC, components in the sample are separated by passing the sample and carrier gas over a stationary phase consisting of an inert solid support coated with a nonvolatile liquid. In GLC the distribution process between the mobile gas phase and liquid stationary phase is *partition*. GLC is by far the more versatile method because of the wide range of liquid stationary phases that are commercially available.

Background Chemistry

A general introduction to the theory of chromatography is given in the Background Chemistry section of Experiment 17. If you are new to chromatography, it is probably advisable to read the section before you continue on into the Background Chemistry section of "Gas Chromatography."

A basic GC system consists of a carrier gas, a heated sample injection port, a separating column, and a detector. Commercially available instruments cost $5,000–$50,000 and often come with a dedicated computer for data collection, storage, and interpretation. The GC flow schematic is shown in Figure 19.1.

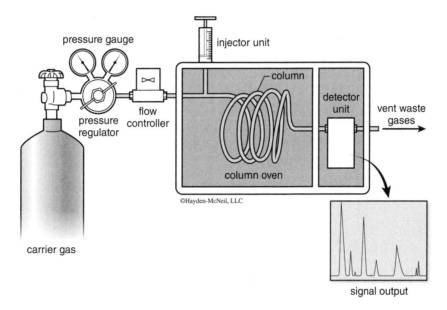

Figure 19.1 Schematic of a typical GC.

The carrier gas is usually a pure, inert gas (e.g., He, H_2, Ar, or N_2) stored in a pressurized tank. The flow rate of the mobile phase must be very carefully controlled in GC because the rates of migration of all components are dependent on it. Various pressure gauges, flow controllers, and meters accomplish exact carrier gas flow control.

The samples to be analyzed by GC may be gases, liquids, or solids. Solid and liquid samples must be volatilized; thus, they must be heated as they are introduced into the injection port. Generally, a very small sample volume is needed—on the order of 0.1 μL to 50 μL. The volatilized sample is swept onto the separating column by a flowing stream of carrier gas. The two main types of columns in general use are shown in Figure 19.2.

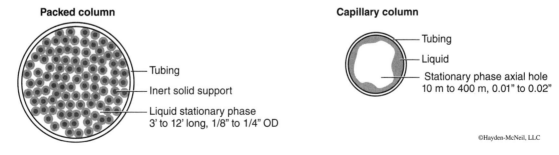

Figure 19.2 Two types of GC columns.

Packed columns are relatively short because of the high pressure required to push the gases through the stationary phase. These columns are inexpensive and therefore widely used. Capillary columns are much narrower and can be much longer because of the hole all the way through the column. Capillary columns are tough to make and are expensive, although the increase in efficiency is worth the price, particularly for the analysis of very complex samples (e.g., gasoline).

Both types of columns are available with any one of several hundred different liquid stationary phases. Selection of the type of liquid stationary phase is based on the type of sample to be analyzed. The real power and flexibility of GC as a method of analysis rest on the fact that the stationary phase can almost be tailored at will to fit the separation problem. The choice is often made on the "like dissolves like" principle, or put in a more sophisticated way, the liquid is chosen on the basis of polarity index. The column is usually placed in an oven, the temperature of which can be raised or lowered (and monitored) in any predetermined manner. The separated components that leave the column are then quantitatively detected by a suitable detector or, in some instances, may be trapped and recovered. Again, one of the tremendous advantages of GC is the variety of sensitive, quantitative detectors that are available, e.g., thermal conductivity, mass spectrometry, and even live male insects (used as detectors of insect pheromones).

Many commercial GCs have three types of built-in detectors: *thermal conductivity* (TCD), *flame ionization* (FID), and *electron capture* (ECD). The detector output (signal) is usually fed to a strip chart recorder or to a dedicated computer (are there any other kind?). A typical GC chromatogram is shown in Figure 19.3.

Gas Chromatogram

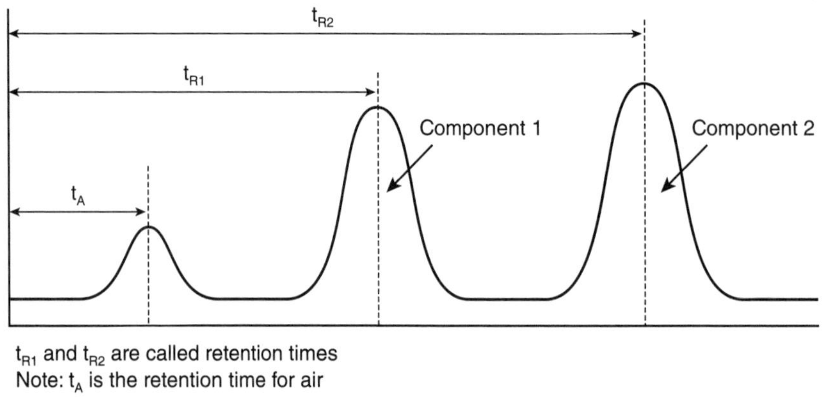

t_{R1} and t_{R2} are called retention times
Note: t_A is the retention time for air

Figure 19.3 A GC chromatogram.

The various components do not have R_f values, in the same sense as in paper chromatography, because the components actually come *out* of the gas chromatograph, and the mobile phase is continuously flowing (compare PC). In GC the retention parameter is called the *retention time* (t_R) and is the time that elapses between the injection of the sample and when the center of the component band is detected by the detector. Almost always, the injection of the sample into a gas chromatograph results in air being injected. Air components (O_2 and N_2) are generally unretained—i.e., have no affinity for the liquid stationary phase—and quickly appear in the detector. The time between sample injection and the detected air peak is called the *retention time of air* (even though it is not retained by the stationary phase). The detectors also produce a concentration profile that, with a suitable calibration line, can be used to quantitatively measure the amount or concentration of any sample component.

A Small-Scale Gas Chromatograph

The Department of Chemistry could not afford to buy a gas chromatograph for each of you (in spite of the current tuition trends!). However, you can build your own working GC for about $0.25. The GC design was developed by the author over a three-year period (between 1974–1977). The column stationary phase is constructed of a glass or straw tube filled with dry Tide detergent ("you can trust Tide!") and uses natural gas as carrier gas. The GC detector is rather unusual in that the principle has been known for 90 years and is only now beginning to be used in some modern instruments. You will be constructing a Beilstein detector—named after a famous German chemist, who incidentally didn't discover the principle; a Swedish chemist, Berthollet, did!

The detector is a copper coil that is placed in a small flame generated at the column exit by burning natural gas. One of the real reasons for using natural gas (methane) as a carrier gas is that it comes from a highly controlled valve and has a convenient useful line pressure of about 6–7 ounces per square inch. The normal gas tap serves as a fine-tuning regulator for the carrier gas flow. The methane is then used as a fuel source for the small-scale premix burner and Beilstein detector.

Normally in commercial GC instruments, the injection port is actually a little oven that quickly converts the liquid sample (often dissolved in a volatile solvent) into vapor. In your GC the samples are halocarbon vapors and, thus, heating is not necessary. The port is made from ordinary Bunsen burner tubing (latex tubing). Surprisingly, the latex is a self-sealing material that will take repeated injections without leaking. The separating column is a short (20 cm × 0.8 cm) tube of soft glass packed with activated Tide detergent. Tide detergent is a complex mixture of about twelve ingredients formulated to get clothes clean. However, from the GC viewpoint, it consists of an inorganic solid ($Na_5P_3O_{10}$, sodium tripolyphosphate) coated with *polar, high molecular weight, organic surfactant*. The organic surfactant probably serves as the liquid stationary phase in GC. The Tide must be activated before use in order to remove the perfume and some water. Activation is carried out by placing a large tray of detergent in an oven at 150 °C for about 4 hours. The particle size of the powder is not ideal, but it is in the correct range to allow a reasonable carrier gas flow through the column (provided the column is not too long). The actual process of putting the Tide into the tube (packing the column) is critical to achieving successful separations. If the column is packed too tightly, there will be no carrier gas flow, and if the column is packed too loosely, channeling will occur, giving rise to poor or no separations. Of course, the larger the Tide column, the longer are the retention times for components and the greater is the band spreading of each component. A column length of 20–50 cm seems to be reasonable for the gas pressures encountered in most schools and universities.

It is worth noting that there are several reports in the scientific literature of the use of solid detergents as stationary phases in gas chromatography. In the GC that you will be building, the Tide-packed column will be used at ambient temperatures. The halocarbon samples that you will be separating have a relatively high vapor pressure at room temperature, and elevated column temperatures are not necessary. The Tide column will separate the sample mixture into individual halocarbon components that then must be sensed by some type of detector. You will be using a Beilstein detector, which is a sensitive device for the detection of compounds containing halogen atoms, but which is not very sensitive, or does not work at all, for other substances.

The *Beilstein detector* is a sensitive, selective GC detector that emits visible light when separated halocarbon components go through it. A quantitative analysis may be obtained by using some type of photodetector (e.g., a CdS cell or photodiode) to transduce emitted light into an electronic effect. Of course, a calibration line is required for each component because the detector and transducer response depend on the chemical structure of the detected substance. A Beilstein detector consists of a copper wire coil that is placed in the relatively cool part of a small flame. As the flame plays over the copper (and the surface copper(II) oxide), the surface reacts with free electrons in the flame and is kept clean and reactive. This phenomenon is very beautiful to watch because the black surface ripples with a golden sheen as the flame reduces Cu^{2+} back to Cu^0. If a halogen-containing vapor is burned in the flame, highly reactive halogen atoms are formed which then quickly react with the fresh copper surface to form volatile copper halides. The halides then rapidly react with OH radicals in the flame to give various copper species (e.g., $CuOH^+$) that are thermally excited by the heat of the flame. The excited copper species emit green-blue light as they return to the ground state. Emission of green-blue light is a definite indication that a halogen-containing component has arrived in the detector. By the way, the Beilstein effect has been used for many years in devices for detecting leaks in air conditioners and refrigerators!

Once you have built the GC, the best way to learn about the technique is to get involved in investigating a practical problem. The next section presents an interesting environmental sciences application that involves the analysis of industrial and commercial products and addresses the general problem of halocarbons in the environment.

Halocarbons and the Environment

A large number of chemical compounds containing carbon–halogen bonds have been made by the chemical industry and have proved to be extremely useful in industry, commerce, and agriculture. The uses are varied and include such applications as pesticides, hydraulic fluids, electrical transformer fluids, solvents, aerosol propellants, anesthetics, refrigerants, air conditioner fluids, foam expanders, plastics, etc. Some specific examples follow.

Insecticide:

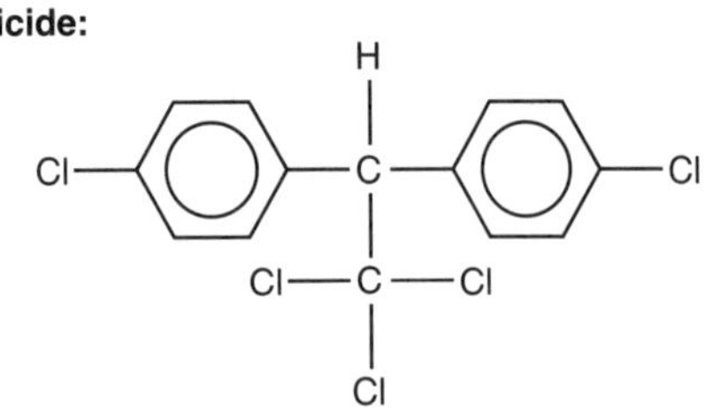

DDT, *dichlorodiphenyltrichloroethane*

Hydraulic fluids and transformer fluids:

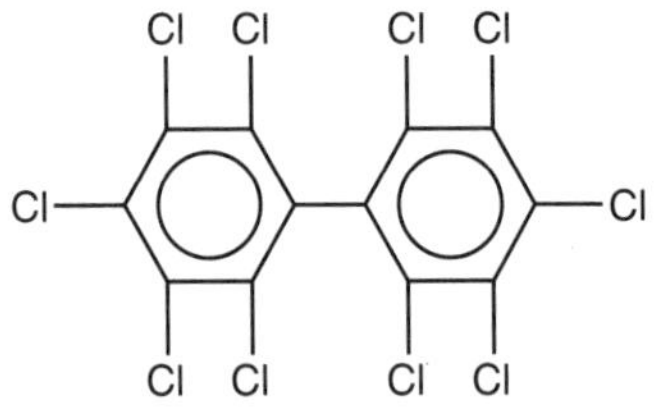

PCB, *polychlorinatedbiphenyl*   PBB, *polybrominatedbiphenyl*

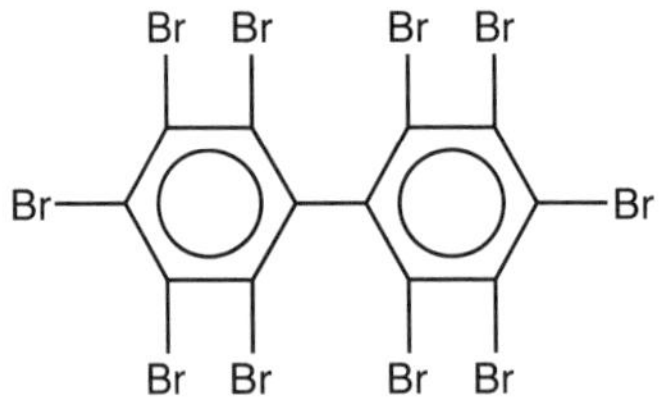

Solvents:

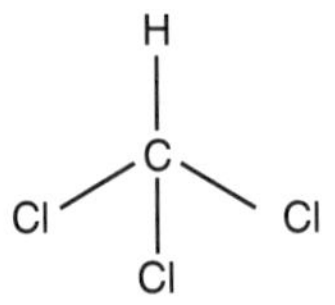

Chloroform 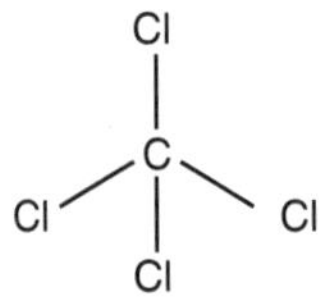   Carbon tetrachloride

Solvents, propellants, refrigerants, foam expanders, air conditioner fluids, etc.:

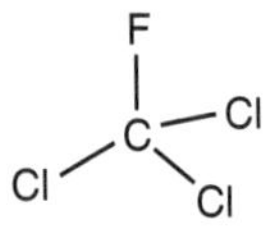

Freon 11 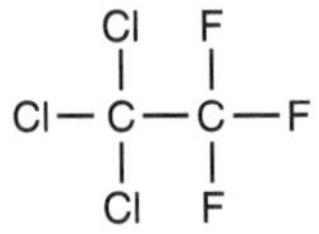   Freon 12   Freon 123   Freon 22   Freon 134a

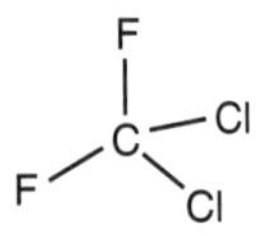

Freon 113

Chloro-fluoro-carbons (CFCs): compounds that contain only Cl, F, and C

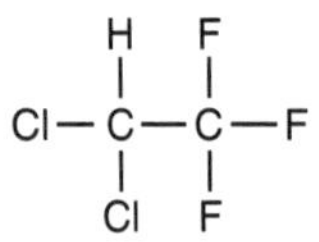

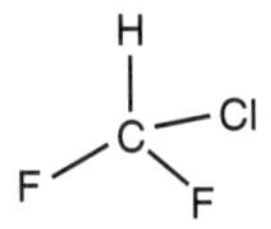

Hydro-chloro-fluoro-carbons (HCFCs): compounds containing only H, Cl, F, and C

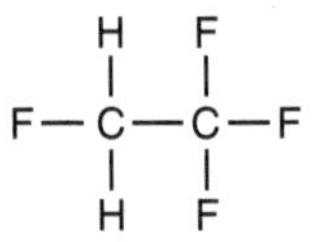

Hydro-fluoro-carbons (HFCs): compounds containing only H, F, and C; 134a is currently the main refrigerant compound

Freons are named according to "the rule of 90." Add 90 to the name of the freon, and the resulting digits indicate the numbers of atoms of C, H, F, and by implication, Cl, in the molecule. For example, Freon 11 + 90 = 101, therefore the molecule has 1 carbon, 0 hydrogens, and 1 fluorine. The remaining 3 bonds to carbon are supplied by chlorine.

The use of many of these halocarbons has been restricted, and some of them have been banned outright because of environmental health problems. The environmental problems have arisen mostly from the chemical and biological properties of these halocarbons. Carbon–halogen covalent bonds are very stable, and these compounds do not break down easily under most environmental conditions. This chemical longevity, together with the fact that many of these compounds are fat soluble, means that halocarbons stay around a long time and concentrate up food chains. (For one interesting aspect, see Experiment 8, "An Introduction to Acids and Bases.")

In this module, it is the smaller molar mass halocarbons (e.g., the freons) that are of interest. The freons, sometimes called chlorofluorocarbons (CFCs), are very stable, volatile, and cheap compounds. These characteristics make them valuable as refrigerants, propellants, and foam expanders. Their stability means that they persist in the air—the troposphere—for a long time (half-life is about 75 years for Freon 12), eventually drifting into the stratosphere.

Unfortunately, the stratosphere is a sink for freons because at this high altitude, the high-energy ultraviolet (UV) light from the sun causes even stable compounds to break down. In a complex sequence of photochemical reactions, the freons are decomposed by light into chlorine atoms:

$$CCl_3F + h\upsilon \rightarrow Cl + CCl_2F$$

$$CCl_2F_2 + h\upsilon \rightarrow Cl + CClF_2$$

The chlorine atoms catalyze the destruction of ozone (O_3) in a series of free radical reactions, one of which is

$$Cl + O_3 \rightarrow ClO + O_2$$

Recently, it was discovered that each year, in September and October, the stratospheric ozone layer over Antarctica shrinks drastically and in many places disappears completely. Again, it appears that chlorofluorocarbons are the culprit. Unusual chemical reactions on the surface of polar stratospheric ice clouds generate chlorine from chlorofluorocarbons, and the ozone is destroyed. The maintenance of normal ozone concentrations in the stratosphere is critical to life on Earth. The stratosphere ozone cycle removes most of the high-energy UV light that would otherwise reach the Earth's surface. The consequences of a reduced ozone concentration in the stratosphere may vary from increased skin cancers to severe chromosome damage and dramatic climate changes.

A recent global conference of CFC producers, users, and scientists agreed that the problem of ozone destruction by chlorofluorocarbons is a real and severe environmental threat. In an unprecedented decision the conference announced CFC production restriction and eventual phase-out of CFCs altogether. This decision has stimulated several large companies to begin research on developing new CFC substitutes for refrigerants and foam-expanding agents. In spite of all the recent furor, it is important to note that most of the CFCs that have *ever* been produced are still present in the atmosphere. The ozone problem is not going to go away for many decades, if ever.

Gas chromatography has played a key role not only in the initial identification of CFCs in the atmosphere, but also in the current research on ozone "holes" in the polar regions. In fact, it could be said that the whole CFC story started about 30 years ago in an English country garden! In 1970 an independent scientist named James Lovelock, who now works in a barn-turned-laboratory in Cornwall, England, invented a new type of GC detector called the *electron capture detector*. He attached the detector to a GC, and his first sample for analysis was English garden air. The GC chromatogram revealed two previously unidentified peaks that were shown to be Freons 11 and 12. Lovelock did a rough calculation based on the freon concentrations measured by the GC experiment and came to the conclusion that all of the freons ever manufactured were still present in the atmosphere—the rest is history.

It is strange but true that the discovery of the CFC-global ozone problem relied on the invention and use of a GC detector. In this laboratory module, you have the opportunity to build your own sophisticated GC equipment, investigate its limitations, and carry out analyses on various samples containing halocarbons.

Additional Reading

1. The Chemical Heritage Foundation has a section on "Faces in the Environment" that covers a lot of the ozone/CFC issue (as of 11/04). http://www.chemheritage.org/educationalservices /faces/env/env.htm

Quiz Outline

Your quiz will NOT cover all of the information below, but it will cover some subset of the information given below.

Explain the differences between stationary and mobile phases and the purpose of each (see Background, Exp. 17).

Be able to compare paper, liquid, and gas chromatography. How are they alike and how do they differ?

Be able to explain how a Beilstein detector works, including what it detects the presence of.

Be able to sketch the gas chromatograph used in this experiment and label the most important parts.

Be able to list some uses of gas chromatography.

NOTE: Please bring an empty aluminum can (beverage flavor of your choice!) to lab for this experiment.

Sample Pre-Laboratory Quiz

1. Describe the main difference between gas chromatography and paper chromatography.

2. Explain how a Beilsten detector works.

3. Why have chlorofluorocarbons (CFCs) and halons been used so extensively industrially—i.e., What are the advantages of their use?

4. List two applications for gas chromatography.

5. Explain why freons pose a threat to our environment. (i.e., What is it about the chemistry of these compounds that makes them environmentally dangerous?) Be as specific as possible.

Laboratory Experiments

Flowchart of the Experiments

Section A.   **The Construction of a Gas Chromatograph**

Section B.   **Measurement of the Retention Time of Air and the Gas Flow Rate**

Section C.   **Measurement of the Retention Times of Halocarbons**

Section D.   **GC Separation of Halocarbon Mixtures**

Section E.   **Quantitative Analysis Using a Commercial GC**

Requires one four-hour class period to complete.

CAUTION: In this series of experiments, you will be using natural gas as a carrier gas in GC. Be aware that natural gas is flammable and in certain circumstances can be dangerous. Please remember that burning gas is hot, and so are metal objects (such as detectors and windbreaks) that come into contact with flames. Please sign out and in for the syringe sample injector you use during the experiment.

Section A.   The Construction of a Gas Chromatograph

Goal:

To build a working small-scale gas chromatograph that is capable of separating several halocarbons.

Before You Begin:

You are about to build the odd-looking device, actually a small-scale gas chromatograph, shown in the diagram below. As you work through Section A, refer to the diagram to compare with your own construction.

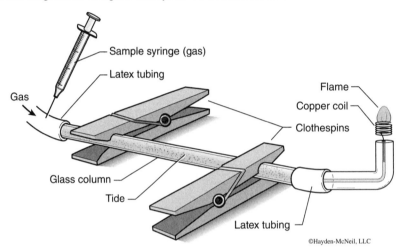

Small-scale gas chromatograph

Experimental Steps:

1. Obtain the following from Reagent Central: 1 × 20 cm piece of 8 mm glass tubing; 1 × 2 ft and 1 × 2 cm pieces of latex tubing; 1 glass L-shaped capillary tube; small bundle of polyester fiber; 1 piece of copper wire approximately 40 cm long; 1 small cup of activated Tide detergent; a 9" large barrel pipet; and a windbreak made from a beverage can.

2. Do not wash the 20 cm piece of glass tubing or it will take a long time to dry. Place a small plug of polyester fiber inside one end of the glass tube.

3. To keep the Tide from falling out of the column, insert a small cork at the end of the tube with the plug.

4. Make a funnel from a 9" large barrel pipet by cutting off half of the bulb and all but 1/2" of the stem. Scoop up some of the activated Tide detergent and pour it thorough the funnel into the vertically-held glass tube.

5. Deliver the detergent at an even rate, tapping the tube gently as you fill it.

NOTE: If the funnel gets blocked, remove and invert it over the cup and tap. Do not attempt to poke it out or it will really clog.

6. Refill the funnel and keep pouring and tapping until the tube is completely filled with Tide. Remove the funnel.

7. Keep the tube vertical and very gently bounce the tube on the table (at the cork end). The Tide will settle a little.

8. Add more Tide until it is about 0.5 cm from the end.

9. Place a plug of polyester fiber into the end of the tube to keep the Tide in. Remove the cork from the other end.

You have now prepared a Tide-packed gas chromatography column. Since this is possibly the first time that you have attempted this high technology endeavor, there might be some probability that the column packing is not perfect. Don't worry—diagnosis of "sick" columns is easy, and repacking takes only a few minutes. It is important that you handle the column carefully. Place it gently on the table and try not to bump it too much. Now you can construct the burner and Beilstein photoionization detector.

GC Detector Construction

10. As demonstrated below, hold the straight part of your glass column (or a round pen) and *tightly* wind a copper wire coil 10 turns. As you wind, keep your thumb tightly on the end and put tension on the wire as you wind it. Leave a tail of copper wire about 2 cm long on one side of the coil.

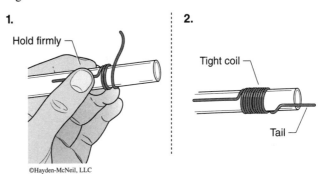

©Hayden-McNeil, LLC

NOTE: Do not worry if your coil is not as tightly compressed as in the second drawing. After heating the coil in Section B it will be easy to compress the coil.

11. Slip the tight coil off the glass tube and adjust the tail so that it is aligned with the center axis of the coil.

12. Now slide the tail into one end of a glass right-angle bend. (This item should be available in the front of the room.)

Presto! You have created a GC detector! Now you are ready to assemble the gas chromatograph.

Gas Chromatograph Construction

13. Push one end of the latex tubing onto the natural gas tap and carefully push the other onto the column. Try to avoid pulling the polyester wad out.

14. Push the small piece of latex on the other end of the column.

15. Attach the GC detector to the small piece of latex. Rotate it if necessary to ensure that the column will lie naturally on the table with the burner vertical.

16. Clip two clothespins onto the column as stabilizers.

17. Sometimes there are drafts in the lab, and a windbreak may be needed to stabilize the flame. If this is the case, then prepare a windbreak by cutting an aluminum can in half. Turn the top piece upside down, and feed the glass bend up through the drinking hole. The can will sit at a little bit of an angle, but it should still work fine.

18. For added stability, tape the gas chromatograph to the table top.

    Congratulations. You have just made a small-scale, packed-column gas chromatograph with a latex injection port and a Beilstein burner photoionization detector.

Section B.   Measurement of the Retention Time of Air and the Gas Flow Rate

Goal: *To "age" the Beilstein detector and measure the retention time for unretained air.*

Discussion: The carrier gas for your gas chromatograph is natural gas. The flow rate of the carrier gas contributes to the rates of migration of the sample components from one gas chromatograph with another or even for the same chromatograph over time (important in the organic laboratories). Therefore, you need to know the flow rate of the carrier gas. Generally, if the flow rate is faster, the sample components will come off the column faster.

To determine the flow rate (linear gas velocity, $\bar{u}$) you need to measure the retention time for air or air peak time, t_R. Since air is not retained by the gas chromatograph, the time that it takes to flow through the gas chromatograph is an indication of the flow rate of the natural gas.

Experimental Steps: **CAUTION: The can windscreen gets HOT!**

1. Turn the gas tap full on. Wait about 5 seconds, strike a match, and hold the flame to the top of the coil.

2. Adjust the gas tap so that the flame is about 0.5–1.0 cm above the top of the coil. Let the heat from the flame "age" the coil.

   The visible blackening of the copper surface is due to $2Cu + O_2 \rightarrow 2CuO(s)$.

3. Wait about 30 seconds, then remove the coil with a pair of tweezers and hold it for a moment to cool. Place it carefully on the table.

   NOTE: Aged detectors are fragile, but malleable. If you need to adjust the shape of your coil, for example to compress the turns, it is best done when the coil is cool.

The rest of this section is done without having the coil in the gas tip.

4. Obtain a plastic, graduated 1.0 mL syringe from your instructor. Your instructor will have you sign for it.

5. Pull the plunger out to the 0.5 mL mark.

6. Push the needle into the latex injection port within a cm or so of the end of the column. Smoothly and quickly, push the plunger in. Using your marker, mark the injection point and continue to inject near this point in subsequent trials.

    Watch the flame carefully and note that after a very short time, the flame will dip smaller and then go back to its regular size. The dip corresponds to a change in air-fuel ratio as the injected air arrives in the burner.

7. Repeat the injection of 0.5 mL of air.

    •   Measure the elapsed time from the injection to the flame dip.

    The elapsed time is the retention time for air—i.e., the time it takes for the injected air to travel unretained through the column and into the flame.

    •   Carry out at least three measurements of the retention time for air and record your data.

    NOTE: From now on, *do not touch the gas tap.* The flow is set.

Questions: Q1.   Calculate the gas flow rate (linear gas velocity) by $\bar{u} = \frac{L}{t_A}$ where $\bar{u}$ is the average linear gas velocity (in cm/sec), L is the length of the GC column (in cm, from point of injection to the tip of the glass burner), and t_A is the average retention time for air (in seconds).

Q2.   What would be a disadvantage of having "too fast" of a gas flow rate?

    NOTE: In any GC experiment the carrier gas flow rate must be measured because *all* retention times for components will be dependent on it. The faster the carrier gas is flowing, the faster the sample components will move through the column.

    Sometimes the carrier gas flow rate is measured in a different way, with a soap bubble flow meter. The soap bubble flow meter is used to measure the gas flow rate on the gas chromatographs in the Instrument Room. The flow of the carrier gas (often helium) is reported as a volumetric flow (i.e., mL per minute).

Section C.   Measurement of the Retention Times of Halocarbons

Goal: *To measure the GC retention times for a series of organic compounds containing carbon–halogen covalent bonds.*

Experimental Steps: 1.   Using tweezers slip the copper coil back into the burner. Relight the burner if necessary.

NOTE: It is very important that the flame be only on top of the coil. When the burner and detector are optimized, the flame will be steady, on top of the coil, and not very luminous. If the flame is burning from the glass tip or inside the coil, the coil will get too hot and the Beilstein effect will not work well. Try and adjust the coil with your tweezers, but do not change the gas flow rate!

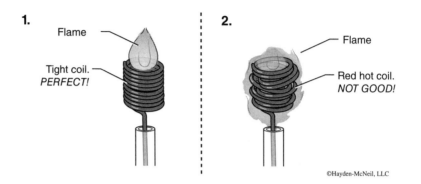

2.   At Reagent Central you will find 25 mL conical flasks stoppered with rubber septa. At your arm's reach station there are two flasks labeled:

Freon 123 ($C_2HCl_2F_3$, dichlorotrifloroethane),

Freon 22 ($CHClF_2$, chlorodifluoromethane).

3.   Pump the syringe plunger several times to clean the syringe with air, ending with the plunger pushed all the way into the barrel of the syringe.

4.   Start with Freon 22. Insert the needle into the septum.

5.   Pull the plunger out to the 0.1 mL mark. Remove the syringe and needle.

6.   Stick the needle into the GC injection port. Be ready to begin timing.

7.   Inject the vapor, using good injection technique, and immediately begin timing.

8.   Watch the detector flame.

Record the elapsed time from injection to:

(a) The first appearance of a green-blue color in the flame.

(b) The maximum intensity of green-blue flame.

(c) The disappearance of green-blue color in the flame.

The first time you try this, everything generally happens too fast to get decent results (it took me 7 times!). *Repeat this measurement two more times. Calculate an average for the three trials.*

You have just measured the times shown in the following diagram.

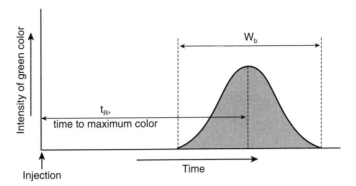

The elapsed time from injection to the maximum green-blue flame color is the retention time, t_R, for that halocarbon. However, with the homemade GC it is often hard to tell when the color is at its maximum. Therefore, in this case, we will define the retention time as the midpoint between the appearance and disappearance of the green-blue flame color.

•   Does this correlate with your estimate of the maximum intensity of the green-blue flame?

The band width of the halocarbon peak, W_b, is the difference in time between the appearance and disappearance of the green-blue flame color.

9.   Repeat the above measurements (steps 3 through 8) on Freon 123.

Freon 123 is less volatile than Freon 22 so use more vapor—0.2 mL–0.3 mL, or whatever is necessary. You may use the same syringe provided that, after injecting each sample, you *remove the plunger entirely, replace, and pump air several times to pump any residual vapor from the needle.*

NOTE: You are going to withdraw vapor, not liquid!

If you think that for some reason the flow rate is changing (e.g., the building gas pressure might change), then redetermine the retention time for air.

•   Calculate the W_b values for each halocarbon peak.

HINT: Assume that the peak is Gaussian, i.e., symmetrical. Note that the units of t_R and W_b in this GC experiment are seconds.

Questions: Q3.   In a table, report for each sample:

(a)   The elapsed time from injection to the first appearance of the green-blue color in the flame

(b)   The elapsed time from injection to the last appearance of the green-blue color in the flame

(c)   The retention time, t_R

(d)   The band width of the halocarbon peak, W_b

(e)   The boiling point at 1 atm of each halocarbon sample*

(f)   Molecular weight of each halocarbon compound

(g) The dipole moment of each halocarbon compound*

(h) The retention time, t_R, for one set of neighbor's data, including their gas flow rate, $\bar{u}$

*Possible sources of boiling point data are the *Chemical Rubber Company (CRC) Handbook of Chemistry and Physics* and the Merck Index.

NOTE: These compounds may be listed under various names. For example, in the *CRC*, Freon 22 ($CHClF_2$) is listed as "methane, chloro-difluoro."

Reference your source.

Q4. (a) Is there any correlation between the boiling points and the retention times, t_R, of the samples? Should there be a correlation? You may want to consider the connection between the boiling point, molecular polarity, and molecular mass of a sample to answer this question. Explain your reasoning.

(b) What are London Dispersion Forces?

(c) What is the relationship between dispersion forces and molecular weight?

Q5. Comparing your retention times and gas flow rate with your neighbor's data, do the numbers make sense? Explain.

Section D.   GC Separation of Halocarbon Mixtures

Goals: *(1) To make a homogeneous mixture of several halocarbons and to obtain a gas chromatographic separation of all of the components. (2) To measure halocarbon retention times and W_b values to determine peak resolution.*

Experimental Steps: 1.   Clean the syringe by pumping with air.

2.   Stick the needle into the septum of the Freon 22 flask. Pull the plunger out to the 0.1 mL mark.

3.   Leaving the plunger set, stick the needle into the Freon 123 septum. Take up an appropriate amount of Freon 123 (the amount that was necessary to see a signal in Section C). For example, if you used 0.3 mL of Freon 123 in Section C, then pull the plunger out to 0.4 mL. You then would have 0.1 mL of Freon 22 and 0.3 mL of Freon 123 in the same syringe.

NOTE: *Do not contaminate* the individual halocarbons in the flasks by pushing the plunger in at any time.

Be ready to record the elapsed times for the appearance and disappearance of green-blue flame color.

4.   Inject the mixture into the gas chromatograph.

•   Record the elapsed times and describe what happens.

5.   Repeat two more times for a total of three trials.

Consider the diagram below which shows the separation of Freon 11 and Freon 12.

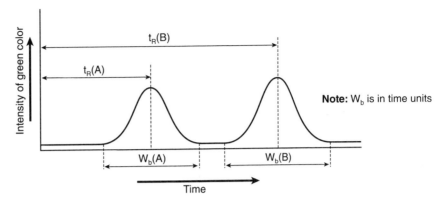

One important parameter in any chromatographic system is the resolution obtained between two successive components, which is defined by

$$\text{Resolution} = \frac{\text{difference between retention times}}{\text{average peak widths}} = \frac{t_R(B) - t_R(A)}{\left(\dfrac{W_b(A) + W_b(B)}{2}\right)}$$

Questions:

Q6. Report your results (t_R and W_b) for the injection of the gas mixture in the chromatograph. Were you able to detect the separate gases? Were their retention times the same as when they were detected separately?

Q7. Why does the width of the peak W_b increase as the t_R increases?

Q8. Calculate the resolution that you obtained experimentally between Freon 22 and Freon 123.

Q9. What does a resolution of 1.0 tell you about the peaks in a chromatographic separation?

Hint: Think about values of t_R and W_b for two peaks that would give you a resolution equal to 1 and then draw a diagram (to scale!) such as the one above.

Q10. Go back to the neighbor that you exchanged data with earlier (Q5). Now exchange data from this section with them. Do the numbers make sense? Explain.

Section E.   Quantitative Analysis Using a Commercial GC

Goals:

(1) To compare your small-scale GC to a commercial unit. (2) To determine the identity and concentration of unknown freon samples dissolved in 1,2-dichloroethane.

Experimental Steps:

1. This part of the experiment will take place in 104 Whitmore Lab, the general chemistry stock room and instrument room. Your unknown sample will be waiting for you when you arrive. Your instructor will inform you when it is time for your class to go to the instrument room.

2. A flask containing unknown concentrations of Freon 123 and Freon 22 dissolved in dichloroethane will be at your station. Record the unknown number. There will be an instructor to acquaint you with the instrument and assist you in taking data.

3. Calibration data will be collected by the GC operator prior to your arrival. A printout of calibration data is available at your GC station. Don't forget this vital piece of information!

4. Each GC has a dedicated computer to handle its data. You will use the PeakSimple program to control the GC and view your data. All GC instructions have been entered into a method that controls the temperature, pressure, and display settings. The software and method will be ready for your use when you arrive.

5. Assign one group member to the computer. He or she will start the run (spacebar) immediately before the sample is injected.

6. Assign one group member to withdraw the unknown sample and inject it into the GC. Use smooth but fast motions while injecting for the best results. You will be instructed on how to draw and inject your samples.

7. The analysis should take 3 to 5 minutes. Have the instructor check your scan. Three peaks should be noted by the computer. These peaks indicate the presence of Freon 123, Freon 22, and dichloroethane.

8. Take your printout back to your laboratory room. Identify the components. Create a calibration table. Plot your calibration data. Calculate the concentration of your freons.

GC Conditions

Instrument used	SRI model 8610C (Buck model 910)
Detector type	FID
Detector temp/voltage	200 °C, −690 V
Column type: Polar	0.2% Carbowax 1500 on Carboblack B
Column dimensions	2 m length × 1/8" diameter (stainless steel)
Column oven temperature	135 °C for 5 minutes
Carrier gas	Nitrogen at 20 mL/min (32 psi)

Questions: Q11.   How does your homemade GC compare to the commercial equipment that you used in terms of the injection, the column, the detector, and the overall process? What components are involved in the commercial GC, but not your homemade GC? Identify possible sources of error for each instrument. In both cases, how did you determine the identity of the compounds injected?

Q12.   Based on the samples you analyzed with your homemade GC, identify which peaks correspond to Freon 22 and Freon 123 in the chromatogram from the commercial GC.

Q13.   What are the retention times of Freon 123 and Freon 22 obtained from the commercial GC? How did these retention times compare with those you obtained using your homemade GC? What are some reasons for any differences?

Q14.   Using the calibration data that was given to your group, make a calibration plot of peak area vs. concentration for Freon 123.

Q15.   Use your calibration plot to determine the concentration of Freon 123 in your unknown sample.

Q16.   Using the calibration data that was given to your group, make a calibration plot of peak area vs. concentration for Freon 22.

Q17.   Use your calibration plot to determine the concentration of Freon 22 in your unknown sample.

Q18.   Are peak intensities the same for different compounds of the same concentration? Why or why not?

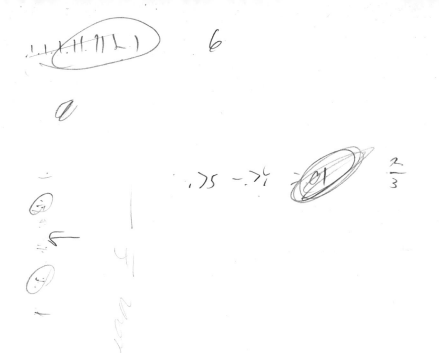